TEACH
Lesson Plan Manual

to accompany

Structure & Function of the Body

Thirteenth Edition

TEACH
Lesson Plan Manual
to accompany

Structure & Function of the Body
Thirteenth Edition

Prepared by
Kathleen M. Reilly Dolin, MSN, RN

MOSBY

ELSEVIER

11830 Westline Industrial Drive
St. Louis, Missouri 63146

TEACH Lesson Plan Manual to accompany   ISBN: 978-0-323-04967-2
STRUCTURE & FUNCTION OF THE BODY

ISBN: 978-0-323-04967-2

Managing Editor: Jeff Downing
Developmental Editor: Karen C. Maurer
Publishing Services Manager: Deborah L. Vogel
Project Manager: Brandilyn Tidwell
Design Direction: Kimberly Denando

Printed in United States of America

Last digit is the print number: 9 8 7 6 5 4 3 2

How to Use This Lesson Plan Manual

Welcome to TEACH, your Total Curriculum Solution!

This Lesson Plan Manual is designed to help you prepare for classes using **Thibodeau and Patton's Structure & Function of the Body.** We hope it will reduce your lesson preparation time, give you new and creative ideas to promote student learning, and help you to make full use of the rich array of resources in the Thibodeau and Patton teaching package.

The lesson plans are designed to promote active student learning and get students involved in class discussions and activities. They include assessment tools to help you gauge your students' understanding of the course material and adapt lessons to their needs.

Each textbook chapter is divided into 50-minute lessons — building blocks that can be sequenced to fit your class schedule. The lesson plans are available in electronic format so that you can customize them to fit the requirements of your course.

Every lesson includes a wide variety of teaching resources. In many cases, our subject matter experts have provided more resources and activities than can be covered in a 50-minute lesson. We encourage you to choose activities that match the needs of your students and your curriculum, and the materials and resources available at your school.

Lesson plans can be a valuable tool for documenting how your curriculum covers learning objectives required by accrediting organizations. Some accrediting organizations require that learning resources be integrated into a program's curriculum to enhance students' learning experiences. The activities in this Lesson Plan Manual will encourage your students to use learning resources such as the library or the Internet to complement their textbook.

Lesson Plan Manual Format

The Lesson Plan Manual is available in 3 formats:
1. In print, with pages 3-hole punched and perforated for your convenience
2. On a CD-ROM included with the printed Lesson Plan Manual; files are in Microsoft Word and PowerPoint
3. Online at *http://TEACH.elsevier.com*. Access codes are available from your sales representative

Lesson Plan Manual Organization

TEACH lesson plans complement Elsevier textbooks; there is a lesson plan chapter for each book chapter. Each lesson plan chapter includes 3 sections:
1. **Preparation:** checklists to help you prepare classes based on the chapter
2. **Lessons:** each chapter is divided into 50-minute lessons, to provide you with the building blocks for your curriculum
3. **Lecture Outlines:** also divided into 50-minute lessons

Preparation

The Preparation section ensures that you're well prepared for class. It includes the following checklists:
- *Teaching Focus* — identifies key student learning goals for the chapter

- *Materials and Resources* — lists materials needed for each lesson within the chapter

- *Lesson Checklist* — includes instructor preparation suggestions

- *Key Terms* — provides page references for each key term in the chapter

- *Additional Resources* — lists instructor resources available for the chapter

- *Terms & Definitions*—provides page references for each key term in the chapter

- *Additional Resources*—lists instructor resources available for this chapter

Lessons

Each lesson includes the following sections:

Pretest and Background Assessment. The first lesson in each chapter includes a Pretest and two Background Assessment questions, designed to help you gauge your students' readiness for the lesson. Depending on students' responses, you may wish to modify your lesson. Students who are comfortable with the topic may need more challenging activities. Students who have difficulty with the topic may need to start by addressing more fundamental concepts.

Critical Thinking Question. Every lesson includes a Critical Thinking Question to motivate students by demonstrating real-world applications of the lesson content.

Lesson Roadmap. The heart of the TEACH lesson plan is the 3-column roadmap that links Objectives and Content from **Thibodeau and Patton's Structure & Function of the Body** with its Teaching Resources. Teaching Resources reference all the elements of the ancillary package and include additional teaching tips such as Class Activities, discussion topics, and much more. This section correlates your textbook and its ancillary materials with the objectives upon which your course is based.

Homework/Assignments, Instructor's Notes/Student Feedback. These sections are provided for you to add your own notes for assignments, for recording student feedback, and for other notes relating to the lesson.

Lecture Outline

The Lecture Outlines include PowerPoint slides to provide a compelling visual presentation and summary of the main chapter points. Lecture notes for each slide highlight key topics and provide questions for discussion—to help create an interactive classroom environment.

We encourage you to select material from the Lesson Plan Manual that meets your students' needs, to integrate TEACH into your existing lesson plans, and to put your own teaching approach into the plans. We hope TEACH will be an invaluable tool in your classroom.

Table of Contents
Structure & Function of the Body, 13th ed.

LESSON PLANS AND LECTURE OUTLINES

Chapter

Lesson Plan

1 An Introduction to the Structure and Function of the Body

TEACHING FOCUS

In this chapter, students will have the opportunity to learn the levels of organization of the body. Students will be introduced to the principal directions, terms, and sections (planes) used to describe the body, along with the abdominopelvic regions, abdominopelvic quadrants, and major cavities of the body. Students will have the opportunity to understand the axial and appendicular subdivisions of the body and the anatomical regions in each area. Students will be exposed to the basics of homeostasis.

MATERIALS AND RESOURCES

☐ Index cards (Lesson 1.1)
☐ List of items that relate to either anatomy or physiology (Lesson 1.1)
☐ Photocopies of Figure 1-1 (p. 4) (Lesson 1.1)
☐ Photocopies of Figure 1-8 (p. 14) (Lesson 1.2)
☐ Photocopies of head-and-torso outline (Lesson 1.2)
☐ Slips of paper with descriptive terms for body regions (Lesson 1.2)
☐ Computer (all Lessons)

LESSON CHECKLIST

Preparations for this lesson include:

- lecture
- guest speakers: medical assistant, physician, nurse, nurse practitioner, physician assistant
- student performance evaluation of all entry-level skills required for student comprehension and application of anatomy and physiology principles including:
  o relevance of studying anatomy and physiology
  o relationship of anatomy to physiology
  o levels of organization of the body
  o principal directional terms and sections used to describe the body
  o relationship of body parts to one another
  o relevance of homeostasis to proper body functioning

KEY TERMS

abdominal cavity (p. 9)
abdominopelvic cavity (p. 9)
anatomical position (p. 6)
anatomy (p. 3)
anterior (p. 7)
appendicular (p. 13)
atrophy (p. 13)
axial (p. 13)
body as a whole (p. 6)
chemical level (p. 4)
control center (p. 14)
cranial cavity (p. 10)
deep (p. 9)
diaphragm (p. 10)
dissection (p. 3)
distal (p. 9)
dorsal body cavity (p. 7)
dorsal cavity (p. 9)
effector (p. 14)
epigastric region (p. 10)
experimental controls (p. 8)
experimentation (p. 8)
feedback loop (p. 13)
four quadrants (p. 11)
frontal (p. 9)
homeostasis (p. 13)
hypogastric region (p. 10)
hypothesis (p. 8)
inferior (p. 6)
lateral (p. 7)

law (p. 8)
left hypochondriac region (p. 11)
left iliac (inguinal) region (p. 11)
left lumbar region (p. 11)
medial (p. 7)
mediastinum (p. 9)
midsagittal plane (p. 9)
negative feedback loop (p. 15)
pelvic cavity (p. 10)
physiology (p. 3)
pleural cavities (p. 10)
posterior (p. 7)
positive feedback loop (p. 13)
prone (p. 6)
proximal (p. 9)
right hypochondriac region (p. 11)
right iliac (inguinal) region (p. 11)
right lumbar region (p. 11)
sagittal (p. 9)
scientific method (p. 8)
sensor (p. 14)
spinal cavity (p. 10)
superficial (p. 9)
superior (p. 6)
supine (p. 6)
theory (p. 8)
thoracic cavity (p. 9)
transverse (p. 9)
umbilical region (p. 11)
ventral body cavity (p. 9)
ventral cavity (p. 10)

ADDITIONAL RESOURCES

AnimationDirect (Book Companion CD)
Instructor's Electronic Resource (IER) (CD)
PowerPoint slides (CD, Evolve)
Test Bank (Evolve)

Legend

ESLR
EVOLVE Student
Learning Resource

EILR TB
EVOLVE Instructor
Learning Resource
Test Bank

AnimationDirect
on Book Companion
CD

PPT
PowerPoint
Slides

SG
Study
Guide

IRM
Instructor's
Resource Manual

Class Activities are indicated in ***bold italic.***

LESSON 1.1

PRETEST

1. The term used to describe the position of the body lying face upward is _____.

2. The plane of the body that runs lengthwise from front to back is the _____.

3. The body cavity that contains the trachea, heart, and blood vessels is _____.

4. The area of the body around the navel is called _____.

5. What is the basic type of control system in the body?
   a. homeostasis
   b. feedback loop
   c. control center
   d. hypothesis

6. What is a systematic approach to discovery called?
   a. scientific method
   b. experimentation
   c. theory
   d. experimental controls

7. What is the anatomical direction term that means *nearer the surface?*
   a. proximal
   b. distal
   c. superficial
   d. deep

8. What is the body cavity that contains the lower colon, rectum, urinary bladder, and reproductive organs?
   a. cranial cavity
   b. pleural cavity
   c. abdominal cavity
   d. pelvic cavity

9. What is the term for the body region of the upper cheek?
   a. zygomatic
   b. volar
   c. popliteal
   d. olecranal

10. What term refers to a degeneration process?
   a. effector loop
   b. negative feedback loop
   c. homeostasis
   d. atrophy

Answers: 1. supine; 2. sagittal; 3. mediastinum; 4. umbilical; 5. b; 6. a; 7. c; 8. d; 9. a; 10. d

BACKGROUND ASSESSMENT

Question: What is the anatomical position? Why is the term used? What are other positions besides anatomical position?

Answer: To assume anatomical position, the body is in an erect, or standing, posture with the arms at the sides and the palms forward. The head and feet also point forward. Discussions about the body, the way it moves, its posture, or the relationship of one area to another assume that the body as a whole is in anatomical position. Other positions are supine and prone. In the supine position, the body is lying face upward, and in the prone position, the body is lying face downward.

Question: What are the two major body cavities? What are the subdivisions of these two major cavities?

ELSEVIER

Answer: The two major body cavities are the *ventral* and *dorsal* body cavities. The ventral body cavity is divided into the *thoracic* cavity, which is further subdivided into the *mediastinum* and *pleural* cavities, and the *abdominopelvic* cavity, which is further subdivided into the *abdominal* and *pelvic* cavities. The dorsal body cavity is divided into the *cranial* and *spinal* cavities.

CRITICAL THINKING QUESTION

You are assisting a physician while she examines a patient. She has asked you to instruct the patient lying on the examination table to take the anatomical position. The patient is unfamiliar with this term. How should you tell the patient to pose?

Guidelines: You should tell the patient to stand up and place his arms at his sides with his palms facing forward. The patient's hands and feet should also face forward. The anatomical position is a reference position that gives meaning to the directional terms used to describe body parts and regions.

OBJECTIVES	CONTENT	TEACHING RESOURCES
Define the terms *anatomy* **and** *physiology.*	■ Introduction (p. 3)	Slide 7 Word Find question 50 (p. 5) Multiple Choice question 5 (p. 6) Fill in the Blanks questions 31-35 (p. 8) Multiple Choice questions 1-2; True or False questions 1-3 **Book Resources** Quick Check question 1 (p. 6) Review question 1 (p. 18) Chapter Test questions 1-2 (p. 20) ▸ Discuss Science Applications: Modern Anatomy (p. 4). Discuss how the history of modern anatomy relates to other fields of study. *Class Activity **Have two students define the terms** anatomy **and** physiology. **Ask the class to offer improvements to their definitions.*** *Class Activity **Divide the class into two or more teams. Give them a series of items (e.g., dissecting the spleen) and ask them to describe how they relate to anatomy and physiology. The team with the most correct answers wins.*** *Class Activity **Have groups of three create a diagram of the process called** the scientific method. **Have them share their diagrams with the class.***
List and discuss in order of increasing complexity the	■ Structural levels of organization (p. 4)	Slides 8-9 Structural Levels of Organization questions 1-5 (p. 2)

OBJECTIVES	CONTENT	TEACHING RESOURCES
levels of organization of the body.		📖 Multiple Choice questions 7, 13 (pp. 6-7) 🅔 Multiple Choice questions 3-4, 36-38; True or False question 58; Short Answer question 4 💿 3D Turntable **Book Resources** Quick Check questions 2-3 (p. 6) Figure 1-1 Structural levels of organization in the body (p. 4) Review question 2 (p. 19) Chapter Test question 3 (p. 20) Clear View of the Human Body ▸ Discuss the scientific method. Define it and discuss why it is important to the study of human biology. *Class Activity **Divide the students into teams. Give each team a blank copy of Figure 1-1 (p. 4; available on EILR) on the structural organization of the body. The goal is for each team to fill in the names of each microscopic and gross level of the body in a set period of time. The team who has the most correct answers wins.***
Define the term *anatomical position.*	■ Anatomical position (p. 6)	🖾 Slide 10 📖 Anatomical Position questions 6-10 (p. 2) 📖 Multiple Choice question 16 (p. 7) 🅔 True or False questions 4-7, 59-60 **Book Resources** Quick Check questions 1-2 (p. 6) Figure 1-2 Anatomical position (p. 6) Review question 3 (p. 19) Chapter Test question 4 (p. 20) *Class Activity **Invite a volunteer to stand in front of the class to demonstrate proper anatomical position. Have the students tell the volunteer how to position his/her arms, legs, hands, feet, and head. Then ask other volunteers to describe or demonstrate the supine and prone positions.***

OBJECTIVES	CONTENT	TEACHING RESOURCES
List and define the principal directional terms and sections (planes) used in describing the body and the relationship of body parts to one another.	■ Anatomical directions (p. 6) ■ Planes or body sections (p. 9)	Slides 11-17 Anatomical Directions questions 11-26 (pp. 2-3) Applying What You Know questions 47-49 (p. 4) Multiple Choice questions 4, 8, 14, 15, 20 (pp. 6-7) Directions and Planes of the Body diagram (p. 10) Multiple Choice questions 5-14, 31-34, 38; True or False questions 8-32, 61, 63; Matching questions 1-7, 15-20; Short Answer questions 5-6 **Book Resources** Figure 1-3 Directions and planes of the body (p. 7) Review question 4 (p. 19) Critical Thinking question 11 (p. 11) Chapter Test questions 5-8, 16-20 (p. 20) *Class Activity **Divide students into pairs. Have each team point out anatomical directions and planes on each other.*** *Class Activity **Have one group of students slice an orange vertically, the other horizontally. Have them discuss the differences.*** *Class Activity **Have students make flash cards of each anatomical direction with its opposite direction. Then have the students form small groups to quiz each other.***

1.1 Homework/Assignments:

Divide the class into teams. Assign each team a different body part. Ask each team to research dissected views of the assigned part and then present their findings to the class. The teams can look for x-ray views, computerized scans, and digitized photographs of thin slices of the body. One source of this information is the Visible Human Project page of the National Library of Medicine Web site.
http://www.nlm.nih.gov/research/visible/visible_human.html

1.1 Teacher's Notes:

LESSON 1.2

CRITICAL THINKING QUESTION

Mr. Shepherd has gone outside to shovel snow on a cold day. How does his body maintain a relatively constant body temperature? What is this process called?

Guidelines: Mr. Shepherd's body is working to maintain homeostasis. The cold weather threatens internal stability. To stay warm, his body employs a highly complex and integrated communication control system called a *negative feedback loop*. Nerve endings, acting as temperature sensors, feed information to a control center in his brain that compares actual body temperature to normal body temperature. In response to a chill, the brain sends nerve signals to muscles to make them shiver. Shivering produces heat that increases his body temperature. He stops shivering when feedback information tells the brain that his body temperature is normal

OBJECTIVES	CONTENT	TEACHING RESOURCES
List the major cavities of the body and the subdivisions of each.	■ Body cavities (p. 9)	Slides 19-22 Body Cavities questions 27-33 (p. 3) Multiple Choice questions 3, 6, 11, 12, 18 (pp. 6-7) Dorsal and Ventral Body Cavities diagram (p. 9) Multiple Choice questions 15-17, 21-22; True or False questions 33-39, 62 **Book Resources** Figure 1-4 Body cavities (p. 10) Figure 1-7 Organs of the major body cavities (p. 12) Table 1-1 Body cavities (p. 10) Quick Check questions 1-3 (p. 12) Review questions 5, 7 (p. 19) Chapter Test questions 11, 12 (p. 20) Clear View of the Human Body *Class Activity* **Divide the students into teams. Give each team a copy of a head-and-torso outline. Ask each team to draw in the appropriate body cavities and subcavities within a certain time limit.**
List the nine abdominopelvic regions and the abdominopelvic quadrants.	■ Body cavities (p. 8)	Slides 23-28 Body Regions questions 34-38 (p. 3) Applying What You Know question 47 (p. 4)

Thibodeau/Patton

OBJECTIVES	CONTENT	TEACHING RESOURCES
		Multiple Choice questions 2, 9, 10 (pp. 5-6)
		Regions of the Abdomen diagram (p. 11)
		Multiple Choice questions 18-20, 23, 27, 28; True or False questions 40-43
		Completion questions 21, 22 (pp. 7-8)
		Book Resources
		Figure 1-5 The nine regions of the abdominopelvic cavity (p. 11)
		Figure 1-6 Division of the abdominopelvic cavity into four quadrants (p. 11)
		Table 1-1 Body cavities (p. 10)
		Review question 6 (p. 19)
		Critical Thinking question 13 (p. 19)
		Chapter Test questions 13, 14 (p. 20)
		Clear View of the Human Body
		Class Activity Create a mock game show. Invite three contestants to the front of the room. You will call out the name of a region or quadrant of the abdominopelvic cavity. The first student to properly give you the name of an organ in that body cavity receives a point. Whoever reaches five points first wins.
		Class Activity Divide students into groups. Have each group come up with ailments that occur in the abdominopelvic cavity (such as cirrhosis of the liver, stomach ulcer, appendicitis, etc.) and then determine which region and quadrant are affected.
Discuss and contrast the axial and appendicular subdivisions of the body. Identify a number of specific anatomical regions in each area.	■ Body regions (p. 12)	Slides 29, 30
		Applying What You Know question 49 (p. 4)
		Multiple Choice questions 17, 19 (p. 7)
		Multiple Choice question 39; True or False questions 54-56, 64, 65; Matching questions 8-14
		Matching questions 23-32 (p. 8)
		Book Resources
		Figure 1-8 Axial and appendicular divisions of the body (p. 14)

OBJECTIVES	CONTENT	TEACHING RESOURCES
		Table 1-2 Descriptive terms for body regions (p. 15)
		Quick Check questions 1, 2 (p. 13)
		Review question 8 (p. 19)
		Chapter Test questions 9, 10 (p. 20)
		Class Activity Print each of the descriptive terms for body regions listed in Table 1-2. Put the names in a "hat" and pass it around the room. Ask each student to choose a piece of paper and then describe the meaning of that term. For example, if a student pulls out "zygomatic," the proper answer is "upper cheek."
		Class Activity Hand out unlabeled copies of Figure 1-8 (p. 14; available on EILR). Divide students into teams and ask them to label the diagram.
Explain the meaning of the term *homeostasis* and give an example of a typical homeostatic mechanism.	■ The balance of body functions (p. 14)	Slides 31-33
		The Balance of Body Functions questions 39-46 (p. 4)
		Multiple Choice question 1 (p. 5)
		Multiple Choice questions 24-26, 29, 30, 40; True or False questions 44-53, 57, 66-67; Short Answer questions 1-3
		Book Resources
		Figure 1-9 Negative feedback loops (p. 16)
		Quick Check questions 1-3 (p. 17)
		Review questions 9, 10 (p. 19)
		Critical Thinking question 12 (p. 19)
		Chapter Test question 15 (p. 20)
		▶ Discuss how exercise affects homeostasis.
		Class Activity Divide the students into teams. Ask each team to come up with an example of a negative feedback loop and a positive feedback loop. Have each team discuss their examples and explain to the class how they work.
Performance Evaluation		Chapter 1 Computerized Test Bank questions

Structure & Function of the Body, 13th ed.
Thibodeau/Patton

OBJECTIVES	CONTENT	TEACHING RESOURCES
		Definitions questions 1-20 (p. 7); Identification question 33 (p. 8)
		Student Post-Test questions
		Book Resource
		Chapter Test (p. 20)

1.2 Homework/Assignments:

1.2 Teacher's Notes:

ELSEVIER

Structure & Function of the Body, 13th ed.

Thibodeau/Patton

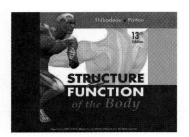

Slide 1

Chapter 1

Introduction to the
Structure and Function
of the Body

Slide 2

Learning Objectives

- Define the terms *anatomy* and *physiology*
- In order of increasing complexity, list and discuss the levels of organization in the body
- Define the term *anatomical position*

Slide 3

Learning Objectives (cont'd.)

- List and define the principal directional terms and sections, or planes, used in describing the body and the relationship of body parts to one another
- List the nine abdominopelvic regions and the abdominopelvic quadrants

Slide 4

Learning Objectives (cont'd.)

- List the major cavities of the body and the subdivisions of each
- Discuss and contrast the axial and appendicular subdivisions of the body. Identify a number of specific anatomical regions in each area

4

Slide 5

Learning Objectives (cont'd.)

- Explain the meaning of the term *homeostasis* and give an example of a typical homeostatic mechanism

5

Slide 6

**Chapter 1
Lesson 1.1**

6

Slide 7

Anatomy and Physiology

- **Anatomy:** the study of the structure of an organism and the relationships of its parts
- **Physiology:** the study of the functions of living organisms and their parts

7

- Andreas Vesalius (1514-1564) was the first to apply a scientific method to the study of the human body.

- Ask students to name other fields to which modern anatomy might apply.

- What is the relationship of anatomy to physiology? (structure determines function)

Thibodeau/Patton

Slide 8

- The body is a single organism constructed of the following smaller units:
  - **Cells:** organizations of various chemicals
  - **Tissues:** organizations of similar cells
  - **Organs:** organizations of different kinds of tissues
  - **Systems:** organizations of many different kinds of organs

- Organization is an outstanding characteristic of body structure. Organism, which denotes a living thing, implies organization.
- The existence of life depends on the proper levels and proportions of chemical substances in the cells.
- Atoms and molecules are referred to as what level of organization in the body? (chemical)
- The functioning of an organism (body) therefore is ultimately dependent on its cellular functions.

Slide 9

- What name is given to groups of several different kinds of tissues arranged to perform a special function? (an organ)

Slide 10

Anatomical Position

- Standing erect with the arms at the sides and palms turned forward

- Discussions about the body and the relationship of one area to another assume that the body as a whole is in the anatomical position.
- What are the two terms used to describe the body when it is not in the anatomical position? (prone and supine)

Slide 11

Anatomical Directions

- **Superior:** toward the head, upper, above
- **Inferior:** toward the feet, lower, below
- **Anterior:** front, in front of (same as ventral in humans)
- **Posterior:** back, in back of (same as dorsal in humans)

- Examples:
  - Lungs are superior to the diaphragm; stomach is inferior to the diaphragm.
  - The nose is on the anterior surface of the body; the shoulder blades are on the posterior surface.
  - What are anatomical directions used to describe? (the relative positions of body parts)

ELSEVIER

Slide 12

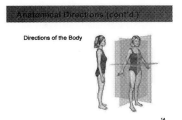

Anatomical Directions (cont'd.)

- **Medial:** toward the midline of a structure
- **Lateral:** away from the midline or toward the side of a structure
- **Proximal:** toward or nearest the trunk, or nearest the point of origin of a structure
- **Distal:** away from or farthest from the trunk, or farthest from a structure's point of origin

Copyright (c) 2008, 2005 by Mosby, Inc., an affiliate of Elsevier Inc. All rights reserved.   12

- Examples:

  - The great toe is at the medial side of the foot; the little toe is at the lateral side.

  - The elbow lies at the proximal end of the lower arm; the hand lies at the distal end.

Slide 13

Anatomical Directions (cont'd.)

- **Superficial:** nearer the body surface
- **Deep:** farther away from the body surface

Copyright (c) 2008, 2005 by Mosby, Inc., an affiliate of Elsevier Inc. All rights reserved.   13

- Examples:

  - The skin of the arm is superficial to the muscles.

  - The bone of the upper arm is deep to the muscles that surround it.

- Why are the anatomical positions listed in pairs? (It is easier to learn.)

- These terms are used frequently in medicine to describe conditions or injuries.

Slide 14

Anatomical Directions (cont'd.)

Directions of the Body

Copyright (c) 2008, 2005 by Mosby, Inc., an affiliate of Elsevier Inc. All rights reserved.   14

- In anatomical directions, does "right" refer to your right or your subject's right? (your subject's right)

Slide 15

Planes or Body Sections

- **Sagittal plane:** runs lengthwise; divides a structure into right and left sections
- **Midsagittal plane:** sagittal plane that divides the body into two equal halves

Copyright (c) 2008, 2005 by Mosby, Inc., an affiliate of Elsevier Inc. All rights reserved.   15

- Which plane divides the body into two equal halves? (midsagittal plane)

Thibodeau/Patton

Slide 16

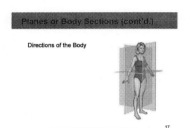

- Which plane runs lengthwise from side to side and divides the body into the front and back? (frontal, or coronal, plane)

Slide 17

- This figure illustrates the division of the body into planes and sections.

- Why is this division helpful to the medical practitioner? (It allows the medical practitioner to be more precise in their description of patients' signs and symptoms.)

Slide 18

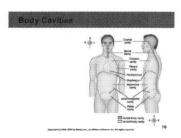

Slide 19

- The body is made up of cavities that contain compact, well-ordered arrangements of internal organs.

- The two major body cavities are the ventral and dorsal body cavities.

- The subbdivisions of the ventral body cavity are: Thoracic (chest) cavity, Pleural (lungs) cavity, Mediastinum, Diaphragm, Abdominal cavity, Abdominopelvic cavity, Pelvic cavity

- The subdivisions of the dorsal cavity are: Cranial cavity, Spinal cavity

Thibodeau/Patton

Slide 20

Body Cavities (cont'd.)

- Ventral
  - Thoracic cavity
    - **Mediastinum:** midportion of thoracic cavity; heart and trachea are located in mediastinum
    - **Pleural cavities:** right lung located in right pleural cavity; left lung is in left pleural cavity

20

- Which organ separates the thoracic cavity from the abdominal cavity? (diaphragm)
- In which cavity is the mediastinum located? (The mediastinum is located in the ventral body cavity.)

Slide 21

Body Cavities (cont'd.)

- Dorsal
  - Cranial cavity contains brain
  - Spinal cavity contains spinal cord

21

Slide 22

Body Cavities (cont'd.)

- Abdominopelvic cavity
  - Abdominal cavity contains stomach, intestines, liver, gallbladder, pancreas, and spleen
  - Pelvic cavity contains reproductive organs, urinary bladder, and the lowest part of the intestine

22

- What is the difference between the abdominal cavity and the abdominopelvic cavity? (The abdominopelvic cavity refers to the abdominal cavity and the pelvic cavity together.)

Slide 23

Abdominopelvic Regions and Quadrants

The Nine Regions of the Abdominopelvic Cavity

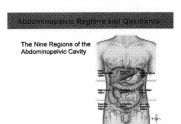

23

- Name the nine regions of the abdominopelvic cavity.

Slide 24

Nine Abdominopelvic Regions

- Upper abdominopelvic regions
  - Right and left hypochondriac regions
  - Epigastric region

24

- The upper regions lie above an imaginary line across the abdomen at the level of the ninth rib cartilages.
- Identify the organs that are located in the upper regions.

Slide 25

Nine Abdominopelvic Regions (cont'd.)

- Middle regions
  - Right and left lumbar regions
  - Umbilical region

25

- The middle regions lie below an imaginary line across the abdomen at the ninth rib cartilages and above an imaginary line across the abdomen at the top of the hip bones.
- Identify the organs that are located in the middle regions.

Slide 26

Nine Abdominopelvic Regions (cont'd.)

- Lower regions
  - Right and left iliac (inguinal) regions
  - Hypogastric region

26

- The lower regions lie below an imaginary line across the abdomen at the level of the top of the hip bones.
- Identify the organs that are located in the lower regions.

Slide 27

Four Quadrants of the Abdominopelvic Cavity

- Right upper/superior
- Right lower/inferior
- Left upper/superior
- Left lower/inferior

27

- What are the four quadrants generally used for by health professionals? (describing the location of pain, tumors, or surgical sites)

Slide 28

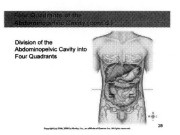

Division of the
Abdominopelvic Cavity into
Four Quadrants

- What is meant by a section of the body? (subdivisions of the body identified by special names)

Slide 29

- **Axial region:** head, neck, and torso or trunk
- **Appendicular region:** upper and lower extremities

Examples of descriptive terms for body regions:

Area	Body region
buccal	cheek
dorsal	back
pedal	foot
volar	palm or sole

- Name some of the regions of the upper extremity and lower extremity. (upper: facial, frontal, cervical; lower: femoral, pedal, tarsal)

Slide 30

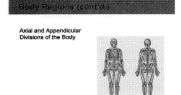

Axial and Appendicular
Divisions of the Body

- What is the difference between the axial and the appendicular portion of the body? (The axial portion consists of the head, neck, and torso or trunk; the appendicular portion consists of the upper and lower extremities.)

Slide 31

The Balance of Body Functions

- Survival depends on the maintenance or restoration of homeostasis
- **Homeostasis:** relative constancy of the internal environment
- **Feedback loops:** the body uses negative feedback loops, and less often, positive feedback loops to maintain or restore homeostasis

- Name some examples of negative feedback loops. (muscles shiver to raise body temperature)
- Name some examples of positive feedback loops. (uterine contractions during the birth of a baby; to stop bleeding, platelets cluster to form a blood clot)

ELSEVIER

Structure & Function of the Body, 13th ed.

Thibodeau/Patton

Slide 32

Negative
Feedback Loops

- How does negative feedback differ from positive feedback?
  (Negative feedback loops oppose or negate a change in the body,
  whereas positive feedback loops temporarily amplify the change
  that is occurring.)

Slide 33

The Balance of Body Functions (cont'd.)

- All organs function to maintain homeostasis
- Body functions are related to age; peak efficiency is
  during young adulthood, diminishing efficiency
  occurs after young adulthood

- Does homeostasis maintain absolutely constant values?
  (No, homeostasis is a state of *relative* constancy, which allows
  some variation)
- Define developmental processes and aging processes.

Structure & Function of the Body, 13th ed.

Thibodeau/Patton

2 Lesson Plan
Chemistry of Life

TEACHING FOCUS

In this chapter, students will have the opportunity to learn how the basic principles of anatomy and physiology are based on the principles of chemistry. Students will be exposed to the terms *atom, element, molecule,* and *compound,* along with the structure of an atom. Students will have the opportunity to learn about chemical bonding, organic and inorganic chemical compounds, the chemical characteristics of water, and the concept of pH. Students will also have the opportunity to understand the following organic molecules: *carbohydrate, lipid, protein,* and *nucleic acid.*

MATERIALS AND RESOURCES

- ☐ Computer (all Lessons)
- ☐ Flash cards (all Lessons)
- ☐ Handouts of Figure 2-4 (Lesson 2.2)
- ☐ Handouts or display of Figures 2-6, 2-8, 2-9, and 2-11 (Lesson 2.3)

LESSON CHECKLIST

Preparations for this lesson include:

- lecture
- guest speakers: biochemist, medical assistant, physician, nurse, radiographer
- student performance evaluation of all entry-level skills required for student comprehension and application of inorganic and organic chemistry principles including:
  - ○ the chemical basis of the structure and function of the human physiology
  - ○ the structure of fundamental particles and the process by which they bond to form building blocks of the human physiology including nucleic acids
  - ○ the fundamental components of the essential structures of the body

KEY TERMS

acid (p. 29)
adenine (p. 35)
adenosine triphosphate (ATP) (p. 27)
alkaline (p. 29)
amino acids (p. 33)
aqueous solution (p. 27)
atherosclerosis (p. 35)
atom (p. 23)
atomic mass (p. 24)
atomic number (p. 24)
base (p. 29)
biochemistry (p. 23)
blood lipoproteins (p. 35)
bond (p. 25)
carbohydrates (p. 31)
carbon (p. 25)
carbon dioxide (p. 25)
cholesterol (p. 33)
compound (p. 24)
covalent bond (p. 26)
cytosine (p. 35)
dehydration synthesis (p. 28)
deoxyribonucleic acid (DNA) (p. 36)
dissociation (p. 25)
double helix (p. 36)
electrolyte (p. 25)
electron (p. 24)
element (p. 24)
energy level (p. 24)
enzyme (p. 34)
functional proteins (p. 34)
glycogen (p. 31)
guanine (p. 35)

hydrogen (p. 24)
hydrolysis (p. 28)
inorganic (p. 27)
ion (p. 25)
ionic bonds (p. 25)
isotopes (p. 30)
lipid (p. 31)
lock-and-key model (p. 35)
matter (p. 23)
molecule (p. 24)
neutron (p. 24)
nitrogen (p. 24)
nucleic acid (p. 35)
nucleotides (p. 35)
nucleus (p. 24)
orbital (p. 24)
organic (p. 27)
oxygen (p. 24)
peptide bond (p. 34)
pH (p. 29)
phospholipids (p. 33)
product (p. 27)
protein (p. 33)
proton (p. 24)
radioactive isotopes (p. 30)
reactant (p. 27)
ribonucleic acid (RNA) (p. 35)
solute (p. 27)
solvent (p. 27)
structural proteins (p. 34)
thymine (p. 35)
triglycerides (p. 31)
uracil (p. 35)

ADDITIONAL RESOURCES

AnimationDirect (Book Companion CD)
Instructor's Electronic Resource (IER) (CD)
PowerPoint slides (CD, Evolve)
Test Bank (Evolve)

Legend

ESLR
EVOLVE Student
Learning Resource

EILR TB
EVOLVE Instructor
Learning Resource
Test Bank

AnimationDirect
on Book Companion
CD

PPT
PowerPoint
Slides

SG
Study
Guide

IRM
Instructor's
Resource Manual

Class Activities are indicated in ***bold italic.***

LESSON 2.1

PRETEST

1. When atoms share electrons, they form a(n) _____.
2. A unit of measurement expressing the degree to which a solution is acidic or basic is termed _____.
3. Two atoms that have the same atomic number but different atomic masses are called _____.
4. The basic building blocks of nucleic acids are _____.
5. The twisted, double-strand arrangement of nucleotides in a DNA molecule is a(n)
   a. uracil.
   b. double helix.
   c. deoxyribose.
   d. guanine.
6. The basic units of proteins are
   a. structural proteins.
   b. enzymes.
   c. amino acids.
   d. adenine.
7. Lipid molecules formed by a glycerol unit joined to three fatty acids are called
   a. triglycerides.
   b. phospholipids.
   c. cholesterol.
   d. carbohydrates.
8. Bases are
   a. weak acids.
   b. salts.
   c. acidic.
   d. alkaline.
9. When water is the solvent, the mixture is considered a(n)
   a. aqueous solution.
   b. solute.
   c. hydrolysis.
   d. dehydration synthesis.
10. An electrically charged atom is called a(n)
   a. electrolyte.
   b. molecule.
   c. ion.
   d. orbital.

Answers: 1. covalent bond; 2. pH; 3. isotopes; 4. nucleotides; 5. b; 6. c; 7. a; 8. d; 9. a; 10. c

BACKGROUND ASSESSMENT

Question: What are the four major elements that make up most of the human body? What is the general name for those elements?

Answer: Oxygen, carbon, hydrogen, and nitrogen make up about 96% of the human body. These elements are also called *atoms.*

Question: What are enzymes? Why are they vital? Describe the lock-and-key model of how they operate.
Answer: Enzymes are chemical catalysts. They help a chemical reaction occur but are not reactants or products themselves. Enzymes are vital to body chemistry, because no reaction in the body occurs quickly enough, unless the specific enzymes needed for that reaction are present. Shape is important to the function of enzyme molecules. Each enzyme has a shape that "fits" the specific molecules it works with, just like a key fits specific locks. This explanation of enzyme action is called the *lock-and-key model.*

CRITICAL THINKING QUESTION

Florence, a regular patient at your practice, has taken an interest in your work and indicates that she might like to become a medical assistant. However, she is somewhat confused by articles she has read describing new developments and cutting-edge technologies in medical science, and she is concerned about her ability to gain sufficient knowledge to respond to questions from patients about new developments in medicine. She asks you what aspects of your training might provide a knowledge base for understanding emerging technologies in medicine. How do you respond?

Guidelines: You can explain to Florence that in addition to acquiring the skills and competencies required for performing the duties of an allied health professional on a daily basis, training also provides fundamental knowledge of the biochemical basis of the structures and functions of the human physiology. This background provides a foundation for understanding new treatments and technologies that have evolved from deeper insights into the genetic, molecular, or cellular basis of disease processes. By acquiring greater familiarity with the fundamental chemical and genetic structure of the human physiology, allied health professionals are better able to understand disease states and how various treatments address an underlying pathology.

OBJECTIVES	CONTENT	TEACHING RESOURCES
Define the terms *atom, element, molecule,* and *compound.*	■ Levels of chemical organization (p. 23) ☐ Atoms (p. 23) ☐ Elements, molecules, and compounds (p. 24)	Slides 5-6 Levels of Chemical Organization questions 1, 2, 5, 7-9, 12 (pp. 14-15) Applying What You Know question 47 (p. 18) Chemistry of Life crossword puzzle (p. 17) Word Find question 49 (p. 19) Check Your Knowledge questions 1, 4 (p. 19) Multiple Choice questions 1-13; True or False questions 1-25; Matching questions 1-15; Short Answer questions 1-5 True or False questions 31-34, 38 (p. 20); Multiple Choice questions 45, 50 (p. 21) Molecule Formation **Book Resources** Quick Check questions 1-3 (p. 25) Outline Summary: Levels of Chemical Organization (p. 37)

OBJECTIVES	CONTENT	TEACHING RESOURCES
		Review question 1 (p. 40)
		Chapter Test questions 1, 2, 5 (p. 40)
		Critical Thinking question 17 (p. 40)
		▶ Discuss Table 2-1 Important Elements in the Human Body (p. 24). Discuss the four primary elements and the trace elements that make up the human body. Why are these important?
		▶ Discuss Clinical Application: Radioactive Isotopes (p. 30). Define radioactive isotopes and how they can both damage tissue and be beneficial. Have students give an example.
		Class Activity Divide the students into four teams. Assign each team one of the following terms: atom, element, molecule, compound. Ask each team to tell the class what their term means and to give examples of that term.
Describe the structure of an atom.	■ Levels of chemical organization (p. 23) □ Atoms (p. 23)	⊠▬ Slides 7-9 ▪ Levels of Chemical Organization questions 3, 4, 6, 10, 11 (pp. 14-15) ▪ Check Your Knowledge questions 2, 3, 5, 6 (p. 19) **Book Resources** Table 2-1 Important Elements in the Human Body (p. 24) Outline Summary: Levels of Chemical Organization (p. 37) Review questions 2, 3 (p. 40) Chapter Test questions 3, 4 (p. 40) ▶ Discuss Figure 2-1 A model of the atom (p. 24). Discuss how the core of an atom contains a nucleus composed of positively charged protons and uncharged neutrons and how the number of protons makes up the atomic number. *Class Activity Divide the class into teams. Assign each team an atom, such as oxygen, carbon, hydrogen or nitrogen. Ask each team to draw a model of the atom, identifying its proton, neutron, nucleus, and energy levels.* *Class Activity Bring in household items such as string, toothpicks, marshmallows, and so on. Have each student create a labeled model of an atom using the household objects.*

OBJECTIVES	CONTENT	TEACHING RESOURCES
Compare and contrast ionic and covalent types of chemical bonding.	■ Chemical bonding (p. 23) ☐ Ionic bonds (p. 23) ☐ Covalent bonds (p. 24)	▦▦ Slides 10-15 📖 Chemical Bonding questions 13-18 (p. 15) ✏ Multiple Choice questions 14-16; True or False questions 26-35 💿 Chemical Bonding **Book Resources** Figure 2-2 Ionic bonding (p. 26) Table 2-2 Important Ions in Human Body Fluids (p. 27) Quick Check questions 1-3 (p. 27) Outline Summary: Chemical Bonding (pp. 37-38) Review questions 4, 5 (p. 40) Critical Thinking question 12 (p. 40) Chapter Test questions 6-8, 21 (pp. 40-41) ▸ Discuss Figure 2-3 Covalent bonding (p. 27). How does covalent bonding occur? Discuss the difference between covalent bonding and ionic bonding. *Class Activity **Show the class Figure 2-2 Ionic bonding on page 27 of the text. After discussing the NaCl example, ask students to provide examples of other ionic bonds. If there are no answers, ask each student to research a type of ionic bond.*** *Class Activity **On separate pieces of paper, write down the symbols of important elements and ions in the human body. (Table 2-1, p. 24 and Table 2-2, p. 27) Hold each up one at a time and have students write down the name of the element or ion and the category in which it falls.*** *Class Activity **Ask pairs of students to take turns comparing and contrasting ionic and covalent types of chemical bonding. Also have them develop a list of important ions in human body fluids. Provide students with a brief explanation of the relevance of ions to health. Pick a pair to share their information with the class.***

2.1 Homework/Assignments:

2.1 Teacher's Notes:

LESSON 2.2

CRITICAL THINKING QUESTION

Mr. Hamilton, a diabetic patient at your clinic, is diagnosed with ketoacidosis by the physician. The physician explains that if a diabetic patient does not take the insulin that is normally prescribed, and if the resulting hyperglycemia is left untreated, it can lead to a critical condition called *ketoacidosis.* **This occurs when ketones, a group of acids that can build up in the bloodstream, accumulate and change the balance of acids in the blood. The patient's wife, Mrs. Hamilton, asks if you can explain, in basic terms, why such a change is potentially life-threatening.**

Guidelines: You can respond that Mr. Hamilton has experienced a change in the blood pH, a measure of the balance of acids in the blood. The pH of body fluids affects body chemistry so greatly that normal body function can be maintained only within a narrow range of pH. A decrease in the pH of blood can cause dangerous abnormalities in various pathways in the body and result in instability of many of the body systems.

OBJECTIVES	CONTENT	TEACHING RESOURCES
Distinguish between organic and inorganic chemical compounds.	■ Inorganic chemistry (p. 27) ☐ Water (p. 27) ☐ Acids, bases, and salts (p. 29)	Slides 17 Chemical Bonding questions 13-18 (p. 15) Inorganic Chemistry questions 19-30 (p. 16) Check Your Knowledge questions 7, 9, 11 (pp. 19-20) Multiple Choice questions 17-29; True or False questions 36-56; Short Answer questions 6, 7 True or False questions 35, 39 (p. 20); Multiple Choice questions 44, 46, 49 (pp. 20-21) **Book Resources** Quick Check question 1 (p. 31) Outline Summary: Inorganic Chemistry (p. 38) Outline Summary: Organic Chemistry (pp. 38-39) Review question 6 (p. 40) Chapter Test questions 8, 9 (p. 40) ▸ Discuss Research, Issues and Trends (p. 31) and how to convert between the metric system and our system of English measurements. Have students share their knowledge or experiences with the metric system. **Class Activity** *Divide students into teams. Have each team create a list of organic and inorganic compounds. See which team can list the most in a 5- or 10-minute period.*

Structure & Function of the Body, 13th ed.

Thibodeau/Patton

OBJECTIVES	CONTENT	TEACHING RESOURCES
Discuss the chemical characteristics of water.	☐ Water (p. 27)	Slides 18-19 Check Your Knowledge question 8 (p. 19) **Book Resources** Figure 2-4 Water-based chemistry (p. 28) Quick Check question 2 (p. 31) Outline Summary: Inorganic Chemistry, Part C (p. 38) Review question 7 (p. 40) Critical Thinking question 13 (p. 40) Chapter Test questions 10, 11, 22 (pp. 40-41) *Class Activity Hand out a copy of Figure 2-4 (p. 28; available on EILR) without the labels "dehydration synthesis" and "hydrolysis." Have students identify each reaction and discuss the processes.* *Class Activity Have small groups collaborate for a presentation on the chemical functions and importance of water in the body. Pick a group to make a presentation to the class.*
Explain the concept of pH.	☐ Acids, bases, and salts (p. 29)	Slides 20-22 Check Your Knowledge questions 10, 12 (p. 20) **Book Resources** Figure 2-5 The pH scale (p. 29) Quick Check question 3 (p. 31) Outline Summary: Inorganic Chemistry, Part D (p. 38) Review questions 8, 9 (p. 40) Critical Thinking question 14 (p. 40) Chapter Test questions 12, 13, 19, 20, 24 (pp. 40-41) ▸ Discuss Figure 2-5 The pH scale (p. 29) and consider some of the ways the body maintains the proper pH balance. Discuss its importance. *Class Activity Divide students into groups. Have them come up with a list of common substances and determine if each is acidic or basic. Have students bring in food products or cleaning agents. Are they acidic or basic?*

ELSEVIER

OBJECTIVES	CONTENT	TEACHING RESOURCES
		Class Activity Ask groups of three to develop an explanation of the concept of pH and to describe the pH scale and give examples of acids and bases. Have each group present their explanation to the class, then ask students which explanation was the most thorough.

2.2 Homework/Assignments:

2.2 Teacher's Notes:

LESSON 2.3

CRITICAL THINKING QUESTION

Mr. Vasquez has been told he is at risk for atherosclerosis. He has been told he has high levels of a "bad" blood protein. What kind of blood protein can cause atherosclerosis, and how does this condition come about? What kind of blood protein reduces the risk of atherosclerosis? What factors can increase and decrease the risk of atherosclerosis?

Guidelines: Mr. Vasquez has high levels of low-density lipoproteins (LDL) in his blood. LDLs carry cholesterol to cells, including the cells that line blood vessels. High-density lipoproteins (HDLs), on the other hand, carry "good" cholesterol away from cells and toward the liver for elimination from the body. A high proportion of HDL in the blood is associated with a low risk of developing atherosclerosis. Factors such as cigarette smoking decrease HDL levels and contribute to the risk of atherosclerosis. Lifestyle factors, such as proper exercise and diet, and medication can reduce the risk of atherosclerosis.

OBJECTIVES	CONTENT	TEACHING RESOURCES
Discuss the structure and function of the following four types of organic molecules: *carbohydrates, lipids, proteins,* **and** *nucleic acids.*	■ Organic chemistry (p. 31) ☐ Carbohydrates (p. 31) ☐ Lipids (p. 31) ☐ Proteins (p. 33) ☐ Nucleic acids (p. 35)	Slides 24-37 Organic Chemistry questions 31-40 (p. 16) Check Your Knowledge questions 13-15 (p. 20) Multiple Choice questions 30-44; True or False questions 57-82; Matching questions 16-30; Short Answer questions 8-10 True or False questions 36, 37, 40 (p. 20); Multiple Choice questions 41-43, 47, 48 (pp. 20-21) **Book Resources** Figure 2-6 Carbohydrates (p. 32) Figure 2-7 Triglyceride (p. 33) Figure 2-8 Phospholipids (p. 33) Figure 2-9 Protein (p. 34) Figure 2-10 Enzyme action (p. 35) Figure 2-11 DNA (p. 36) Table 2-4 Components of Nucleotides (p. 35) Quick Check questions 1-3 (p. 36) Outline Summary: Organic Chemistry (pp. 38-39) Review questions 10, 11 (p. 40) Critical Thinking question 15 (p. 40) Chapter Test questions 14-18, 23, 25 (pp. 40-41)

ELSEVIER

OBJECTIVES	CONTENT	TEACHING RESOURCES
		▶ Discuss Table 2-3 Major Types of Organic Compounds (p. 32). Define carbohydrates, lipids, proteins, and nucleic acids and list the functions of each.
		▶ Discuss the definition of a lipoprotein and the difference between HDL and LDL cholesterol and its link to atherosclerosis, as indicated in Clinical Application: Blood Lipoproteins (p. 35).
		▶ Discuss Biochemistry: Rosalind Franklin (p. 37). Consider how Franklin's work has helped us understand the human body and its functions.
		*Class Activity **Show the class Figure 2-6 Carbohydrates (p. 32), Figure 2-8 Phospholipids (p. 33), Figure 2-9 Protein (p. 34), and Figure 2-11 DNA (p. 36). Ask students to point out the key aspects of each figure.***
		*Class Activity **Have students share experiences of cholesterol testing and results.***
Performance Evaluation		Chapter 2 Computerized Test Bank questions
		Matching questions 1-15 (p. 19); Definitions questions 16-30 (p. 19); True or False questions 31-40 (p. 20); Multiple Choice questions 41-50 (pp. 20-21)
		Student Post-Test questions
		Book Resources
		Review questions (p. 40)
		Chapter Test (pp. 40-41)

Structure & Function of the Body, 13th ed.

Thibodeau/Patton

2.3 Homework/Assignments:

Divide the students into four groups. Ask each group to research the following terms: *carbohydrates, lipids, proteins,* and *nucleic acids.* Have the groups list the components of the compounds and the function of each.

Have students explore an area of interest related to this chapter's content, for example, cholesterol management, radiation therapy, acidosis, and alkalosis.

2.3 Teacher's Notes:

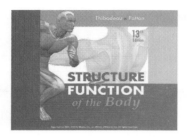

Slide 1

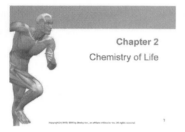

Chapter 2

Chemistry of Life

Slide 2

Learning Objectives

- Define the terms *atom, element, molecule,* and *compound*
- Describe the structure of an atom
- Compare and contrast ionic and covalent types of chemical bonding
- Distinguish between *organic* and *inorganic* chemical compounds

2

Slide 3

Learning Objectives (cont'd.)

- Discuss the chemical characteristics of water
- Explain the concept of pH
- Discuss the structure and function of the following types of organic molecules: *carbohydrate, lipid, protein,* and *nucleic acid*

3

Slide 4

Chapter 2
Lesson 2.1

Slide 5

Levels of Chemical Organization

- Elements, molecules, and compounds
  - **Element:** a pure substance; made up of only one kind of atom
  - **Molecule:** a group of atoms bound together to form a larger chemical unit
  - **Compound:** substances whose molecules have more than one kind of element

- What are the three subatomic particles? (protons, electrons, and neutrons)

Slide 6

Levels of Chemical Organization (cont'd.)

Important Elements in the Human Body

- What makes up molecules? (Atoms)

Slide 7

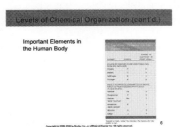

Levels of Chemical Organization (cont'd.)

- Atoms
  - **Nucleus:** central core of atom
    - **Proton:** positively charged particle in nucleus
    - **Neutron:** noncharged particle in nucleus
    - **Atomic number:** number of protons in the nucleus; determines the type of atom

- What makes up an atom's atomic mass? (The number of protons and neutrons combined.)

Thibodeau/Patton

Slide 8

A Model of the Atom

Neutron   Proton

Electron

Energy
levels
(shells)

Nucleus

- What is an orbital? (An orbital describes the limits within which electrons can move.)

- How many electrons can an orbital hold? (It can hold two.)

Slide 9

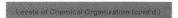

- **Energy levels:** Regions surrounding atomic nucleus that contain electrons
  - **Electron:** Negatively charged particle
  - May contain up to two electrons in the level closest to the nucleus
  - May contain up to eight electrons in the remaining levels
  - Energy increases with distance from the nucleus

- Describe an energy level. (Energy levels, or shells, are how orbitals are arranged.)

Slide 10

Chemical Bonding

- Chemical bonds form to make atoms more stable
  - Outermost energy level of each atom is full
  - Atoms may share electrons, or they may donate or borrow them to become stable

- What is a chemical bond? (the energy that holds two atoms together)

Slide 11

- Ionic bonds
  - Ions form when an atom gains or loses electrons in its outer energy level to become stable
    - **Positive ion:** Has lost electrons; indicated by superscript positive sign(s), as in Na^+ or Ca^+
    - **Negative ion:** Has gained electrons; indicated by superscript negative sign(s), as in Cl^-

- How is an ion formed? (Ions form when an atom gains or loses an electron to become stable.)

Structure & Function of the Body, 13th ed.
Thibodeau/Patton

Slide 12

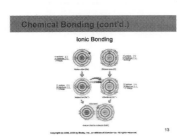

Chemical Bonding (cont'd.)

- Ionic bonds form when positive and negative ions attract each other because of electrical attraction
- **Electrolyte:** Molecule that dissociates, or breaks apart, in water to form individual ions; an ionic compound

- What is dissociation? (When molecules dissolve in water, because water molecules wedge between the ions and force them apart.)

Slide 13

Chemical Bonding (cont'd.)

Ionic Bonding

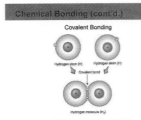

- What is the name given to molecules that form ions when dissolved in water? (Ionic bonds)

Slide 14

Chemical Bonding (cont'd.)

- Covalent bonds
  - Covalent bonds form when atoms that share electrons in their outer energy shell fill up and thus become stable
  - Covalent bonds do not ordinarily dissociate in water

- What is covalent chemical bonding? (When atoms fill up their energy levels by sharing electrons rather than by donating or receiving them.)

Slide 15

Chemical Bonding (cont'd.)

Covalent Bonding

- Are covalent bonds easily broken? Why or why not? (No, because the atoms must stay close to each other in covalent bonds.)

Slide 16

Chapter 2
Lesson 2.2

Slide 17

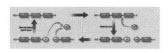

Inorganic Chemistry

- *Organic* molecules contain carbon–carbon covalent bonds and/or carbon–hydrogen covalent bonds; *inorganic* molecules do not
- Examples of inorganic molecules: water and some acids, bases, and salts

- Does the human body contain organic or inorganic molecules? (The human body contains both.)

Slide 18

Inorganic Chemistry (cont'd.)

- Water
  - Water is a solvent, a liquid into which solutes are dissolved, that forms aqueous solutions in the body
  - Water is involved in chemical reactions
    - **Dehydration synthesis:** Chemical reaction in which water is removed from small molecules, so they can be strung together to form a larger molecule
    - **Hydrolysis:** Chemical reaction in which water is added to the subunits of a large molecule to break it apart into smaller molecules

- What is an aqueous solution? (An aqueous solution is one in which water is the solvent for a mixture.)

Slide 19

Inorganic Chemistry (cont'd.)

Water-Based Chemistry

- Define dehydration synthesis. (A reaction in which small molecules are assembled into large molecules by removing water.)

Structure & Function of the Body, 13th ed.

Thibodeau/Patton

Slide 20

- Acids and Bases
  - Water molecules dissociate to form equal amounts of H⁺ (hydrogen ion) and OH⁻ (hydroxide ion)
  - **Acid:** Substance that shifts the H⁺/OH⁻ balance in favor of H⁺; opposite of base
  - **Base:** Substance that shifts the H⁺/OH⁻ balance against H⁺; also known as an *alkaline*; opposite of acid

- What solutions have an excess of hydrogen ions? (acids)
- How do acids differ from bases? (differ in amount of hydrogen atoms)

Slide 21

- **pH:** Mathematical expression of relative H⁺ concentration in an aqueous solution
  - A value of 7 is neutral (neither acid nor base)
  - Values above 7 are basic; pH values below 7 are acidic
  - Neutralization occurs when acids and bases mix and form salts
  - Buffers are chemical systems that absorb excess acids or bases and thus maintain a relatively stable pH

- What is pH? (a mathematical expression of relative H⁺ concentration in an aqueous solution)

Slide 22

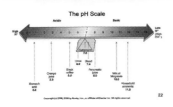

- What is a strong acid? (A strong acid is an acid that completely, or almost completely, dissociates to form H⁺ ions.)
- What is a weak acid? (A weak acid dissociates very little and therefore produces few excess H⁺ ions in solution.)

Slide 23

Chapter 2
Lesson 2.3

Slide 24

Organic Chemistry

- **Carbohydrates:** Sugars and complex carbohydrates
  - Contain carbon (C), hydrogen (H), oxygen (O)
  - Made up of six carbon subunits called *monosaccharides* or *single sugars* (e.g., glucose)
  - **Disaccharide:** Double sugar made up of two monosaccharide units (e.g., sucrose, lactose)

24

● What is the name of a substance in which many saccharides join together? (polysaccharide)

Slide 25

Organic Chemistry (cont'd.)

- **Polysaccharide:** Complex carbohydrate made up of many monosaccharide units (e.g., glycogen made up of many glucose units)
- The function of carbohydrates is to store energy for later use

25

Slide 26

Organic Chemistry (cont'd.)

26

● What is the advantage to the body (cells) of ingesting monosaccharides? (more energy readily available)

Slide 27

Organic Chemistry (cont'd.)

- **Lipids:** Fats and oils
  - Triglycerides
    - Made up of one glycerol unit and three fatty acids
    - Store energy for later use

27

● What are the three main types of lipids in the body? (trigylcerides, phospholipids, and cholesterol)

● How are they useful to the body? (Store energy, form cell membranes, and are useful in hormone production)

Thibodeau/Patton

Slide 28

Organic Chemistry (cont'd.)

Triglyceride

Glycerol —

Fatty acids

28

Slide 29

Organic Chemistry (cont'd.)

- Phospholipids
  - Similar to triglyceride structure, except with only two fatty acids and a phosphorus-containing group attached to a glycerol molecule
  - The hydrophilic head attracts water, and the double tail repels water, thus forming stable double layers (bilayers) in water
  - Form membranes of cells

29

Slide 30

Organic Chemistry (cont'd.)

Phospholipids

30

Slide 31

Organic Chemistry (cont'd.)

- Cholesterol
  - Molecules have a steroid structure made up of multiple rings
  - Stabilizes the phospholipid tails in cellular membranes
  - Converted into steroid hormones, such as estrogen, testosterone, and cortisone by the body

31

- Cholesterol is needed in the body.
- What are some examples of how excess cholesterol can cause harm? (Excess cholesterol can lead to high blood pressure, coronary heart disease, and stroke)

Slide 32

Organic Chemistry (cont'd.)

- Proteins
  - Very large molecules made up of amino acids held together in long, folded chains by peptide bonds
  - Structural proteins form the structures of the body
    □ Collagen is a fibrous protein that holds many tissues together
    □ Keratin forms tough waterproof fibers in the outer layer of the skin

32

- What is the lock-and-key model and how does it relate to enzymes? (Each enzyme has a shape that "fits" with the specific molecules it works on, similar to the way a key fits specific locks.)

Slide 33

Organic Chemistry (cont'd.)

- Functional proteins
  □ Participate in chemical processes (examples: hormones, cell membrane channels and receptors, enzymes)
  □ Enzymes
    ○ Catalysts help chemical reactions occur
    ○ Lock-and-key—each enzyme fits a particular molecule that it acts on, in the same way as only one key fits a lock
- Proteins can combine with other organic molecules to form glycoproteins or lipoproteins

33

- How do enzymes work? (they speed up chemical processes)

Slide 34

Organic Chemistry (cont'd.)

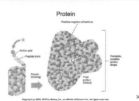

34

Slide 35

Organic Chemistry (cont'd.)

- Nucleic acids
  - Made up of nucleotide units
    □ Sugar (ribose or deoxyribose)
    □ Phosphate
    □ Nitrogen base (adenine, thymine or uracil, guanine, cytosine)
  - By directing the formation of structural and functional proteins, nucleic acids ultimately direct overall body structure and function

35

- What are the two forms of nucleic acid? (The two forms are deoxyribonucleic acid [DNA] and ribonucleic acid [RNA].)

Structure & Function of the Body, 13th ed.

Thibodeau/Patton

Slide 36

Organic Chemistry (cont'd.)

- DNA (deoxyribonucleic acid)
  - Used as the cell's "master code" for assembling proteins
  - Composed of deoxyribose (the sugar), phosphate, and four bases: cytosine, guanine, adenine, and thymine
  - Forms a double helix

- What is the role of DNA in the body? (It makes up the genetic code in the body.)

Slide 37

Organic Chemistry (cont'd.)

- RNA (ribonucleic acid)
  - Used as a temporary "working copy" of a gene (a portion of the DNA code)
  - Composed of ribose (the sugar), phosphate, and four bases: adenine, uracil, cytosine, and guanine

3 Lesson Plan
Cells and Tissues

TEACHING FOCUS

In this chapter, students will have the opportunity to learn about the basic structure and function of a cell, including the major cell parts. Students will be exposed to the major passive and active transport processes that move substances into and out of cells. Students will also have the opportunity to understand DNA, RNA, cellular reproduction, and the components of a neuron. Finally, students will be exposed to different types of tissues, including epithelial, connective, and muscle tissues.

MATERIALS AND RESOURCES

- ☐ Computer (all Lessons)
- ☐ Index cards (all Lessons)

LESSON CHECKLIST

Preparations for this lesson include:

- lecture
- guest speakers: biologist, medical assistant, physician, nurse
- student performance evaluation of all entry-level skills required for student comprehension and application of the principles of cellular biology, including:
  - ○ composition and function of cells
  - ○ movement of substances through cell membranes
  - ○ cell reproduction
  - ○ composition and function of tissues

KEY TERMS

active transport (p. 52)
adenosine triphosphate (ATP) (p. 50)
adipose tissue (p. 66)
anaphase (p. 59)
apoptosis (p. 48)
areolar connective tissue (p. 66)
arrangement (p. 60)
axon (p. 69)
basement membrane (p. 62)
blood (p. 67)
body composition (p. 70)
bone (p. 67)
cardiac muscle tissue (p. 68)
cartilage (p. 67)
cell body (p. 69)
centrioles (p. 48)
centromere (p. 58)
chondrocytes (p. 67)
chromatids (p. 58)
chromatin granules (p. 48)
chromosomes (p. 48)
cilia (p. 48)
cleavage furrow (p. 59)
collagen (p. 66)
complementary base pairing (p. 55)

connective tissue (p. 63)
crenation (p. 54)
cytoplasm (p. 45)
dendrites (p. 69)
deoxyribonucleic acid (DNA) (pp. 48, 55)
dialysis (p. 51)
diffusion (p. 50)
DNA replication (p. 57)
endoplasmic reticulum (p. 45)
epithelial tissue (p. 60)
fat tissue (p. 66)
fibrous connective tissue (p. 66)
filtration (p. 51)
flagellum (p. 48)
gene (p. 55)
genome (p. 57)
glia (p. 69)
goblet cells (p. 62)
Golgi apparatus (p. 46)
hematopoietic tissue (p. 67)
hypertonic (p. 54)
hypotonic (p. 54)
interphase (p. 57)
interstitial fluid (p. 44)
ion pump (p. 52)

ADDITIONAL RESOURCES

AnimationDirect (Book Companion CD)
Instructor's Electronic Resource (IER) (CD)
PowerPoint slides (CD, Evolve)
Test Bank (Evolve)

Legend

ESLR
EVOLVE Student
Learning Resource

EILR TB
EVOLVE Instructor
Learning Resource
Test Bank

AnimationDirect
on Book Companion
CD

PPT
PowerPoint
Slides

SG
Study
Guide

IRM
Instructor's
Resource Manual

Class Activities are indicated in **_bold italic_**.

Structure & Function of the Body, 13th ed.

Thibodeau/Patton

LESSON 3.1

PRETEST

1. _____ are the small structures that make up much of the cytoplasm.
2. _____ is the uphill movement of a substance through a living cell membrane.
3. An abnormal mass of proliferating cells is called a(n) _____.
4. Fat tissue is also called _____.
5. The small sphere in the center of the cell that controls cell reproduction is the
   _____.
6. Which of the following is NOT a type of muscle tissue?
   a. hematopoietic
   b. skeletal
   c. cardiac
   d. smooth
7. Which of the following is found in the lining of the inner surface of the stomach?
   a. stratified transitional epithelium
   b. pseudostratified epithelium
   c. simple columnar epithelium
   d. stratified squamous epithelium
8. The production of identical new cells is called
   a. DNA replication.
   b. mitosis.
   c. prophase.
   d. anaphase.
9. All the DNA in each cell of the body is called
   a. a centromere.
   b. transcription.
   c. messenger RNA.
   d. a genome.
10. The movement of water and solutes through a membrane because of a greater pushing force on one
    side of the membrane is called
    a. filtration.
    b. active transport.
    c. osmosis.
    d. dialysis.

Answers: 1. Organelles; 2. Active transport; 3. neoplasm; 4. adipose; 5. nucleus; 6. a; 7. c; 8. b; 9. d; 10. a

BACKGROUND ASSESSMENT

Question: What are the three main parts of a cell and, briefly, what does each do?
Answer: The three main parts of a cell are *plasma membrane, cytoplasm,* and *nucleus.* The plasma membrane surrounds the entire cell, forming its outer boundary. The cytoplasm is the living material inside the cell with the exception of the nucleus. The nucleus is the large, membrane-bound structure in most cells that contains the genetic code.

Question: How do the structures of different types of cells affect their functions? What are some examples of this?
Answer: Every human cell performs certain functions; some maintain the cell's survival, while others help maintain the body's survival. In many cases, the number and type of organelles allow cells to differ dramatically in terms of their specialized functions. For example, cells that contain large numbers of mitochondria, such as heart muscle cells, are capable of sustained work. The numerous mitochondria found in these cells supply the necessary energy required for the heart's rhythmic and ongoing contractions. The flagellum of a sperm cell is another example of the way a specialized organelle has a specific function. The sperm's flagellum propels it through the female's reproductive tract, increasing the chances of successful fertilization.

CRITICAL THINKING QUESTION

Bob is told that he has a benign tumor in his abdomen. He is scared and confused about what the tumor is and how it got there. How should you explain to Bob what a tumor is and how it develops?

Guidelines: Explain to Bob that as people age, their damaged, destroyed, or less functional cells are constantly replaced with new ones. This process is called *mitosis.* Tell Bob that the tumor is a mass of proliferating (reproducing and growing) cells called a *neoplasm,* which forms when the body loses the ability to control mitosis. You can also explain the four stages of mitosis, if he wants to know more about the process, but make sure he understands what you are explaining. Since Bob is concerned about the tumor, your scientific information may be too much for him to handle. Patients usually do not want to hear detailed, physiological descriptions.

OBJECTIVES	CONTENT	TEACHING RESOURCES
Identify and discuss the basic structure and function of the three major components of a cell.	■ Cells (p. 42) ☐ Size and shape (p. 43) ☐ Composition (p. 44) ☐ Parts of the cell (p. 44) – Plasma membrane (p. 44) – Cytoplasm (p. 45) – Nucleus (p. 48)	Slides 6-15 Cells questions 1-5 (p. 22) Check Your Knowledge question 1 (p. 29) Multiple Choice questions 1-13, 36-40; True or False questions 1-11, 13-16, 50-62; Matching questions 1-13; Short Answer questions 1, 2 **Book Resources** Figure 3-1 Structure of the plasma membrane (p. 44) Figure 3-2 General characteristics of the cell (p. 46) Table 3-1 Structure and Function of Some Major Cell Parts (p. 47) Science Applications: Microscopy (p. 49) Quick Check questions 1, 2 (p. 50) Review questions 1, 2 (p. 75) Critical Thinking questions 17 (p. 75) Chapter Test question 1 (p. 76) *Class Activity **Divide the students into three teams. Assign each team one of the following terms: plasma membrane, cytoplasm, and nucleus. Ask each team to research the term and then tell the class what their term means and how the terms relate to each other.***

ELSEVIER

Structure & Function of the Body, 13th ed.

Thibodeau/Patton

OBJECTIVES	CONTENT	TEACHING RESOURCES
List and briefly discuss the functions of the primary cellular organelles.	■ Relationship of cell structure and function (p. 47)	Slide 16 Cells questions 6-20 (p. 22) Check Your Knowledge questions 2-4 (p. 29) Matching questions 11, 12 (p. 30) Cell Structure diagram (p. 31) *e* Multiple Choice question 14; True or False question 12; Short Answer question 9 **Book Resources** Quick Check questions 3, 4 (p. 50) Review questions 3, 4 (p. 75) Chapter Test questions 2, 17-25 (pp. 76-77) *Class Activity* **Hand out the Cell Structure diagram (Study Guide p. 31). Ask each student to label the parts of a cell.** *Class Activity* **Divide students into teams. Ask each team to draw the parts of a cell, such as ribosomes and mitochondria, then have the teams discuss the function of each part. Have them refer to Table 3-1 (p. 47) for help.**

Compare the major passive and active transport processes that act to move substances through cell membranes.	■ Movement of substances through cell membranes (p. 50)
	
	□ Passive transport processes (p. 50)
	
	  − Diffusion (p. 50)
	
	  − Filtration (p. 51)
	
	□ Active transport processes (p. 52)
	
	  − Ion pumps (p. 52)
	
	  − Phagocytosis and pinocytosis (p. 53)
		Slides 17-24
		
		Movement of Substances Through Cell Membranes questions 21-32 (pp. 23-24)
		
		Applying What You Know questions 50, 51 (p. 27)
		
		Check Your Knowledge questions 3, 5 (p. 29)
		
		Matching questions 14-16 (p. 30)
		
		e Multiple Choice questions 15-24, 41, 42; True or False questions 17-27, 63-67; Short Answer questions 7, 10
		
		Passive Transport
		
		Active Transport
		
		Book Resources
		
		Table 3-2 Passive Transport Processes (p. 51)
		
		Figure 3-3 Diffusion (p. 52)

Thibodeau/Patton

OBJECTIVES	CONTENT	TEACHING RESOURCES
		Clinical Application: Tonicity (p. 54)
		Table 3-3 Active Transport Processes (p. 53)
		Figure 3-4 Sodium-potassium pump (p. 54)
		Quick Check questions 1-4 (p. 55)
		Review questions 6, 7 (p. 75)
		Critical Thinking question 18 (p. 75)
		Chapter Test questions 3, 4, 11 (p. 76)
		Class Activity ***Divide students into six teams. Assign each team a form of active or passive transport:*** **diffusion, osmosis, filtration, ion pump, phagocytosis,** *or* **pinocytosis.** ***Ask each group to sketch how that process works and to give real-life examples.***

3.1 Homework/Assignments:

3.1 Teacher's Notes:

LESSON 3.2

CRITICAL THINKING QUESTION

Jill, a patient at your office, is planning to start a family with her husband, Ed. She is concerned that, because one of Ed's family members suffers from multiple sclerosis, her children could be predisposed to the disease. What should you tell her?

Guidelines: Though it has not been proven, many scientists believe genes and heredity can play a role in developing MS. This is called *genetic susceptibility.* This means that there is a chance that Jill and Ed's children could be predisposed to the disease. It is not a certainty. Explain the concept of heredity and genetics to Jill in basic terms that are easy to understand, and let her know about any tests or new information about the disease. Couples who are concerned about genetic susceptibilities should be referred to a genetic specialist.

OBJECTIVES	CONTENT	TEACHING RESOURCES
Compare and discuss DNA and RNA and their function in protein synthesis.	■ Cell reproduction and heredity (p. 55) □ DNA molecules and genetic information (p. 55) — Genetic code (p. 55) — RNA molecules and protein synthesis (p. 56)	Slides 26-32 Cell Reproduction questions 33-41 (p. 24) Check Your Knowledge question 7 (p. 29) Matching questions 13, 17 (p. 30) Multiple Choice questions 25, 26, 43; True or False questions 28-34, 68-70; Short Answer questions 4-6, 8, 11, 12 **Book Resources** Table 3-4 Components of Nucleotides (p. 55) Figure 3-5 Protein synthesis (p. 56) Quick Check questions 1-3 (p. 59) Review questions 8-10 (p. 75) Critical Thinking questions 19, 20 (p. 75) Chapter Test questions 5-9 (p. 76) *Class Activity Divide students into small groups. Have each group discuss the differences and similarities between DNA and RNA.* *Class Activity Assign each student either* **transcription** *or* **translation.** *Ask selected students to describe his/her term and compare it with the other term.*
Discuss the stages of mitosis and explain the importance of cellular reproduction.	□ Cell division (p. 57) — DNA replication (p. 57) — Prophase (p. 58) — Metaphase (p. 58)	Slides 33-39 Word Find (p. 27) Crossword Puzzle (p. 28) Check Your Knowledge question 8 (p. 29)

Thibodeau/Patton

OBJECTIVES	CONTENT	TEACHING RESOURCES
	– Anaphase (p. 59) – Telophase (p. 59) – Results of cell division (p. 59)	Matching questions 18, 19 (p. 30) Mitosis diagram (p. 32) Multiple Choice questions 27-31; True or False questions 35-42; Matching questions 14-18; Short Answer question 3 **Book Resources** Figure 3-6 Mitosis (p. 58) Table 3-5 Stages of Cell Division (p. 59) Quick Check questions 4 (p. 59) Review questions 10-12 (p. 75) Chapter Test questions 12-16 (p. 76) *Class Activity **Have students create models of mitosis using household materials.*** *Class Activity **Have students explain the meaning of** daughter cells (p. 57).* *Class Activity **Divide students into four teams: prophase, metaphase, anaphase, and telophase. Ask each group to present their term to the class in the order in which the process occurs.***

3.2 Homework/Assignments:

3.2 Teacher's Notes:

LESSON 3.3

CRITICAL THINKING QUESTION

Jane's mother has always told her to take good care of her skin and to avoid chapping and scratches. Aside from aesthetic reasons, why is this a good idea? Describe the types and functions of skin cells.
Guidelines: Skin is made up of stratified squamous epithelium, consisting of several layers of closely packed cells. These multiple layers protect the body from microscopic invasion. Most microbes cannot work their way through a barrier of stratified squamous tissue, such as the tissue that composes the surface of skin and mucous membranes. However, if skin cracks because of chapping or if it is scratched, the solid barrier is broken, and microorganisms can enter the body and cause infection.

OBJECTIVES	CONTENT	TEACHING RESOURCES
Explain how epithelial tissue is grouped according to shape and arrangement of cells.	■ Tissues (p. 59) ☐ Epithelial tissue (p. 60) — Shape of cells (p. 60) — Arrangement of cells (p. 60) — Simple squamous epithelium (p. 61) — Stratified squamous epithelium (p. 61) — Simple columnar epithelium (p. 61) — Stratified transitional epithelium (p. 62) — Pseudostratified epithelium (p. 62) — Cuboidal epithelium (p. 63)	⊠ Slides 41-45 Tissues question 42, Epithelial section (p. 25) Check Your Knowledge question 10 (p. 30) Tissues diagram (pp. 33-34) *e* Multiple Choice question 32; True or False questions 43, 44; Matching questions 19, 24, 27, 30, 33, 35 **Book Resources** Table 3-6 Epithelial Tissues (p. 60) Table 3-7 Connective Tissues (p. 61) Table 3-8 Muscle and Nervous Tissue (p. 62) Figure 3-7 Classification of epithelial tissues (p. 63) Figure 3-8 Simple squamous and simple cuboidal epithelium (p. 64) Figure 3-9 Stratified squamous epithelium (p. 64) Figure 3-10 Simple columnar epithelium (p. 65) Figure 3-11 Stratified transitional epithelium (p. 65) Figure 3-12 Simple cuboidal epithelium (p. 66) Quick Check question 1 (p. 69) Review question 13 (p. 75) Chapter Test question 10 (p. 76) *Class Activity Have students create flashcards of the different types of epithelial tissues. Then have them quiz each other on the differences between them.*

OBJECTIVES	CONTENT	TEACHING RESOURCES
		*Class Activity **Call out a type of epithelial tissue and ask students to come up with examples of that tissue.***
List and briefly discuss the major types of connective and muscle tissue.	☐ Connective tissue (p. 63) – Areolar and adipose connective tissue (p. 66) – Fibrous connective tissue (p. 66) – Bone and cartilage (p. 67) – Blood and hematopoietic tissue (p. 67) ☐ Muscle tissue (p. 68) – Skeletal muscle tissue (p. 68) – Cardiac muscle tissue (p. 68) – Smooth muscle tissue (p. 68)	⊠▣ Slides 46-50 📖 Tissues question 42, Connective and Muscle sections (p. 25) 📖 Applying What You Know question 52 (p. 27) 📖 Check Your Knowledge question 9 (p. 30) 📖 Matching question 20 (p. 30) *e* Multiple Choice questions 33, 35; True or False questions 46, 47, 49; Matching questions 21-23, 26, 29, 31, 32 **Book Resources** Figure 3-13 Adipose tissue (p. 66) Figure 3-14 Dense fibrous connective tissue (p. 67) Figure 3-15 Bone tissue (p. 67) Figure 3-16 Cartilage (p. 67) Figure 3-17 Blood (p. 68) Figure 3-18 Skeletal muscle (p. 68) Figure 3-19 Cardiac muscle (p. 69) Figure 3-20 Smooth muscle (p. 69) Quick Check questions 2, 3 (p. 69) Review questions 14, 15 (p. 75) *Class Activity **Hand out copies of the Tissues diagram (Study Guide pp. 33-34). Ask each student to label each tissue drawing. Next, ask students to describe how to differentiate between the types of tissues.*** *Class Activity **Identify various parts of the body—such as blood, lungs, and tendons—and ask students to name the tissue type.***
List the three structural components of a neuron.	☐ Nervous tissue (p. 69)	⊠▣ Slide 51 📖 Tissues question 42, Nervous section (p. 25) *e* Multiple Choice question 34; True or False questions 45, 48; Matching questions 20, 25, 28, 34

Thibodeau/Patton

OBJECTIVES	CONTENT	TEACHING RESOURCES
		Book Resources
		Quick Check question 4 (p. 69)
		Review question 16 (p. 75)
		*Class Activity **Hand out unlabeled copies of Figure 3-21 (p. 69; available on EILR or IER). Ask students to label the parts of the nervous tissue.***
Performance Evaluation		*e* Chapter 3 Computerized Test Bank questions
		Critical Thinking questions (p. 33); Classroom Application (p. 34); Lab Activities (p. 34); Practical/Creative Learning Activities (p. 34); Student Assignment (pp. 35-37)
		e Student Post-Test questions
		Book Resources
		Review questions (p. 75)
		Critical Thinking questions (p. 75)
		Chapter Test (pp. 75-76)

3.3 Homework/Assignments:

3.3 Teacher's Notes:

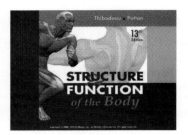

Slide 1

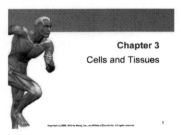

Chapter 3
Cells and Tissues

Slide 2

Learning Objectives

- Identify and discuss the basic structure and function of the three major components of a cell
- List and briefly discuss the functions of the primary cellular organelles
- Compare the major passive and active transport processes that function to move substances through cell membranes

---

Slide 3

Learning Objectives (cont'd.)

- Compare and discuss DNA and RNA and their functions in protein synthesis
- Discuss the stages of mitosis and explain the importance of cellular reproduction

---

ELSEVIER

Structure & Function of the Body, 13th ed.

Thibodeau/Patton

Slide 4

Learning Objectives (cont'd.)

- Explain how epithelial tissue is grouped according to shape and arrangement of cells
- List and briefly discuss the major types of connective and muscle tissue
- List the three structural components of a neuron

4

Slide 5

Chapter 3
Lesson 3.1

5

Slide 6

Size and Shape

- Human cells vary considerably in size
- All are microscopic
- Cells differ notably in shape
- Cytoplasm contains specialized organelles surrounded by a plasma membrane

6

- An ovum has a diameter of 150 micrometers.

- A red blood cell has a diameter of 7.5 micrometers.

- What are some of the shapes of different cell types? (some are flat, brick shaped, and irregular)

Slide 7

Composition

- Cytoplasm contains specialized organelles
- A plasma membrane surrounds each cell
- Organization of cytoplasmic substances is important for life
- The small, circular body called the *nucleus* is inside the cell

7

- What is interstitial fluid? (fluid between the cells)

- What does the word "organelles" mean? (small structures "little organs" that comprise cells)

Thibodeau/Patton

Slide 8

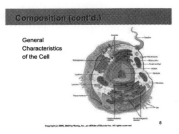

Composition (cont'd.)

General
Characteristics
of the Cell

- What are the three major parts of a cell? (plasma membrane, cytoplasm, and nucleus)

- Ask students to cite the functions of specific cell components.

Slide 9

Parts of a Cell

- Plasma membrane
  - Forms outer boundary of cell
  - Only 7 nm (3/10,000,000 of an inch) thick
  - Thin, two-layered membrane of phospholipids containing proteins form the framework of the plasma membrane
  - Is selectively permeable

- What is cholesterol, and what is its function? (Cholesterol is a fat, and it is a component of the plasma membrane)

- What are some of the other functions of the plasma membrane? (acts as a gateway for passage of substances, allows for tissue typing, and contains receptors for protein binding)

Slide 10

Parts of a Cell (cont'd.)

- Cytoplasm
  - Internal living material of cells
  - **Organelles:** Small structures that make up most of the cytoplasm
- **Ribosomes:** May attach to rough endoplasmic reticulum (ER) or lie free in cytoplasm

- What is the primary function of ribosomes? (to manufacture proteins)

Slide 11

Parts of a Cell (cont'd.)

- Endoplasmic Reticulum (ER)
  - Network of connecting sacs and canals
  - Carries substances through cytoplasm

- What are the two types of ER? How do they function? (smooth and rough; the smooth ER makes new membranes for the cell; the rough ER receives and transports newly made proteins)

ELSEVIER

Thibodeau/Patton

Slide 12

Parts of a Cell (cont'd.)

- Golgi apparatus
  - Group of flattened sacs stacked on one another near nucleus
- Mitochondria
  - Composed of inner and outer membranes
  - Each contains one DNA molecule

Copyright (c) 2008, 2005 by Mosby, Inc., an affiliate of Elsevier Inc. All rights reserved.   12

- Explain how the Golgi apparatus works. What is its primary function? How does this process take place? (The primary function of the Golgi apparatus is to make mucus. It does this by chemically processing molecules received from the ER.)

- What are vesicles? (little sacs contained within the Golgi apparatus)

Slide 13

Parts of a Cell (cont'd.)

- Lysosomes
  - Membranous-walled organelles
  - Contain digestive enzymes
- Centrioles
  - Paired organelles
  - Fine tubules that lie at right angles to each other near the nucleus

Copyright (c) 2008, 2005 by Mosby, Inc., an affiliate of Elsevier Inc. All rights reserved.   13

- Describe the protective function of lysosomes. (They digest and destroy microbes that may enter the cell.)

- What is the role that centrioles play during cell division? (Centrioles move away from each other during mitosis to form a network of spindle fibers. These fibers serve as "guidewires" to assist chromosomes to move to opposite ends of the cell in a later mitotic phase.)

Slide 14

Parts of a Cell (cont'd.)

- Cilia
  - Fine hairlike extensions found on free or exposed surfaces of some cells
- Flagellum
  - Single projection extending from cell surfaces
  - Much larger than cilia

Copyright (c) 2008, 2005 by Mosby, Inc., an affiliate of Elsevier Inc. All rights reserved.   14

- What are two additional properties of cilia? (capable of moving in a wavelike fashion; often have highly specialized functions, such as to propel mucus upward from the respiratory tract)

- What is unique about flagella with regard to humans? (Sperm cells are the only human cells that contain flagella.)

Slide 15

Parts of a Cell (cont'd.)

- Nucleus
  - Controls every organelle in the cytoplasm
  - Controls cell reproduction
  - Contains the genetic code
  - Component structures include nuclear envelope, nucleoplasm, and chromatin granules

Copyright (c) 2008, 2005 by Mosby, Inc., an affiliate of Elsevier Inc. All rights reserved.   15

- What is the genetic code? (information stored in each gene)

- Why is the genetic code relevant to our study? (determines cell structure and function and therefore heredity; diseases can be inherited)

ELSEVIER

Structure & Function of the Body, 13th ed.
Thibodeau/Patton

Slide 16

Relationship Between Cell Structure and Function

- Regulation of life processes
- Survival of species through reproduction of the individual
- Relationship of structure to function is apparent in number and type of organelles seen in different cells

16

- What are some examples of specialized organelles? (Lysosomes, ribosomes, golgi apparatus)

Slide 17

Movement of Substances Through Cell Membranes

- Passive transport processes
  - Do not require added energy and result in movement "down a concentration gradient"
- Types of passive transport include
  - Diffusion
    - Osmosis
    - Dialysis
  - Filtration

17

- What are the two transport processes for moving substances into and out of cells? (Active and passive)

- How are they different? (Active transport requires cellular energy, passive does not.)

Slide 18

Movement of Substances Through Cell Membranes (cont d.)

Passive Transport Processes

18

- To form urine in the kidney, wastes are filtered out of the blood into the kidney tubules because of differences in hydrostatic pressure (filtration).

Slide 19

Movement of Substances Through Cell Membranes (cont d.)

- Passive transport processes
  - Diffusion
    - Substances scatter themselves evenly throughout an available space
    - It is unnecessary to add energy to the system
    - Movement is from high to low concentration
    - Osmosis and dialysis are specialized examples of diffusion

19

- What are osmosis and dialysis? (Osmosis is the movement of water through a semipermeable membrane. In dialysis, solutes also can cross the membrane.)

- What are solutes? (substances dissolved in water)

- How is equilibrium achieved? (A concentration gradient exists. Movement of water and solutes occur. Equilibrium is achieved when there is an equilibration between concentrations of two solutions after an interval of time.)

Structure & Function of the Body, 13th ed.
Thibodeau/Patton

Slide 20

- Passive transport processes
  - Filtration
    - Movement of water and solutes through a membrane because of a greater pushing force on one side of the membrane
    - This force is called *hydrostatic pressure*
    - Responsible for urine formation

20

- Give some additional examples of filtration.

Slide 21

Movement of Substances Through Cell Membranes (cont'd)

- Active transport processes
  - Occurs only in living cells
  - Movement of substances is "up the concentration gradient"
  - Requires energy from adenosine triphosphate (ATP)

21

- What is adenosine triphosphate (ATP)? (energy produced by the mitochondria that is used for active transport)

Slide 22

Active Transport Processes

22

Slide 23

- Active transport processes
  - Ion pumps
    - An ion pump is a protein complex in the cell membrane called a *carrier*
    - Ion pumps use energy from ATP to move substances across cell membranes against their concentration gradients

23

- Energy is needed!

Structure & Function of the Body, 13th ed.
Thibodeau/Patton

Slide 24

Movement of Substances Through Cell Membranes (cont'd)

- Active transport processes
  - Phagocytosis and Pinocytosis
    - Both are active transport mechanisms, because they require cell energy
    - Phagocytosis is a protective mechanism often used to destroy bacteria
    - Pinocytosis is used to incorporate fluids or dissolved substances into cells

24

- How do phagocytosis and pinocytosis work? (Phagocytosis process permits a cell to engulf and "eat" foreign material. Pinocytosis is a mechanism that incorporates fluid or solutes into cells and traps them.)

- The body uses both active and passive transport processes in order to function.

Slide 25

Chapter 3
Lesson 3.2

25

Slide 26

Cell Reproduction

- Mitosis
  - The process of cell reproduction
  - During the process, one cell divides to become two cells
  - Tied closely to the production of proteins

26

- What molecules play a crucial role in protein synthesis and mitosis? (DNA and RNA)

Slide 27

Cell Reproduction (cont'd)

- DNA molecule and genetic information
  - Chromosomes are composed largely of DNA
    - DNA are shaped like a long, narrow spiral staircase
    - Each step in the DNA ladder consists of a pair of bases
      - Only two combinations of bases occur
      - This is called *complementary base pairing*

27

- What are the components of DNA? (sugar, phosphate, nitrogen bases)

- What are the base pairs? (adenine-thymine and guanine-cytosine)

ELSEVIER

Thibodeau/Patton

Slide 28

Genetic Code

- DNA molecule and genetic information
  - Genes dictate formation of enzymes and other proteins by ribosomes
  - Although the types of base pairs in all chromosomes are the same, the sequence varies
  - Each gene directs the synthesis of a specific protein
  - **Genetic code:** The storage of information in each gene

Copyright (c) 2008, 2005 by Mosby, Inc., an affiliate of Elsevier Inc. All rights reserved.   28

- How many chromosomes are in human body cells? (46)

Slide 29

Genetic Code (cont'd.)

- RNA molecules and protein synthesis
  - Ribonucleic acid (RNA) transfers genetic information from the nucleus to the cytoplasm
  - RNA composition
    - **Sugar:** Ribose
    - **Phosphate**
    - **Nitrogen bases:** Cytosine, guanine, adenine, uracil

Copyright (c) 2008, 2005 by Mosby, Inc., an affiliate of Elsevier Inc. All rights reserved.   29

- Where does protein synthesis occur? (ribosomes and endoplasmic reticulum)

Slide 30

Genetic Code (cont'd.)

- RNA molecules and protein synthesis
  - Transcription
    - Double-stranded DNA separates to form messenger RNA (mRNA)
    - Each strand of mRNA duplicates a particular gene (base-pair sequence) from a segment of DNA
    - mRNA molecules pass from the nucleus to the cytoplasm, where they direct protein synthesis in ribosomes and ER

Copyright (c) 2008, 2005 by Mosby, Inc., an affiliate of Elsevier Inc. All rights reserved.   30

Slide 31

Genetic Code (cont'd.)

- Translation
  - Involves synthesis of proteins in cytoplasm by ribosome
  - Requires use of information contained in mRNA to direct the choice and sequencing of the building blocks called amino acids
  - As blocks of amino acids are assembled into proper sequence, a protein strand forms

Copyright (c) 2008, 2005 by Mosby, Inc., an affiliate of Elsevier Inc. All rights reserved.   31

- What happens after the protein strand is formed? (The protein strand either folds in, on itself, or combines with another strand to form a complete protein molecule.)

ELSEVIER

Slide 32

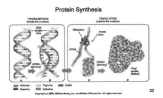

- Go through the steps of transcription and translation as shown in the figure.

Slide 33

Cell Division

- Reproduction of cell by division of the nucleus (mitosis) and the cytoplasm
- DNA replication
  - Process by which each half of a DNA molecule becomes a whole molecule identical to the original DNA molecule
  - Precedes mitosis

- What is interphase? (A "resting" cellular phase, where no active cell division occurs)

Slide 34

Cell Division (cont'd.)

- Mitosis
  - Process in cell division in which identical chromosomes (DNA molecules) to each new cell are formed when the original cell divides
  - Enables cells to reproduce their own kind

- Name the four stages of mitosis. (prophase, metaphase, anaphase, telophase)

Slide 35

Cell Division (cont'd.)

Mitosis

- What are some of the distinctive characteristics of each stage of mitosis?

  - Interphase: Resting

  - Prophase: Organization

  - Metaphase: Chromosome alignment

  - Anaphase: Cleavage furrow, beginning of cell division

  - Telophase: Cell division completed

Structure & Function of the Body, 13th ed.

Thibodeau/Patton

Slide 36

Stages of Mitosis

- Prophase—first stage
  - Chromatin granules become organized
  - Chromosomes (pairs of linked chromatids) appear
  - Chromatids are held together by a beadlike structure called a *centromere*
  - Centrioles move away from each other
  - Spindle fibers form between centrioles
  - The nuclear envelope disappears, freeing genetic material

Slide 37

Stages of Mitosis (cont'd.)

- Metaphase—second stage
  - The nuclear envelope and nucleolus have disappeared
  - Chromosomes align across the center of each cell
  - Spindle fibers attach themselves to each chromatid

- What do spindle fibers resemble? (a network of tubules)

Slide 38

Stages of Mitosis (cont'd.)

- Anaphase—third phase
  - Centromeres break apart
  - Separated chromatids are now called chromosomes once again
  - Chromosomes are pulled to opposite ends of the cell
  - A cleavage furrow develops at end of anaphase
    - Beginning to divide cell into two daughter cells

- Daughter cells have identical genetic characteristics. Each may later undergo mitosis.

- *Daughter cells* is the term used to define the "new" cells formed, somewhat like "offspring."

Slide 39

Stages of Mitosis (cont'd.)

- Telophase—fourth stage
  - Cell division is completed
  - Nuclei appear in daughter cells
  - Nuclear envelope and nucleoli appear
  - Cytoplasm and organelles divide equally
  - Daughter cells become fully functional

- What are the results of cell division? (the production of identical new cells)

- Discuss neoplasm.

Thibodeau/Patton

Slide 40

Chapter 3
Lesson 3.3

Slide 41

Tissues

- Epithelial tissue
  - Covers body and lines body cavities
  - Cells packed closely together with little matrix
  - Classified by shape and arrangement of cells

- What are the four shapes of epithelial cells? (squamous, cuboidal, columnar, transitional)

- In what ways can they be arranged? (simple or stratified)

- What is the purpose of the various arrangements; remember structure determines function. (to facilitate bodily activities)

Slide 42

Tissues (cont'd.)

- Epithelial tissue
  - Simple squamous epithelium
    - Single layer of very thin, irregularly shaped cells
    - Transport is function (such as absorption of oxygen into blood)
    - Located in alveoli of lungs, lining of blood and lymphatic vessels
  - Stratified squamous epithelium
    - Several layers of closely packed cells
    - Protection is primary function

- Where can stratified squamous cells be found? (surface of skin and mucous membranes)

Slide 43

Tissues (cont'd.)

- Epithelial tissue
  - Simple columnar epithelium
    - Single layer of tall, narrow cells
    - Contain mucus-producing goblet cells
  - Stratified transitional epithelium
    - Up to 10 layers of roughly cuboidal-shaped cells that distort to squamous shape when stretched
    - Functions as protection
    - Found in body areas subject to stress and that stretch, such as urinary bladder

- What is the special function of simple columnar epithelium? (mucus production)

- Where can these cells be found? (lining the inner surface of the stomach, intestines, and some areas of the respiratory and reproductive tracts)

ELSEVIER

Structure & Function of the Body, 13th ed.

Thibodeau/Patton

Slide 44

- Epithelial tissue
  - Pseudostratified epithelium
    - Single layer of tall cells that wedge together to appear as if there are two or more layers
  - Simple cuboidal epithelium
    - Form tubules specialized for secretory activity
    - Usually form clusters called *glands*

44

- How does pseudostratified epithelium differ from stratified epithelium? (Each cell touches basement membrane.)

- What are examples of substances secreted through glands of tubules made up of simple cuboidal epithelial cells? (saliva, digestive juices, sweat, and hormones)

Slide 45

Classification of Epithelial Tissues

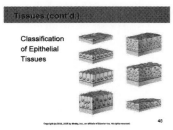

45

- Note these structural differences.

Slide 46

- Connective tissue
  - Most abundant tissue in body
  - Most widely distributed tissue in body
  - Multiple types, appearances, and functions
  - Relatively few cells in intercellular matrix

46

- Where is connective tissue found? (skin, membranes, muscles, bones, nerves and all internal organs)

Slide 47

- Connective tissue
  - Types
    - **Areolar:** Glue that holds organs together
    - **Adipose (fat):** Lipid storage is primary function
    - **Fibrous:** Consists of strong, white collagen fibers

47

- What is the most widely distributed of all connective tissue? (areolar)

- What type of tissue provides great strength and flexibility but no stretch? (fibrous)

- What type of tissue helps insulate? (adipose)

Slide 48

- Connective tissue types
  - Bone—matrix is hard and calcified
    - Forms structural building blocks called *osteons*
    - Function in support and protection, stores calcium
  - Cartilage—chondrocyte is cell type
    - Differs from bone; matrix is consistency of a firm plastic or gristle-like gel
  - Blood and hematopoietic
    - Blood—matrix is fluid
    - Hematopoietic—bloodlike connective tissue found in marrow cavities

48

- ● Osteons are also called *Haversian systems*.

- ● What is the function of hematopoietic tissue? (to produce blood cells)

Slide 49

- Muscle tissue
  - Types
    - Skeletal—also called *striated* or *voluntary*
      - Attaches to bones
      - Control is voluntary
      - Striations apparent when viewed under a microscope

49

- ● Describe the structure and distinctive traits of skeletal muscle cells.

Slide 50

- Muscle tissue types
  - Cardiac—also called *striated involuntary*
    - Produces regular, involuntary contractions of cardiac muscle to produce heartbeat
    - Has faint cross striations and thicker dark bands called *intercalated disks*
  - Smooth—also called *visceral*
    - Involuntary control
    - Appears smooth; without cross striations
    - Has only one nucleus per fiber
    - Forms walls of blood vessels, hollow organs such as intestines and other tube-shaped structures

50

- ● Give some examples of smooth muscles. (digestive tract, respiratory tubes)

Slide 51

- Nervous tissue
  - Provides rapid communication between body structures and for control of body functions
  - Example is spinal cord tissue
  - Consists of two cell types: *neuron* and *glia*
    - Glia (neuroglia)—supportive and connecting cells
    - Neurons—conducting cell

51

- ● Give a general description of a neuron.

- ● What does an axon do? (transmits impulse away from cell body)

- ● What does a dendrite do? (carries impulses toward the cell body)

ELSEVIER

Structure & Function of the Body, 13th ed.

Thibodeau/Patton

4 Lesson Plan
Organ Systems of the Body

TEACHING FOCUS

In this chapter, students will have the opportunity to learn about the terms *organs* and *organ systems*. They will be exposed to the 11 organ systems of the body and will have the opportunity to understand each system's organs and functions. Students will also have the opportunity to identify and discuss the major subdivisions of the male and female reproductive systems.

MATERIALS AND RESOURCES

☐ Computer (all Lessons)
☐ Index cards (Lesson 4.1)

LESSON CHECKLIST

Preparations for this lesson include:

- lecture
- guest speakers: medical assistant, physician, nurse
- method of student evaluation for entry-level knowledge to achieve competency, including comprehension of:
  - definitions of organs and organ systems
  - the 11 major organ systems of the body
  - the location of the major organs of each major organ system
  - the functions of each major organ system
  - the major subdivisions of the reproductive system

KEY TERMS

accessory organ (p. 90)
adrenal glands (p. 85)
alveoli (p. 86)
accessory structures (p. 80)
appendicitis (p. 88)
arteries (p. 85)
bladder (p. 88)
bronchi (p. 86)
capillaries (p. 85)
cardiac muscle (p. 83)
cardiovascular system (p. 85)
circulatory system (p. 85)
digestive system (p. 88)
endocrine system (p. 84)
fallopian tubes (p. 90)
gastrointestinal (GI) tract (p. 88)
genitalia (p. 90)
gonads (p. 90)
hormones (p. 84)
hypothalamus (p. 84)
integumentary system (p. 80)
involuntary muscle (p. 83)
joints (p. 83)
larynx (p. 86)
kidneys (p. 88)
lymph nodes (p. 86)
lymphatic system (p. 86)
lymphatic vessels (p. 86)
mammary glands (p. 90)
nerve impulses (p. 84)
nervous system (p. 83)
nose (p. 86)
organ (p. 79)
ova (p. 90)
ovaries (p. 90)

pancreas (p. 85)
parathyroid (p. 85)
penis (p. 90)
pineal gland (p. 84)
pituitary gland (p. 84)
prostate (p. 90)
radiography (p. 89)
reproductive system (p. 90)
respiratory system (p. 86)
scrotum (p. 90)
sense organs (p. 84)
skeletal system (p. 80)
smooth muscle (p. 83)
sperm (p. 90)
spleen (p. 86)
stimuli (p. 84)
system (p. 79)
testes (p. 90)
thoracic duct (p. 86)
thymus (p. 85)
thymus gland (p. 86)
thyroid (p. 85)
tonsils (p. 86)
trachea (p. 86)
urethra (p. 88)
urinary system (p. 88)
urine (p. 89)
uterine tubes (p. 90)
uterus (p. 90)
vagina (p. 90)
vas deferens (p. 90)
veins (p. 85)
voluntary muscles (p. 83)
vulva (p. 90)

ADDITIONAL RESOURCES

AnimationDirect (Book Companion CD)
Instructor's Electronic Resource (IER) (CD)
PowerPoint slides (CD, Evolve)
Test Bank (Evolve)

Legend

ESLR
EVOLVE Student
Learning Resource

EILR TB
EVOLVE Instructor
Learning Resource
Test Bank

AnimationDirect
on Book Companion
CD

PPT
PowerPoint
Slides

SG
Study
Guide

IRM
Instructor's
Resource Manual

Class Activities are indicated in ***bold italic.***

ELSEVIER

Structure & Function of the Body, 13th ed.

Thibodeau/Patton

LESSON 4.1

PRETEST

1. The body system that includes skin and hair is the _____.
2. The brain, spinal cord, and nerves are organs of the _____ system.
3. Tiny, thin-walled sacs of the lungs are called _____.
4. The mammary glands are part of the _____ system.
5. Which of the following is NOT a type of endocrine gland?
   a. spleen
   b. pituitary gland
   c. hypothalamus
   d. thyroid gland
6. A structure made up of two or more kinds of tissue that can perform a more complex function than any tissue alone is a(n)
   a. system.
   b. appendage.
   c. organ.
   d. joint.
7. Skeletal muscles are also called
   a. cardiac muscles.
   b. voluntary muscles.
   c. involuntary muscles.
   d. smooth muscles.
8. Arteries and veins are part of what system?
   a. nervous
   b. endocrine
   c. lymphatic
   d. circulatory
9. The whitish, watery fluid that contains lymphocytes, proteins, and some fatty molecules is called
   a. lymph.
   b. blood.
   c. pancreatic juice.
   d. urine.
10. Which of the following is classified as an accessory organ of the digestive system?
   a. pharynx
   b. esophagus
   c. liver
   d. rectum

Answers: 1. integumentary system; 2. nervous; 3. alveoli; 4. female reproductive; 5. a; 6. c; 7. b; 8. d; 9. a; 10. c

BACKGROUND ASSESSMENT

Question: What is the name for a group of organs arranged in such a way that they can perform a more complex function than any organ alone? Give a few examples of these groups and describe what they do.
Answer: A group of organs is called an organ *system.* Examples of systems include the skeletal system, which provides a rigid framework for support and protection of the body, and the muscular system, which produces movement, maintains body posture, and generates the heat required for maintaining a constant core body temperature.

ELSEVIER

Structure & Function of the Body, 13th ed.
Thibodeau/Patton

Question: What is the purpose of the integumentary system? What makes up this system?

Answer: The integumentary system is composed of the skin, hair, nails, sense receptors, sweat glands, and oil glands. Its primary function is protection. The skin protects underlying tissue against invasion by harmful bacteria, bars entry of most chemicals, and minimizes the chances of mechanical injury to underlying structures. In addition, the skin regulates body temperature by sweating, and it synthesizes important chemicals and functions as a sophisticated sense organ.

CRITICAL THINKING QUESTION

Roger lost one of his kidneys due to an accident as a child. His doctor has advised him to avoid contact sports. Why did the doctor recommend this? What are the advantages of having two kidneys?

Guidelines: Roger's doctor wants him to avoid contact sports because she does not want Roger to damage his remaining kidney. If it is damaged, he could completely lose kidney function and would have to rely on dialysis to clean his blood of waste, because kidney function—natural or artificial—is essential for life. The reason people are born with two kidneys is that a paired-organ arrangement allows for the accidental loss of one organ without immediate threat to survival.

OBJECTIVES	CONTENT	TEACHING RESOURCES
Define and contrast the terms *organ* and *organ system*.	■ Organ systems of the body (p. 79)	Slide 4 Unscramble the Words (p. 38) Check Your Knowledge questions 4, 10 (p. 41) Multiple Choice question 1; True or False questions 1-3, 51; Short Answer questions 1, 2 Student Assignment question 23 (p. 47); Completion questions 21-30 (p. 47) 3D Turntable **Book Resources** Science Applications: Radiography (p. 89) Outline Summary: Definitions and Concepts (p. 93) Review question 1 (p. 95) Clear View of the Human Body *Class Activity Divide students into two teams. Assign each team either **organ** or **organ system**. Have the teams write a description of each term and list examples of each. Have students match up their organs with their organ systems.*
List the 11 major organ systems of the body.	■ Organ systems of the body (p. 79)	Word Find question 41 (p. 39) **Book Resource** Review question 8 (p. 96) Clear View of the Human Body

OBJECTIVES	CONTENT	TEACHING RESOURCES
		Class Activity **Dictate the list of organ systems to the class, but delete several systems. Ask students to identify the missing systems.**
Identify and locate the major organs of each major organ system.	■ Organ systems of the body (p. 79) ☐ Integumentary system (p. 80) ☐ Skeletal system (p. 80) ☐ Muscular system (p. 83) ☐ Nervous system (p. 83) ☐ Endocrine system (p. 84) ☐ Cardiovascular (circulatory) system (p. 85) ☐ Lymphatic system (p. 86) ☐ Respiratory system (p. 86) ☐ Digestive system (p. 88) ☐ Urinary system (p. 88) ☐ Reproductive system (p. 90) ■ The body as a whole (p. 92)	⊠▀ Slides 5-14 ▓ Organ Systems of the Body questions 1-22 (p. 36) ▓ Multiple Choice questions 2, 7 (p. 41) ▓ Matching questions 11-20 (p. 42) *e* Multiple Choice questions 2, 4-6, 8, 11, 14-17, 19, 20, 23, 24, 26, 27, 30, 36, 38-41; True or False questions 4, 5, 9-12, 14, 15, 18, 23, 25-29, 31, 32, 35, 37-40, 52-55, 57-59 ▓ Student Assignment questions 3, 9, 11-20, 24, 26, 31-34 (pp. 46-48) **Book Resources** Figure 4-1 Body systems and their organs (p. 81) Figure 4-2 Integumentary system (p. 82) Figure 4-3 Skeletal system (p. 82) Figure 4-4 Muscular system (p. 83) Figure 4-5 Nervous system (p. 84) Figure 4-6 Endocrine system (p. 85) Quick Check questions 2, 4 (p. 85) Figure 4-7 Cardiovascular (circulatory) system (p. 86) Figure 4-8 Lymphatic system (p. 87) Figure 4-9 Respiratory system (p. 87) Figure 4-10 Digestive system (p. 88) Figure 4-11 Urinary system (p. 90) Figure 4-12 Male reproductive system (p. 91) Figure 4-13 Female reproductive system (p. 91) Quick Check questions 3-4 (p. 92) Outline Summary: Organ Systems (pp. 93-95) Review questions 6, 9 (p. 95) Chapter Test question 1 (p. 96) Clear View of the Human Body

OBJECTIVES	CONTENT	TEACHING RESOURCES
		Class Activity *Have the students make flash cards that list the organ system on one side and its included organs on the other. Then divide students into pairs and have them quiz each other.*
		Class Activity *Create a mock game show. Have three contestants stand at the front of the room. Have another student call out an organ. The contestant who names the right body system gets a point. Continue until someone reaches 10 points. Make it even more fun. Give each contestant a different noisemaker to "ring in."*

4.1 Homework/Assignments:

4.1 Teacher's Notes:

LESSON 4.2

CRITICAL THINKING QUESTION

Audrey is visiting your clinic for a routine checkup. Following the checkup, she mentions that her older sister was recently diagnosed with ovarian cancer, and Audrey is concerned that she may eventually get cancer as well. What should you tell her?

Guidelines: Let Audrey know how important it is for women to have regular gynecological checkups to maintain reproductive health. Routine checkups allow physicians to detect irregular growths and tumors early, which makes them easier to treat and usually allows for better survival rates. Provide Audrey with any information, such as brochures and Web site addresses, that may help her to understand the benefits of routine checkups.

OBJECTIVES	CONTENT	TEACHING RESOURCES
Briefly describe the major functions of each major organ system.	■ Organ systems of the body (p. 79) 　□ Integumentary system (p. 80) 　□ Skeletal system (p. 80) 　□ Muscular system (p. 83) 　□ Nervous system (p. 83) 　□ Endocrine system (p. 84) 　□ Cardiovascular (circulatory) system (p. 85) 　□ Lymphatic system (p. 86) 　□ Respiratory system (p. 86) 　□ Digestive system (p. 88) 　□ Urinary system (p. 88) 　□ Reproductive system (p. 90) ■ The body as a whole (p. 92)	Slides 16-30 Organ Systems of the Body questions 1-33 (pp. 36-37) Organ Systems crossword puzzle (p. 40) Multiple Choice questions 1, 5, 6, 8, 9 (pp. 40-41) Multiple Choice questions 3, 7, 9, 10, 12-13, 18, 21, 22, 25, 28, 29; True or False questions 6-8, 13, 16, 17, 19-22, 24, 30, 33-34, 36, 41, 42, 56, 60-62; Matching questions 1-11; Short Answer questions 3-6 Student Assignment questions 1, 4-8, 10, 22, 25, 27, 28, 30 (pp. 46-47); Multiple Choice questions 31-34 (p. 48) **Book Resources** Quick Check questions 1, 3 (p. 85) Quick Check questions 1, 2 (p. 92) Health and Well-Being: Paired Organs (p. 92) Outline Summary: Organ Systems (pp. 93-95) Review questions 2-5, 7, 9 (p. 96) Critical Thinking questions 11, 12 (p. 96) Chapter Test questions 2-6, 9-20 (pp. 96-97) *Class Activity **Divide students into groups and assign each group one or more different body systems. Have groups present the basics of the systems to the class. Encourage creativity in the presentations.***

OBJECTIVES	CONTENT	TEACHING RESOURCES
		Class Activity **Divide the class into small teams. Hand out copies of Figures 4-2 through 4-13 to each team, deleting the titles of the figures. Have each team identify the organ systems based on the diagram.**
		Class Activity **Invite a medical assistant or nurse to speak to the class about organ donations.**
Identify and discuss the major subdivisions of the reproductive system.	☐ Reproductive system (p. 90)	▨▤ Slides 27-30
		▥ Applying What You Know question 39 (p. 38)
		▥ Check Your Knowledge question 3 (p. 41)
		e Multiple Choice questions 31-35, 43-50, 63
		▤ Student Assignment questions 2, 21, 29 (pp. 46-47); Completion questions 9, 10 (p. 49)
		Book Resources
		Figure 4-12 Male reproductive system (p. 91)
		Figure 4-13 Female reproductive system (p. 91)
		Health and Well-Being: Cancer Screening Tests (p. 92)
		Outline Summary: Reproductive System (p. 94)
		Review question 10 (p. 95)
		Chapter Test questions 7, 8 (p. 96)
		Class Activity **Divide students into small groups. Have each group identify the organs and structures of the male and female reproductive systems and describe what each structure does.**
Performance Evaluation		*e* Chapter 4 Computerized Test Bank questions
		▤ Student Assignment (pp. 46-49)
		e Student Post-Test questions
		Book Resources
		Review questions (p. 96)
		Critical Thinking questions (p. 96)
		Chapter Test (pp. 96-97)

4.2 Homework/Assignments:

4.2 Teacher's Notes:

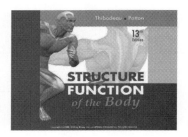

Slide 1

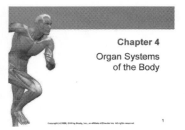

Chapter 4

Organ Systems
of the Body

Slide 2

Learning Objectives

- Define and contrast the terms *organ* and *organ system*
- List the 11 major organ systems of the body
- Identify and locate the major organs of each major organ system
- Briefly describe the major functions of each major organ system
- Identify and discuss the major subdivisions of the reproductive system

Slide 3

Chapter 4
Lesson 4.1

Slide 4

Organ Systems

- **Organ:** A structure made up of two or more kinds of tissues organized in such a way that they can together perform a more complex function than can any tissue alone
- **Organ system:** A group of organs arranged in such a way that they can together perform a more complex function than can any organ alone

- What is the difference between an organ and an organ system? (Organs are the components [smaller units] of the organ system.)

- Recall the levels of organization. (cells-tissues-organs-organ system)

Slide 5

Organ Systems (cont'd.)

- Integumentary System
  - Structure—organs
    - Skin
    - Hair
    - Nails
    - Sense receptors
    - Sweat glands
    - Oil glands
  - Functions
    - Protection
    - Regulation of body temperature
    - Synthesis of chemicals
    - Sense organ

- In adults, approximately how much does the skin weigh? (approximately 20 pounds or more—typically 16% of total body weight)

- How does the skin function as a sense organ? (It allows body to respond to stimuli.)

Slide 6

Organ Systems (cont'd.)

Integumentary System

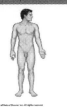

- What are some functions of the skin? (Skin protects against invasion of harmful bacteria, bars entry of most chemicals, and minimizes chances of mechanical injury to underlying structures.)

- The skin is considered the first line of defense in protecting the body.

Slide 7

Organ Systems (cont'd.)

- Skeletal system
  - Structure
    - Bones
    - Joints
  - Functions
    - Support
    - Movement (with joints and muscles)
    - Storage of minerals
    - Blood cell formation

- How many organs (bones) are there in the human skeletal system? (206)

ELSEVIER

Structure & Function of the Body, 13th ed.
Thibodeau/Patton

Slide 8

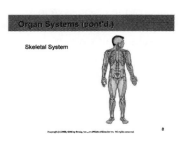

Organ Systems (cont'd.)

Skeletal System

8

- Related tissue such as cartilage, ligaments, and joints are part of the skeletal system. What are their functions? (They provide the body with a framework for support and protection. Joints allow movement.)

- Name another function of bones. (to store important minerals)

- What is the function of red bone marrow? (to create red blood cells)

- Red blood cell formation is an essential function.

Slide 9

Organ Systems (cont'd.)

- Muscular system
  - Structure
    - Muscles
      - Voluntary or striated
      - Involuntary or smooth
      - Cardiac
  - Functions
    - Movement
    - Maintenance of body pressure
    - Production of heat

9

- What is the difference between voluntary (striated) and involuntary (smooth) muscle? (They differ in appearance and function. Striated means "striped"; smooth is called nonstriated. Voluntary muscles allows control of muscle movement; smooth muscle functions automatically.)

- What is cardiac muscle? (specialized muscle tissue present in the heart)

Slide 10

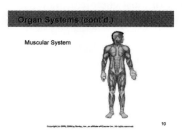

Organ Systems (cont'd.)

Muscular System

10

Slide 11

Organ Systems (cont'd.)

- Nervous system
  - Structure
    - Brain
    - Spinal cord
    - Nerves
    - Sense organs
  - Functions
    - Communication between body functions
    - Integration of body functions
    - Control of body functions
    - Recognition of sensory stimuli

11

- What are some examples of functions of the nervous system? (transmit impulses, coordinate body activities, interpret stimuli)

- What are nerve impulses, and what do they do? (specialized signals of the nervous system that allow for the rapid and precise control of diverse bodily activities)

ELSEVIER

Structure & Function of the Body, 13th ed.

Thibodeau/Patton

Slide 12

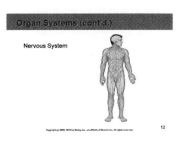

- What are the major functions of the nervous system? (communication, integration, control, and recognition)

- What are examples of stimuli? (heat, light, and pressure) Ask students to provide other examples.

Slide 13

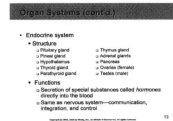

- What is another name for the organs of the endocrine system? (ductless glands)

Slide 14

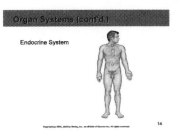

- What are some examples of hormone regulation? **(Hormones regulate metabolism and reproduction.)**

Slide 15

Slide 16

Organ Systems (cont'd.)

- Cardiovascular (Circulatory) System
  - Structure
    - Heart
    - Blood vessels
      - Arteries
      - Veins
      - Capillaries
  - Functions
    - Transportation
    - Regulation of body temperature
    - Immunity (body defense)

16

- Why is a "transportation system" so important to bodily functions? (Nutrients and gases need to get to and from all body cells.)

- What elements are transported by the cardiovascular system? (oxygen and carbon dioxide)

- How does this system regulate body temperature? (Blood vessels dilate to release heat; blood vessels constrict to conserve heat.)

- What do we mean by immunity? (the body's ability to protect itself)

Slide 17

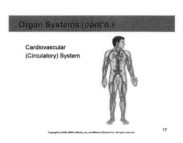

Organ Systems (cont'd.)

Cardiovascular
(Circulatory) System

17

- How is blood pumped through the cardiovascular system? What is the blood's pathway? (via the heart through a closed system of arteries; veins and capillaries).

Slide 18

Organ Systems (cont'd.)

- Lymphatic system
  - Structure
    - Lymph nodes
    - Lymphatic vessels
    - Thymus
    - Spleen
  - Functions
    - Transportation
    - Immunity (body defense)

18

- What is lymph? (a whitish, watery fluid that contains lymphocytes, proteins, and fatty molecules)

- How is lymph formed? (from the fluid around the body cells that diffuse into lymph vessels)

- What does the lymphatic system transport? (fluids, certain large molecules, and fat nutrients)

Slide 19

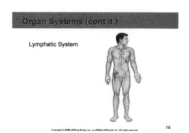

Organ Systems (cont'd.)

Lymphatic System

19

- How does lymph move through the system? (Lymph flows through lymphatic vessels and reenters the circulatory system.)

- How does lymph enter the circulatory system? (through the thoracic duct)

Structure & Function of the Body, 13th ed.

Thibodeau/Patton

Slide 20

Organ Systems (cont'd.)

- Respiratory system
  - Structure
    - Nose
    - Pharynx
    - Larynx
    - Trachea
    - Bronchi
    - Lungs
  - Functions
    - Exchange of waste gas (carbon dioxide) for oxygen in the lungs
    - Area of gas exchange in the lungs called *alveoli*
    - Filtration of irritants from inspired air
    - Warms and humidifies air
    - Regulation of acid–base balance

20

- How does the respiratory system filter irritants? (Irritants are filtered by the sticky mucus that covers the lining of many respiratory passages.)

- What are alveoli? (air sacs of the lungs)

Slide 21

Organ Systems (cont'd.)

Respiratory System

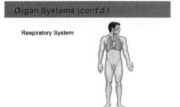

21

- Describe the passage of air through the respiratory system

Slide 22

Organ Systems (cont'd.)

- Digestive system
  - Structure
    - Primary organs
      - Mouth
      - Pharynx
      - Esophagus
      - Stomach
      - Small intestine
      - Large intestine
      - Rectum
      - Anal canal
    - Accessory organs
      - Teeth
      - Salivary glands
      - Tongue
      - Liver
      - Gallbladder
      - Pancreas
      - Appendix

22

- What is the form and function of the primary organs of the digestive system? (They form a tube, open at both ends, called the *gastrointestinal tract,* that takes in food, absorbs its nutrients, and eliminates the waste.)

Slide 23

Organ Systems (cont'd.)

- Digestive system
  - Functions
    - Mechanical and chemical breakdown (digestion) of food
    - Absorption of nutrients

23

- What is the function of the secondary (accessory) organs in the digestive system? (They assist in the mechanical and chemical breakdown of ingested food.)

- How is the appendix different from the other organs in the digestive system? (It is not a functional part of the system.)

- What is appendicitis? (inflammation of the appendix)

ELSEVIER

Slide 24

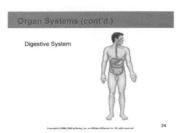

- How do the primary and accessory organs work together? (The accessory organs support the actions of the primary organs. The primary organs digest food, absorb nutrients, and eliminate wastes. The accessory organs secrete substances into the alimentary canal that assist in the mechanical and chemical breakdown of food.)

Slide 25

- What is the function of the kidneys? (clears waste products from the blood)

- How is the passage of urine different for males and females? (The male urethra passes urine and sperm. The female urethra is not part of the female reproductive system and only passes urine.)

Slide 26

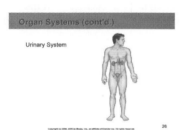

- How are other organs involved in eliminating body waste? (The digestive system eliminates food wastes, the respiratory system eliminates carbon dioxide.)

Slide 27

- What is the function of the male reproductive system? (to produce testosterone and sperm)

Structure & Function of the Body, 13th ed.

Thibodeau/Patton

Slide 28

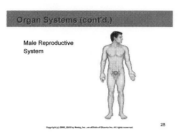

- Prostate and other accessory organs add fluids and nutrients to the sex cells as they pass through the ducts.

Slide 29

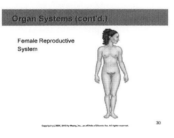

- What are some unique characteristics of the reproductive system? (Ensures survival of the human race and permits development of sexual characteristics.)

Slide 30

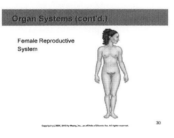

- How do the ova pass through the female reproductive system? (by way of the fallopian tubes to the uterus)

5 | Lesson Plan
The Integumentary System and Body Membranes

TEACHING FOCUS

In this chapter, students will have the opportunity to learn about the various types of epithelial and connective tissue body membranes, including the function and structure of the skin. Furthermore, students will have the opportunity to learn to identify the appendages of the skin, such as hair, receptors, nails, and skin glands, as well as learn how to classify burns.

MATERIALS AND RESOURCES

- ☐ Computer (Lesson 5.1)
- ☐ Copies of Figure 5-1 Types of body membranes (p. 101) (Lesson 5.1)
- ☐ Copies of Figure 5-2 Microscopic view of the skin (p. 103) (Lesson 5.1)
- ☐ Flash cards (Lesson 5.1)
- ☐ Mannequin (Lesson 5.2)

LESSON CHECKLIST

Preparations for this lesson include:
- lecture
- guest speakers: dermatologist, medical assistant, physician, nurse
- student performance evaluation of all entry-level skills required for student comprehension and application of anatomical structures including:
  - ○ structure of each type of body membrane
  - ○ structure and function of the integumentary system
  - ○ classification of burns

KEY TERMS

accessory structures (p. 99)
acne (p. 108)
apocrine (p. 109)
apocrine sweat gland (p. 109)
arrector pili (p. 107)
basal cell carcinoma (p. 110)
basement membrane (p. 100)
blackhead (p. 109)
blisters (p. 104)
burns (p. 112)
bursae (p. 102)
connective tissue membranes (p. 100)
cutaneous membrane (p. 100)
cuticle (p. 108)
cyanosis (pp. 105, 110)
decubitus ulcers (pressure sores) (p. 112)
dehydration (p. 109)
dermal–epidermal junction (p. 104)
dermal papillae (p. 105)
dermis (p. 102)
eccrine (p. 108)
eccrine sweat glands (p. 108)
epidermis (p. 102)
epithelial membranes (p. 100)
first-degree burn (p. 112)

full-thickness burn (p. 112)
follicles (p. 106)
free nerve endings (p. 108)
hair papilla (p. 106)
hypodermis (p. 102)
integument (p. 99)
integumentary system (p. 99)
Kaposi sarcoma (KS) (p. 109)
keratin (p. 103, 110)
Krause's end bulbs (p. 108)
lanugo (p. 106)
lunula (p. 108)
malignant melanoma (p. 109)
Meissner's corpuscle (p. 108)
melanin (pp. 104, 110)
melanocytes (p. 104)
membranes (p. 99)
mucocutaneous junction (p. 102)
mucous membranes (p. 100)
nail bed (p. 108)
nail body (p. 108)
Pacinian corpuscle (p. 108)
parietal peritoneum (p. 100)
parietal pleura (p. 100)
parietal portion (p. 100)

ELSEVIER

Thibodeau/Patton

partial-thickness burns (p. 11)
peritoneum (p. 100)
perspiration (p. 108)
pigment (p. 104)
pleura (p. 100)
pleurisy (p. 100)
pores (p. 109)
root (hair) (p. 106)
root (nail) (p. 108)
rule of nines (pp. 112, 113)
sebaceous glands (p. 102)
sebum (p. 110)
second-degree burn (p. 112)
serous membrane (p. 100)
severity of the burn (p. 111)
shaft (p. 106)
skin (p. 100)

squamous cell carcinoma (p. 110)
stratum corneum (p. 103)
stratum germinativum (p. 102)
sudoriferous glands (p. 108)
subcutaneous injection (p. 106)
subcutaneous tissue (p. 102)
sweat (p. 109)
sweat glands (p. 109)
synovial fluid (p. 102)
synovial membranes (p. 102)
third-degree burn (p. 112)
tinea pedis (p. 108)
total area involved (p. 111)
visceral pleura (p. 100)
visceral portion (p. 100)
visceral peritoneum (p. 100)

ADDITIONAL RESOURCES

AnimationDirect (Book Companion CD)
Instructor's Electronic Resource (IER) (CD)
PowerPoint slides (CD, Evolve)
Test Bank (Evolve)

Legend

ESLR
EVOLVE Student
Learning Resource

EILR TB
EVOLVE Instructor
Learning Resource
Test Bank

AnimationDirect
on Book Companion
CD

PPT
PowerPoint
Slides

SG
Study
Guide

IRM
Instructor's
Resource Manual

Class Activities are indicated in ***bold italic.***

ELSEVIER

Structure & Function of the Body, 13th ed.

LESSON 5.1

PRETEST

1. Epithelial membranes that line body surfaces opening to the exterior are called _____.
2. The innermost layer of epidermis is termed _____.
3. Small, cushionlike sacs that are found between moving body parts are called _____.
4. The soft, fine hair covering the skin of a newborn infant is the _____.
5. The sebaceous gland secretion that lubricates the hair and skin
   a. keratin
   b. sweat
   c. synovial fluid
   d. sebum
6. The crescent-shaped white area of the nail
   a. lunula
   b. root
   c. cuticle
   d. Meissner's corpuscle
7. A burn that involves the deep epidermal layers and causes injury to the upper layers of the dermis
   a. first-degree burn
   b. third-degree burn
   c. full-thickness burn
   d. second-degree burn
8. The very thin, gluelike connective tissue that holds and supports the epithelial cells
   a. pleura
   b. visceral peritoneum
   c. basement membrane
   d. lanugo
9. The transitional area that serves as a point of fusion where skin and mucous membranes meet
   a. synovial membranes
   b. mucocutaneous junction
   c. stratum corneum
   d. dermal–epidermal junction
10. The receptors deep in the dermis that are capable of detecting pressure on the skin surface
    a. free nerve endings
    b. Meissner's corpuscles
    c. Pacinian corpuscles
    d. Krause's end bulbs

Answers: 1. mucous membranes; 2. stratum germinativum; 3. bursae; 4. lanugo; 5. d; 6. a; 7. d; 8. c; 9. b; 10. c

BACKGROUND ASSESSMENT

Question: What are connective tissue membranes called and what do they do?

Answer: Connective tissue membranes are called *synovial membranes.* They line the spaces between bones and joints that move. These membranes are smooth, slick, and secrete a thick, colorless lubricating fluid called *synovial fluid.* The synovial membrane and the synovial fluid help reduce friction between opposing surfaces of bones in movable joints.

Question: How does skin play a role in temperature regulation?

Answer: Skin regulates body temperature by regulating sweat secretion and the flow of blood close to the body surface. When sweat evaporates from the body surface, heat is lost. When increased quantities of blood are allowed to fill the vessels close to the skin, heat is also lost by radiation. Blood supply to the skin far exceeds the amount needed by the skin. This abundant blood supply primarily enables the regulation of body temperature.

ELSEVIER

Structure & Function of the Body, 13th ed.
Thibodeau/Patton

CRITICAL THINKING QUESTION

During her regular physical examination, Courtney, a 14-year-old girl, asks her physician about the blackheads on her nose. What causes them and why has she been getting blackheads?

Guidelines: Sebaceous glands secrete oil for the skin and hair. Oil, or sebaceous, glands have tiny ducts that open into hair follicles so that their secretion, called *sebum,* lubricates the skin and hair. Sebum secretion increases during adolescence, stimulated by the increased blood levels of the sex hormones. Frequently, sebum accumulates in and enlarges some of the ducts of the sebaceous glands, forming white pimples. This sebum often darkens, forming a blackhead.

OBJECTIVES	CONTENT	TEACHING RESOURCES
Classify, compare the structure of, and give examples of each type of body membrane.	■ Classification of body membranes (p. 99) ☐ Epithelial membranes (p. 100) – Cutaneous membrane (p. 100) – Serous membranes (p. 100) – Mucous membranes (p. 101) ☐ Connective tissue membranes (p. 102)	Slides 4-10 Classification of Body Membranes questions 1-8 (p. 44) Unscramble the Words questions 44-49 (p. 46) Skin/Body Membranes crossword puzzle (p. 48) Check Your Knowledge questions 1, 11-16, 23, 24 (pp. 49-50) Multiple Choice questions 1-8, 31-33; True or False questions 1-13, 53-59; Short Answer questions 1, 2, 17 Serous Membrane Mucous Membrane Connective Tissue and Synovial Membrane **Book Resources** Figure 5-1 Types of body membranes (p. 101) Quick Check questions 1-3 (p. 102) Review questions 1-4 (p. 118) Chapter Test questions 1-5 (pp. 118-119) Clear View of the Human Body ***Class Activity Divide the students into four teams. Assign each team one of the following topics: cutaneous membrane, serous membranes, mucous membranes, or synovial membrane. Have each team write a description of the term and list examples of that term.***

OBJECTIVES	CONTENT	TEACHING RESOURCES
		Class Activity Hand out unlabeled copies of Figure 5-1 Types of body membranes (p. 101; available on EILR). Divide students into groups and have each group label the figure.
Describe the structure and function of the epidermis and dermis.	■ The skin (p. 102) □ Structure of the skin (p. 102) — Epidermis (p. 102) — Dermis (p. 105)	Slides 11-16 The Skin questions 9-28 (pp. 44-45) Applying What You Know question 50 (p. 46) Check Your Knowledge questions 2-6, 16, 21, 22 (pp. 49-50) Longitudinal Section of the Skin diagram (p. 51) Multiple Choice questions 9-15, 34-36; True or False questions 14-24, 60-63; Matching questions 21-28; Short Answer questions 3-6 **Book Resources** Figure 5-2 Microscopic view of the skin (p. 103) Figure 5-3 Photomicrograph of the skin (p. 104) Quick Check questions 1, 2 (p. 109) Review questions 5, 6 (p. 118) Critical Thinking question 14 (p. 118) Chapter Test questions 6-8 (p. 119) ▶ Discuss Clinical Application: Subcutaneous Injection (p. 106). ▶ Discuss the two layers of skin: dermis and epidermis. *Class Activity Create a mock game show with three contestants. Give each contestant a copy of Figure 5-2 Microscopic view of the skin (p. 103), taking care to delete the labels. The first student who correctly labels the figure wins.* *Class Activity Assign each student a disorder of the skin, such as squamous cell carcinoma, basal cell carcinoma, or malignant melanoma. Have each student research the disorder and present a brief synopsis of it to the class. Ask students to show photos or drawings if possible.*

OBJECTIVES	CONTENT	TEACHING RESOURCES
		Class Activity **Have students engage in a discussion regarding the effects of the sun on the skin. Explore options for patient education.**
List and briefly describe each accessory organ of the skin.	☐ Appendages of the skin (p. 106) – Hair (p. 106) – Receptors (p. 106) – Nails (p. 109) – Skin glands (p. 109)	Slides 17-25 The Skin questions 31-38 (p. 45) Check Your Knowledge questions 6-10, 17-20, 29, 30 (pp. 49-51) Multiple Choice questions 16-27; True or False questions 25-40, 42, 64, 65; Matching questions 1-10; Short Answer questions 7-11, 16 **Book Resources** Figure 5-5 Hair shaft and follicle (p. 107) Figure 5-6 Structure of nails (p. 108) Quick Check questions 3-4 (p. 109) Review questions 7-12 (p. 118) Chapter Test questions 9-11, 13-20 (p. 119) *Class Activity* **Divide students into small teams. Ask each team to describe the attributes of the hair, receptors, nails, and skin glands.** *Class Activity* **Have students report on pertinent medical information that can be gathered from assessing hair, nails, and skin.** *Class Activity* **Ask each student to create flash cards of the various accessory organs of the skin. Have them include all the structures of the appendages. Divide students into teams and have them quiz each other.**

5.1 Homework/Assignments:

5.1 Teacher's Notes:

LESSON 5.2

CRITICAL THINKING QUESTION

Mr. MacPherson came into the emergency department with burns on both arms, both hands, and his face due to a grease fire in his kitchen. He complained of severe pain. His burns showed signs of blistering, swelling, and fluid loss. What percentage of his body was burned? What classification is his burn and why?

Guidelines: Mr. MacPherson burned approximately 13.5% of his body. Each arm and hand represents 4.5% of the total body surface and the face is an additional 4.5%. His burn is classified as a *second-degree burn*. Because he is experiencing severe pain, we know that he did not destroy the nerve endings, which means it is not a third-degree burn.

OBJECTIVES	CONTENT	TEACHING RESOURCES
List and discuss the three primary functions of the integumentary system.	☐ Functions of the skin (p. 110) – Protection (p. 110) – Temperature regulation (p. 110) – Sense organ activity (p. 110)	Slides 27-29 The Skin questions 29, 30 (p. 45) Applying What You Know question 51 (p. 46) Multiple Choice questions 28, 29; True or False questions 41, 43-52; Matching questions 11-20; Short Answer questions 12, 13 **Book Resources** Quick Check questions 1, 2 (p. 113) Critical Thinking question 15 (p. 118) Chapter Test question 12 (p. 119) Clear View of the Human Body *Class Activity Divide students into teams. Ask each team to come up with examples of skin functions. For example, students can discuss how the skin serves as a source of protection. Make sure the students list the hazards the skin protects against.*
Classify burns and describe how to estimate the extent of a burn injury.	☐ Burns (p. 112) – Estimating body surface area (p. 112) – Classification of burns (p. 112)	Slides 30-32 The Skin questions 39-43 (p. 45) Applying What You Know question 50 (p. 46) Check Your Knowledge questions 25-28 (pp. 50-51) "Rule of Nines" for Estimating Skin Surface Burned diagram (p. 52) Multiple choice questions 30, 37; Short Answer questions 14, 15

Structure & Function of the Body, 13th ed.

Thibodeau/Patton

OBJECTIVES	CONTENT	TEACHING RESOURCES
		⊙ Burns
		Book Resources
		Figure 5-8 The "Rule of Nines" (p. 113)
		Figure 5-9 Classification of burns (p. 114)
		Quick Check question 3 (p. 113)
		Review question 13 (p. 118)
		Critical Thinking question 16 (p. 118)
		Class Activity Have students demonstrate the Rule of Nines on a mannequin or on a drawing of a body.
		Class Activity Divide students into small groups. Have them discuss the classification system for burns. Create practice problems for students to complete. The students could discuss the impact of burns on patients and their families.
Performance Evaluation		𝒆 Chapter 5 Computerized Test Bank questions
		📖 Student Assignment (pp. 59-61)
		𝒆 Student Post-Test questions
		Book Resources
		Review questions (p. 118)
		Critical Thinking questions (p. 118)
		Chapter Test questions 1-20 (pp. 118-119)

5.2 Homework/Assignments:

5.2 Teacher's Notes:

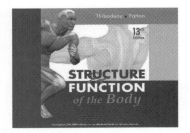

Slide 1

Chapter 5

The Integumentary
System and
Body Membranes

1

Slide 2

Learning Objectives

- Classify, compare the structure of, and give examples of each type of body membrane
- Describe the structure and function of the epidermis and dermis
- List and briefly describe each accessory organ of the skin
- List and discuss the three primary functions of the integumentary system
- Classify burns and describe how to estimate the extent of a burn injury

2

Slide 3

Chapter 5
Lesson 5.1

3

Thibodeau/Patton

Slide 4

Classifications of Body Membranes

- Classifications of body membranes
  - Epithelial membranes: Composed of epithelial tissues and an underlying layer of connective tissue
  - Connective tissue membranes: Composed largely of various types of connective tissue

4

- A membrane is a thin, sheetlike structure that covers and protects the body's surface, lines body cavities, and covers the inner surfaces of hollow organs such as the digestive, reproductive, and respiratory passageways.

- What are some of the other functions performed by membranes? (secrete fluids for lubrication and provide protection from irritants)

Slide 5

Epithelial Membranes

- Cutaneous membrane: The skin
  - Accounts for approximately 16% of body weight
  - The largest, most visible organ

5

- What are the three types of epithelial membranes? (skin, serous, and mucous)

- The cutaneous membrane is the primary organ of the integumentary system.

- It has a superficial layer of epithelial cells and an underlying layer of supportive connective tissue.

Slide 6

Epithelial Membranes (cont'd.)

- Serous membrane: Two layers: simple squamous epithelium lies on basement membrane
  - Types
    - Parietal: Lines walls of body cavities
    - Visceral: Covers organs found in body cavities

6

- The serous membrane that lines body cavities and covers the surfaces of organs is a single, continuous sheet of tissue.

- The name of the serous membrane is determined by its location.

- What are some examples of serous membranes? (parietal and visceral pleura and the peritoneum)

- What are their functions? (cover and protect internal organs)

Slide 7

Epithelial Membranes (cont'd.)

- Serous membrane
  - Diseases
    - Pleurisy: inflammation of the serous membranes that line the chest cavity and cover the lungs
    - Peritonitis: inflammation of the serous membranes that line the walls of the abdominal cavity and cover the abdominal organs

7

- Serous membranes secrete a thin, watery fluid that helps to reduce friction and serves as a lubricant when organs rub against one another and against the walls of the cavities that contain them.

- Pleurisy is also known as *pleuritis*.

- Why might peritonitis sometimes be a serious complication of an infected appendix? (If the appendix ruptures, the contents spill into the abdominal cavity onto the peritoneum, which then becomes infected.)

Thibodeau/Patton

Slide 8

Epithelial Membranes (cont'd.)

- Mucous membranes
  - Line body surfaces that open directly to the exterior
  - Produce mucus, a thick secretion that keeps the membranes soft and moist

- What are some examples of mucous membranes in the body? (those lining the respiratory, urinary, reproductive, and intestinal tracts)

- What is the mucocutaneous junction? (where skin and mucous membranes meet)

- The epithelial component of a mucous membrane varies depending on location and function.

- The esophagus has a tough, abrasion-resistant stratified squamous epithelium.

- The lower segment of the digestive tract has simple columnar epithelium.

Slide 9

Connective Tissue Membranes

- Do not contain epithelial components
- Produce a lubricant called *synovial fluid*

- What are some examples of connective tissue membranes, and what are the functions that they serve? Remember that structure determines function. (Synovial membranes reduce friction in the joints; synovial membranes are also found in cushionlike sacs called bursae.)

Slide 10

Types of Body Membranes

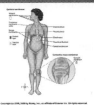

- This figure illustrates the various types of epithelial and connective tissue membranes.

- What are the functions performed by each of the membranes in the figure? (The mucous membrane secretes mucus for lubrication and protection. The cutaneous membrane protects the underlying structures. The serous membranes lubricate organ linings. The connective tissue membranes lubricate joints.)

Slide 11

The Skin

- The skins structure includes two primary layers
  - Epidermis
  - Dermis

- One square inch of skin contains: 500 sweat glands, 1,000 nerve endings, yards of blood vessels, 100 oil (sebaceous) glands, 150 sensors for pressure, 75 sensors for heat, and 10 sensors for cold.

- What type of membrane is the skin? (cutaneous)

ELSEVIER

Structure & Function of the Body, 13th ed.
Thibodeau/Patton

Slide 12

Epidermis

- Outermost and thinnest primary layer of skin
- Composed of several layers of stratified squamous epithelium
- Stratum germinativum: innermost layer of cells that continually reproduce
- As cells approach the surface, they are filled with *keratin* and eventually flake off

12

- Describe the process of cell reproduction performed by the stratum germinavitum.

- What purposes does this process serve? (allows skin to repair itself as needed)

- What is keratin and what purpose does it serve? (Keratin is a tough, waterproof material that protects the skin)

Slide 13

Epidermis (cont'd.)

- **Stratum corneum:** Outermost layer of keratin-filled cells
  - **Pigment-containing layer:** Epidermal layer that contains pigment cells called *melanocytes,* which produce the brown pigment melanin
  - **Blisters:** Caused by breakdown of union between cells or primary layers of skin
  - **Dermal-epidermal junction:** Specialized area between two primary skin layers

13

- Pigment comes from Latin term meaning "paint."

- The higher the concentration of melanin, the deeper the color of skin.

- What is the primary function of melanin? (absorb UV radiation from the sun)

- How is the amount of melanin in the skin determined? (heredity)

- Cyanosis: change in skin color (bluish tinge in light-skinned individuals) if blood oxygen levels or blood flow are reduced.

Slide 14

Dermis

- Deeper and thicker than the epidermis
- Composed largely of connective tissue
- Upper area of dermis characterized by parallel rows of peglike dermal papillae
- Ridges and grooves in dermis form pattern unique to each individual
  - Basis of fingerprinting
  - Improves grip for tool use and walking

14

- Cells of the dermis are scattered far apart, with many fibers in between.

- What types of fibers are in the dermis and what are their characteristics? (Both tough and elastic fibers are present, providing stability as well as elasticity.)

Slide 15

Dermis (cont'd.)

- Deeper areas of dermis are filled with a network of tough collagenous and stretchable elastic fibers
- The number of elastic fibers decreases with age
- The dermis also contains nerve endings, muscle fibers, hair follicles, sweat and sebaceous glands, and many blood vessels

15

- The dermis contains a specialized network of nerves and nerve endings to process sensory information such as pain, pressure, touch, and temperature.

- What results from the elastic fibers in the dermis decreasing with age? Why would this happen? (As the elastic fibers decrease, wrinkles develop. Biological aging also reduces the amount of fat stored in the subcutaneous layers of the skin, which further contributes to wrinkling.)

ELSEVIER

Slide 16

- This figure shows the layers of the skin and its various structures.

- What are the functions performed by the parts of the skin shown in the figure? (Protection, storage, secretion)

Slide 17

Accessory Organs of the Skin

- Hair
  - Hair growth requires an epidermal tubelike structure called a *hair follicle*
  - Hair growth begins from hair papillae located at the base of the follicle
  - Hair root lies hidden in the follicle
  - The visible part of the hair is called the shaft

- Are there any parts of the body that are hairless? If so, which? (yes, palms of the hands and the soles of the feet)

- What is lanugo? (fine hairs present on body in a fetus/newborn)

- What is the arrector pili? (a tiny, smooth muscle present in the dermal skin layer) What function does it perform and why? (These muscles contract when one is frightened or cold.)

Slide 18

Accessory Organs of the Skin (cont'd.)

Hair Follicle

- This figure illustrates the relationship of a hair follicle and related structures to the epidermal and dermal layers of the skin.

- What parts of the hair are in the dermis? (hair papilla, root, and follicle)

- What part/parts is/are in the epidermis? (The visible portion of the hair shaft is in the epidermis.)

Slide 19

Accessory Organs of the Skin (cont'd.)

- Receptors
  - Specialized nerve endings that make it possible for skin to act as a sense organ
  - Relays messages to the brain of touch, pain, temperature, and pressure

- What are the names and functions of receptors located in the skin? (The names indicate their functions; touch, pain, temperature, and pressure.)

- Receptors are widely distributed in the skin.

Slide 20

Accessory Organs of the Skin (cont'd.)

Skin Receptors

20

- This figure illustrates the Meissner's corpuscle and the Pacinian corpuscle.

- What stimuli do these corpuscles respond to? (light touch [meissner] and pressure [pacinian])

Slide 21

Accessory Organs of the Skin (cont'd.)

- Nails
  - Produced by epidermal cells over terminal ends of fingers and toes
  - Visible part is called *nail body*
  - Root lies in a groove and is hidden by the cuticle
  - Crescent-shaped area nearest root is called *lunula*
  - Nail bed may change color with change in blood flow

21

- How are nails formed? (by action of the epidermal cells; nails are filled with keratin, making them hard)

- What purposes might the nails serve? (protection, assessment of circulation)

Slide 22

Accessory Organs of the Skin (cont'd.)

Structure of Nails

22

- These two illustrations view the fingernail from above and in sagittal section (divided into right and left portions).

- What might cause the nail bed to change color? (impaired blood flow)

Slide 23

Accessory Organs of the Skin (cont'd.)

- Skin glands
  - Sweat (sudoriferous) glands
    - Eccrine
      - Most numerous, important, and widespread of the sweat glands
      - Produce perspiration (sweat), which flows out through pores on skin surface
      - Function throughout life and assist in body heat regulation

23

- A single square inch of skin on the palms contains about 3,000 eccrine sweat glands.

- What is the difference between eccrine and apocrine glands? (eccrine secrete sweat and are found throughout the body. Apocrine secret sweat, are larger, present in axilla and genital area, and secrete a thicker substance.)

ELSEVIER

Structure & Function of the Body, 13th ed.

Thibodeau/Patton

Slide 24

Accessory Organs of the Skin (cont'd.)

- Skin glands
  - Sweat (sudoriferous) glands
    - Apocrine
      - Found primarily in axilla (armpit) and around genitalia
      - Larger than eccrine glands
      - Secrete a thicker secretion quite different from eccrine perspiration

24

- Apocrine glands enlarge and begin to function at puberty.

- What causes the odor sometimes associated with secretions of the apocrine glands? (skin bacteria)

Slide 25

Accessory Organs of the Skin (cont'd.)

- Skin glands
  - Sebaceous glands
    - Secrete oil, or sebum, for hair and skin
    - Level of secretion increases during adolescence
    - Amount of secretion is regulated by sex hormones
    - Sebum in sebaceous gland ducts may darken to form a blackhead

25

- Sebum secretion decreases in late adulthood, contributing to increased wrinkling and cracking of the skin.

- Why would sebum be referred to as "nature's skin cream"? (prevents drying and cracking of skin)

- Think of the skin changes that occur from infancy to old age.

Slide 26

Chapter 5
Lesson 5.2

26

Slide 27

Functions of the Skin

- Protection
  - First line of defense against
    - Infection by microbes
    - Ultraviolet rays from the sun
    - Harmful chemicals
    - Cuts and tears

27

- How does the skin protect the body against the potential hazards listed in this slide? (Skin acts a barrier to microbes entering underlying surfaces, melanin prevents damage from UV rays, keratin-filled cells of the stratum corneum resist chemicals and protect from cuts and tears.)

- What are the defensive properties of keratin? (Keratin is waterproof.)

- What are the defensive properties of melanin? Melanin is a pigment that prevents UV rays from penetrating the body.

Thibodeau/Patton

Slide 28

Functions of the Skin (cont'd.)

- Temperature regulation
  - The skin can release almost 3,000 calories of body heat per day
    - Mechanisms of temperature regulation
      - Regulation of sweat secretion
      - Regulation of flow of blood close to the body surface

28

- How is heat lost through the skin? (Through evaporation and radiation)

- Blood supply to the skin far exceeds the amount needed by the skin.

Slide 29

Functions of the Skin (cont'd.)

- Sense organ activity
  - Skin functions as an enormous sense organ
  - Receptors serve as receivers for the body, keeping it informed of changes in its environment
    - Meissner's corpuscles detect light touch
    - Pacinian corpuscles detect pressure
    - Other receptors detect pain, heat, and cold

29

- How do receptors respond to environmental changes? (Receptors act as antennae, keeping body informed. The body can then react to the change.)

- What does SPF mean? Is it important? Why? (SPF means *sun protection factor*. It is important to protect one from damaging UV rays. Excess exposure to UV rays has been associated with skin cancer.)

Slide 30

Burns

- Burns are one of the most serious and frequent problems affecting the skin
- Treatment and recovery or survival depend on total area involved and severity or depth of burn
- Body surface area is estimated using the "rule of nines" in adults
  - Body is divided into 11 areas of 9% each

30

- In what ways can the skin be burned? (fire, contact with hot surfaces, UV light, chemicals, and electrical currents)

- What are the 11 body areas defined by the *Rule of Nines*? (Head—front and back; torso—front and back; arms—right and left; front and back; legs—right and left, front and back; genitalia: see textbook, Figure 5-8, p. 113)

Slide 31

Burns (cont'd.)

The Rule of Nines

31

- This figure illustrates the division of the body into 11 areas of 9% each to estimate the amount of skin surface burned in an adult.

- What percentage of the body is covered if a person suffers burns to the face and both arms? (22.5%)

Structure & Function of the Body, 13th ed.

Thibodeau/Patton

Slide 32

- Classification of burns
  - First-degree (partial-thickness) burns: Only the surface layers of epidermis are involved
  - Second-degree (partial-thickness) burns: Involve the deep epidermal layers
  - Third-degree (full-thickness) burns: Characterized by complete destruction of the epidermis and dermis

- The classification system used to describe the severity of burns is based on the number of tissue layers involved.

- The terms *partial-thickness* and *full-thickness* are now more readily used to describe burns.

- The most severe burns destroy not only layers of skin and subcutaneous tissue but underlying tissues as well.

- What are some examples of how one might receive first-, second-, and third-degree burns? What are the symptoms and what tissues are damaged?

  - First degree can result from a typical sunburn. Symptoms of a first degree burn are minor discomfort and some reddening. The epidermis is injured.

  - Second degree from scalding. Second degree burns blister. They involve injury to the epidermis as well as the dermis.

  - Third degree from a fire. Third degree burns may show blackened skin and the damage is extended into the subcutaneous tissues.

Lesson Plan

6 The Skeletal System

TEACHING FOCUS

In this chapter, students will have the opportunity to learn about the generalized functions and growth of the skeletal system. They will be introduced to the major anatomical structures of long bones, along with the microscopic structure of bones and cartilage. Students will have the opportunity to list the bones found in each major subdivision of the skeleton and to understand the major joints of the body.

MATERIALS AND RESOURCES

- ☐ Figure 6-1 and Figure 6-2 handouts (Lesson 6.1)
- ☐ Flash cards (all Lessons)
- ☐ Hardware implements (Lesson 6.2)
- ☐ Computer (all Lessons)

LESSON CHECKLIST

Preparations for this lesson include:

- lecture
- guest speakers: orthopedic surgeon, physical therapist, sports trainer, radiologist, medical assistant, nurse
- student performance evaluation of all entry-level skills required for student comprehension and application of principles of anatomy including:
  - ○ functions of the skeletal system
  - ○ major anatomical structures in a typical long bone
  - ○ microscopic structure of bone and cartilage
  - ○ formation of bones

KEY TERMS

abduct (p. 145)
adduct (p. 145)
acetabulum (p. 139)
amphiarthroses (p. 143)
appendicular skeleton (p. 127)
articular cartilage (pp. 122, 144)
articulations (p. 121)
axial skeleton (p. 127)
bone (p. 122)
calcaneus (p. 139)
canaliculi (p. 123)
carpal (p. 136)
cartilage (p. 123)
central canal (p. 124)
chest (p. 134)
chondrocytes (p. 124)
circumduct (p. 145)
clavicle (p. 135)
compact bone (p. 123)
concave curves (p. 134)
concentric lamella (p. 123)
convex curves (p. 134)
coronal suture (p. 130)
coxa (p. 139)
cranium (p. 127)

dense bone (p. 123)
diaphysis (pp. 122, 125)
diarthroses (p. 143)
endochondral (p. 125)
endosteum (p. 122)
epiphyseal line (p. 125)
epiphyseal plate (p. 125)
epiphyses (p. 122)
extend (p. 145)
extension (p. 144)
face (p. 127)
false ribs (p. 135)
femur (p. 139)
fibula (p. 139)
flex (p. 145)
flexion (p. 144)
floating ribs (p. 135)
fontanels (p. 130)
frontal sinusitis (p. 130)
Haversian systems (p. 123)
hematopoiesis (p. 122)
hip (p. 139)
humerus (p. 136)
ilium (p. 139)
ischium (p. 139)

ADDITIONAL RESOURCES

AnimationDirect (Book Companion CD)
Instructor's Electronic Resource (IER) (CD)
PowerPoint slides (CD, Evolve)
Test Bank (Evolve)

Legend

ESLR	EILR TB	AnimationDirect	PPT	SG	IRM
EVOLVE Student Learning Resource	EVOLVE Instructor Learning Resource Test Bank	on Book Companion CD	PowerPoint Slides	Study Guide	Instructor's Resource Manual

Class Activities are indicated in **bold italic.**

ELSEVIER

Structure & Function of the Body, 13th ed.

Thibodeau/Patton

LESSON 6.1

PRETEST

1. The hollow area inside the diaphysis of a bone that contains yellow bone marrow is called the _____.
2. Living bone cells are called _____.
3. Cartilage cells are called _____.
4. The bone that forms the lower, back part of the nasal septum is called the _____.
5. There are _____ (number) _____ bones in the face.
6. The immovable joints of the skull are called
   a. sutures.
   b. incus.
   c. sphenoid.
   d. ethmoid.
7. The series of separate bones of the spine are called
   a. humerus.
   b. coccyx.
   c. sacrum.
   d. vertebrae.
8. The posterior surface of the humerus is called
   a. olecranon process.
   b. radius.
   c. olecranon fossa.
   d. ulna.
9. The joints in which cartilage connects the articulating bones are called
   a. amphiarthroses.
   b. synarthroses.
   c. diarthroses.
   d. ligaments.
10. Bending a joint, making the angle between the two bones smaller, is called
   a. adduction.
   b. extension.
   c. flexion.
   d. circumvention.

Answers: 1. medullary cavity; 2. osteocytes; 3. chondrocytes; 4. vomer; 5. 14; 6. a; 7. d; 8. c; 9. a; 10. c

BACKGROUND ASSESSMENT

Question: What are the four types of bones in the body? Give an example of each.
Answer: The names of the four types of bones suggest their shapes. *Long bones* include the humerus. *Short bones* include the carpals. *Flat bones* include the frontal bone. *Irregular bones* include the vertebrae.
Question: What is an epiphyseal fracture? What can happen if this type of fracture is not treated properly?
Answer: The point of articulation between the epiphysis and diaphysis of a growing long bone is susceptible to injury if overstressed, especially in the young child or preadolescent athlete. In these individuals, the epiphyseal plate can be separated from the diaphysis or epiphysis. Without successful treatment, an epiphyseal fracture may inhibit normal growth. Stunted bone growth, in turn, may cause the affected limb to be shorter than the normal limb.

Thibodeau/Patton

CRITICAL THINKING QUESTION

Julie is a 14-year-old girl who is 5 feet 2 inches tall. She seems short compared to her tall parents. Julie's mother is concerned, and she asks her daughter's physician if Julie will grow any more. How can a physician tell if Julie has completed her growth?

Guidelines: If Julie's physician wanted to tell if she was going to grow more, he could have an x-ray study performed on her wrist. If it shows a layer of epiphyseal cartilage, he knows that additional growth will occur. However, if it shows no epiphyseal cartilage, he knows that her growth has stopped and she has attained adult height. This is because growth ceases when all epiphyseal cartilage is transformed into bone, and all that remains is an epiphyseal line that marks the location of where two centers of ossification have fused together.

OBJECTIVES	CONTENT	TEACHING RESOURCES
List and discuss the generalized functions of the skeletal system.	■ Functions of the skeletal system (p. 122) □ Support (p. 122) □ Protection (p. 122) □ Movement (p. 122) □ Storage (p. 122) □ Hematopoiesis (p. 122)	Slide 5 Functions of the Skeletal System, Types of Bones, Structure of Long Bones questions 5, 6 (p. 54) Word Find (p. 60) Check Your Knowledge question 1 (p. 61) Multiple Choice questions 1, 2; True or False questions 1, 2, 56-58; Short Answer question 1 Student Assignment question 6 (p. 70) **Book Resources** Quick Check question 2 (p. 123) Review question 1 (p. 152) Chapter Test question 13 (p. 152) Clear View of the Human Body ***Class Activity Divide the class into teams of two. Have them write down the five major functions of the skeletal system and provide examples of each function.***
Identify the major anatomical structures found in a typical long bone.	■ Types of bones (p. 122) ■ Structure of long bones (p. 122) – Diaphysis (p. 122) – Medullary cavity (p. 122) – Epiphysis (p. 122) – Articular cartilage (p. 122) – Periosteum (p. 122) – Endosteum (p. 122)	Slides 6-9 Functions of the Skeletal System, Types of Bones, Structure of Long Bones questions 1-10 (p. 54) Check Your Knowledge questions 2, 3, 12, 13 (pp. 61-62) Longitudinal Section of Long Bone diagram (p. 64)

Structure & Function of the Body, 13th ed.

Thibodeau/Patton

OBJECTIVES	CONTENT	TEACHING RESOURCES
		e Multiple Choice questions 3-9, 36, 37; True or False questions 3-9, 59-61; Matching questions 2, 4, 6-8, 10; Short Answer questions 2, 3
		Student Assignment questions 3, 4, 38 (pp. 70, 72)
		Book Resources
		Figure 6-1 Longitudinal section of a long bone (p. 123)
		Quick Check question 3 (p. 123)
		Chapter Test questions 1, 2, 14-17 (pp. 152, 153)
		*Class Activity **Hand out an unlabeled copy of Figure 6-1 Longitudinal section of a long bone (available on EILR). Go around the room and have each student identify the appropriate label.***
		*Class Activity **Have students copy these six terms and their definitions on flash cards: diaphysis, medullary cavity, epiphysis, articular cartilage, periosteum, endosteum. Have students quiz each other about the meanings of these terms.***
Discuss the microscopic structure of bone and cartilage, including the identification of specific cell types and structural features.	■ Microscopic structure of bone and cartilage (p. 123)	Slides 11, 12
		Microscopic Structure of Bone and Cartilage questions 11-20 (p. 54)
		Applying What You Know question 93 (p. 59)
		Check Your Knowledge question 6 (p. 62)
		e Multiple Choice questions 10-13, 15, 38; True or False questions 10-14, 62-67; Matching questions 5, 9; Short Answer questions 4, 5
		Student Assignment question 2 (p. 70)
		Book Resources
		Figure 6-2 Microscopic structure of bone (p. 124)
		Figure 6-3 Compact bone (p. 125)
		Figure 6-4 Cartilage tissue (p. 125)
		Quick Check questions 1-3 (p. 127)

ELSEVIER

Structure & Function of the Body, 13th ed.

Thibodeau/Patton

OBJECTIVES	CONTENT	TEACHING RESOURCES
		Review questions 2, 3 (p. 152)
		Critical Thinking questions 13, 14 (p. 152)
		Chapter Test questions 3-5 (p. 152)
		Class Activity Divide the class into two teams. Assign each one the term **bone** *or* **cartilage.** *Have each group tell the rest of the class about the attributes of the term they were assigned. Have the students discuss how bone and cartilage are different.*
		Class Activity Make copies of Figure 6-2 without labels (available on EILR or IER) for each student. Have each student fill in the labels and research any unknown terms.
Explain how bones are formed, how they grow, and how they are remodeled.	■ Bone formation and growth (p. 125)	Slides 13, 14
		Bone Formation and Growth questions 21-30 (pp. 54-55)
		Applying What You Know questions 94, 95 (p. 59)
		Skeletal System crossword puzzle (p. 61)
		Multiple Choice questions 14, 16, 17; True or False questions 15-22, 68, 69; Matching questions 1, 3; Short Answer questions 6, 8
		Classroom Application (p. 68); Student Assignment questions 1, 5, 32-34, 44 (pp. 70, 71, 72)
		Bone Formation and Growth
		Book Resources
		Figure 6-5 Endochondral ossification (p. 126)
		Figure 6-6 Bone development in a newborn (p. 127)
		Quick Check question 4 (p. 127)
		Review questions 4, 5 (p. 152)
		Chapter Test questions 6-9 (p. 152)
		▶ Discuss Clinical Application/Epiphyseal Fracture (p. 130)
		Class Activity Divide the class into teams. Have each team research the bone development of a newborn. Ask each team to point out the bones that have not yet ossified in a newborn.

6.1 Homework/Assignments:

6.1 Teacher's Notes:

LESSON 6.2

CRITICAL THINKING QUESTION

Margie, who plays center on the women's varsity basketball team, ended up at the bottom of a pile-up during a game. When she arrives at the doctor's office, she complains that her knee is very sore. She mentions that she felt a "pop" at the time of the injury, and the knee buckles under her weight. What will the physician check?

Guidelines: The physician will check Margie's knee for strain on the collateral ligaments. Even though the knee is the largest joint, it is very vulnerable to forces applied from the wrong angle, particularly from the lateral side. If Margie's collateral ligaments are sprained, the doctor will likely recommend therapeutic exercise, ice packs to control pain and swelling, and use of a brace to support and stabilize the knee.

OBJECTIVES	CONTENT	TEACHING RESOURCES

Identify the two major subdivisions of the skeleton and list the bones found in each area.	■ Divisions of skeleton (p. 127)
	☐ Axial skeleton (p. 127)
	  – Skull (p. 127)
	  – Spine (vertebral column) (p. 131)
	  – Thorax (p. 134)
	☐ Appendicular skeleton (p. 135)
	  – Upper extremity (p. 135)
	  – Lower extremity (p. 139)
		⊠▬ Slides 16-26
		
		📖 Divisions of the Skeleton questions 31-58 (pp. 55-57)
		
		📖 Bone Markings questions 64-76 (p. 58)
		
		📖 Unscramble the Bones questions 87-92 (p. 59)
		
		📖 Check Your Knowledge questions 4, 5, 7-9, 14-17 (p. 62)
		
		📖 Anterior View of Skeleton diagram (p. 64)
		
		📖 Posterior View of Skeleton diagram (p. 65)
		
		📖 Skull Viewed from the Right Side diagram (p. 66)
		
		📖 Skull Viewed from the Front diagram (p. 67)
		
		🅔 Multiple Choice questions 18-32, 39-41; True or False questions 23-42, 70-75; Matching questions 11-20
		
		📄 Student Assignment questions 7-9, 36, 37, 40, 42, 43, 46 (pp. 8-11)
		
		Book Questions
		
		Figure 6-7 Human skeleton (pp. 128-129)
		
		Table 6-1 Main Parts of the Skeleton (p. 130)
		
		Table 6-2 Bones of the Skull (p. 131)
		
		Figure 6-8 The skull (p. 132)
		
		Figure 6-9 The spinal column (p. 133)
		
		Table 6-3 Bones of the Vertebral Column (p. 134)

OBJECTIVES	CONTENT	TEACHING RESOURCES
		Figure 6-10 The third lumbar vertebra (p. 134)
		Figure 6-11 Spinal curvature of an infant (p. 135)
		Quick Check questions 1-4 (p. 135)
		Figure 6-12 Bones of the thorax (p. 136)
		Table 6-4 Bones of the Thorax (p. 135)
		Figure 6-13 Bones of the arm, elbow joint, and forearm (p. 137)
		Table 6-5 Bones of the Upper Extremities (p. 138)
		Figure 6-14 Bones of the right hand and wrist (p. 138)
		Figure 6-15 Bones of the thigh, knee joint, and leg (p. 140)
		Figure 6-16 Bones of the right foot (p. 141)
		Table 6-6 Bones of the Lower Extremities (p. 141)
		Figure 6-17 Arches of the foot (p. 142)
		Quick Check questions 1-3 (p. 142)
		Clinical Application/Palpable Bony Landmarks (p. 145)
		Review questions 6-8 (p. 152)
		Chapter Test questions 10, 18-35 (pp. 152-153)
		Clear View of the Human Body
		Class Activity** **Have each student label the bones on the anterior and posterior view of a human skeleton (Figure 6-7; available on EILR). Have them also label the bones and parts of the skull; the bones of the spinal column; the bones of the thorax; the bones of the arm, elbow joint, and forearm; the bones of the hand and wrist; and the bones of the thigh, knee, and leg.
		Class Activity** **Create a mock quiz show. Have three students volunteer as contestants. Ask the contestants ten questions that involve the description of bones (use the descriptions in Tables 6-2, 6-3, 6-4, 6-5, 6-6). The contestants should come up with the corresponding names of bones. The student who gets the most questions right wins.

OBJECTIVES	CONTENT	TEACHING RESOURCES
		Class Activity Have each student create flash cards listing the various bones of the body, the number of bones of each type, and the description of each bone type.
		Class Activity Create a bingo board listing the proper anatomical names of the bones. Announce only the lay terms. The first student with a verified bingo wins.

List and compare the major types of joints in the body and give an example of each.	■ Differences between a man's and a woman's skeleton (p. 139)
	■ Joints (articulations) (p. 142)
	 □ Kinds of joints (p. 142)
	  – Synarthroses (p. 142)
	  – Amphiarthroses (p. 143)
	  – Diarthroses (p. 143)
		Slides 28-33
		
		Differences Between a Man's and a Woman's Skeleton questions 59-63 (p. 57)
		
		Joints (Articulations) questions 77-86 (p. 58)
		
		Check Your Knowledge questions 10, 18-20 (p. 62)
		
		Structure of a Diarthrotic Joint diagram (p. 68)
		
		Multiple Choice questions 33-35; True or False questions 43-55; Matching questions 21-28; Short Answer questions 9, 10
		
		Student Assignment questions 10, 35, 39, 41, 45 (pp. 8-10)
		
		Types of Joint Movement
		
		Book Resources
		Quick Check question 4 (p. 142)
		Critical Thinking question 15 (p. 152)
		Figure 6-18 Comparison of the male and female pelvis (p. 143)
		Figure 6-19 Joints of the skeleton (p. 144)
		Figure 6-20 Structure of a diarthrotic joint (p. 146)
		Figure 6-21 Types of diarthrotic joints (p. 147)
		Quick Check questions 1-4 (p. 146)
		Table 6-7 Types of Joint Movements (pp. 148-149)
		Review questions 9-12 (p. 152)
		Chapter Test questions 11, 12 (p. 152)
		
		Class Activity Ask students to point out the three types of joints on a skeleton or on each other. Have them discuss the differences between these three joint types.

Thibodeau/Patton

OBJECTIVES	CONTENT	TEACHING RESOURCES
		Class Activity **Go to a hardware store and find representatives of diarthrotic joints (ball and socket, hinge, pivot, saddle, gliding, and condyloid). Show them to the students and ask them to list examples of that type of joint in the body.**
		Class Activity **Divide the class into teams. Have them perform the types of joint movements shown on pp. 148-149. After they move their joints, have them name the bones involved in the movement.**
Performance Evaluation		✏ Chapter 6 Computerized Test Bank questions
		📖 Classroom Application (p. 68); Lab Activities (p. 69); Practical/Creative Learning Activities (p. 69); Student Assignment (pp. 70-73)
		✏ Student Post-Test questions
		Book Resources
		Review Questions (p. 152)
		Critical Thinking questions (p. 152)
		Chapter Test (pp. 152-153)

6.2 Homework/Assignments:

6.2 Teacher's Notes:

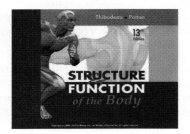

Slide 1

Chapter 6

The Skeletal System

Slide 2

Learning Objectives

- List and discuss the generalized functions of the skeletal system
- Identify the major anatomical structures found in a typical long bone
- Discuss the microscopic structure of bone and cartilage, including the identification of specific cell types and structural features
- Explain how bones are formed, how they grow, and how they are remodeled

2

Slide 3

Learning Objectives (cont'd.)

- Identify the two major subdivisions of the skeleton and list the bones found in each area
- List and compare the major types of joints in the body and give an example of each

3

Thibodeau/Patton

Slide 4

Chapter 6
Lesson 6.1

Slide 5

Functions of Bone

- Supports and gives shape to the body
- Protects internal organs
- Helps make movement possible
- Stores calcium
- Hematopoiesis

- What are the primary functions of bone? (Bones form the body's supporting framework. The hard structure of bones protects delicate structures enclosed within them. The skull protects the brain; the breastbone and ribs protect the heart and lungs.)

- Muscles are anchored to bones. As muscles contract, they pull on bones and move them.

- What is the role of bone in maintaining homeostasis of blood calcium? (Calcium storage: bones help maintain homeostasis of blood calcium, necessary for nerve and muscle function.)

- Hematopoiesis: the process of blood cell formation is carried on in the red bone marrow.

Slide 6

Examples of Bones

- Long
  - Humerus (upper arm)
- Short
  - Carpals (wrist)
- Flat
  - Frontal (skull)
- Irregular
  - Vertebrae (spinal cord)

- Ask students to name other examples of the four different types of bones.

Slide 7

Structure of Long Bones

- Structural components
  - Diaphysis or shaft
  - Medullary cavity—hollow area inside diaphysis containing yellow marrow
  - Epiphyses or ends of the bone—spongy bone contains red bone marrow

- Diaphysis–hollow tube made of hard, compact bone; rigid, strong, yet light enough to permit easy movement

- Epiphyses–ends of the bones; contain red marrow

- Yellow bone marrow–inactive, fatty form of marrow found in adult skeletons

- Articular cartilage covers the ends of bones where they form a joint.

Structure & Function of the Body, 13th ed.
Thibodeau/Patton

Slide 8

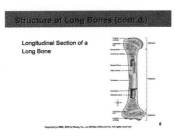

Structure of Long Bones (cont'd.)

Longitudinal Section of a
Long Bone

- Epiphyseal cartilage—presence indicates bone growth not yet complete; significant in children

- Discuss the significance of the epiphyseal line that divides the diaphysis from the epiphysis.

Slide 9

Microscopic Structure of Bone and Cartilage

- Bone types
  - Spongy
    - Texture results from needlelike threads of bone called *trabeculae* surrounded by a network of open spaces
  - Compact (Dense)
    - Structural units are called *osteons, Haversian systems*

- What are the two major types of connective tissue? (bone and cartilage)

- What are the two types of bone? (compact and spongy)

- Describe osteocytes, canaliculi, lacunae.

- Why is the end of the bone spongy rather than dense? (contains marrow)

Slide 10

Microscopic Structure of Bone and Cartilage (cont'd.)

- Cartilage
  - Cell type called *chondrocyte*
  - Has the flexibility of firm plastic
  - Matrix is gel-like and lacks blood vessels
  - Has no blood vessels, so nutrients must diffuse through the matrix to reach cells

- Cartilage resembles bone in that it consists more of intercellular substance than of cells. In cartilage, the collagenous fibers that reinforce the matrix are embedded in a firm gel, rather than the calcified cement substance in bone.

- Why does cartilage rebuild slowly after an injury? (Because it lacks blood vessels.)

- What body parts are made of cartilage? (outer ear, tip of nose)

Slide 11

Microscopic Structure of Bone and Cartilage (cont'd.)

Microscopic Structure of Bone

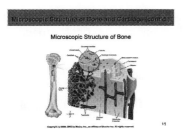

- Discuss the construction of the shell of the bone.

Structure & Function of the Body, 13th ed.
Thibodeau/Patton

Slide 12

- The process of "remodeling"
  - A newborn's skeleton has many bones that have not completely ossified.
  - Cartilage models replaced by calcified bone matrix
- Osteoblasts form new bone
- Osteoclasts resorb bone
- As long as the epiphyseal plate remains between epiphyses and diaphysis, growth continues
- The epiphyseal line marks where two centers of ossification have fused together

- What is the process of *remodeling* a bone? (*Remodeling* a growing bone as it changes from a small cartilage model to an adult bone requires continuous activity by osteoblasts.)

- What is responsible for *sculpting* bones? (The process of *sculpting* by osteoblasts and osteoclasts allows bones to respond to stress and injury by changing size, shape, and density.)

- Think of it this way—blasts build, clasts cut away.

- Osteoblasts and osteoclasts work together to repair and/or enlarge a bone.

Slide 13

Bone Formation and Growth (cont'd.)

Endochondral Ossification

- Endochondral ossification is the process of forming bones from cartilage models.

Slide 14

Chapter 6
Lesson 6.2

Slide 15

Divisions of the Skeleton

- **Skeleton:** Two divisions and their subdivisions
  - Axial skeleton
    - Skull
    - Spine
    - Thorax
    - Hyoid bone
  - Appendicular skeleton
    - Upper extremities, including shoulder girdle
    - Lower extremities, including hip girdle

- Ask students to identify the various parts of the axial skeleton and the appendicular skeleton.

Structure & Function of the Body, 13th ed.
Thibodeau/Patton

Slide 16

Divisions of the Skeleton (cont'd.)

- Axial skeleton
  - Skull
  - Spine (Vertebral Column)
    - Consists of a series of separate bones called vertebrae
    - Sections called *cervical, thoracic, lumbar, sacrum, coccyx*
    - Curves of the spine give strength to support body

16

- How many bones form the head? (The skull consists of 8 bones that form the cranium, 14 bones that form the face, and 6 bones in the middle ear.)

- The bones that give shape to the top of the skull form immovable joints, called *sutures*.

- The parietal bones meet with the occipital bone at the lambdoidal suture; the parietal bones meet with the temporal bone at the junction called the *squamous suture*. The *coronal suture* is the name of the joint between the parietal and the frontal bone. The joint between the two parietal bones is labeled the *sagittal suture*.

Slide 17

Divisions of the Skeleton (cont'd.)

The Skull

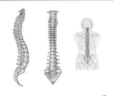

17

- Ask students to identify the bones and sutures of the skull.

Slide 18

Divisions of the Skeleton (cont'd.)

The Spinal Column

18

- The vertebral column consists of separate bones connected in a way that forms a flexible, curved rod.

- Point out the cervical region, thoracic region, lumbar region, sacrum, and coccyx.

- Discuss the physiologic reasons for the four curves of the spine.

Slide 19

Divisions of the Skeleton (cont'd.)

- Axial skeleton
  - Thorax is formed by
    - 12 pairs of ribs
    - The sternum (breastbone)
    - Thoracic vertebrae

19

- What is another name for the breastbone? (sternum)

- What is the difference between *true ribs* and *false ribs*?

  - The first seven pairs of ribs are called *true ribs* and are attached to the sternum.

  - The eighth, ninth, and tenth ribs are attached to the cartilage of the seventh pair of ribs; they are called *false ribs*.

  - The last two pairs of ribs are not attached to costal cartilage; in fact they are not attached anteriorly at all. Thus, they are called *floating cartilage*.

ELSEVIER

Structure & Function of the Body, 13th ed.

Thibodeau/Patton

Slide 20

Divisions of the Skeleton (cont'd.)

Bones of the Thorax

20

Slide 21

Divisions of the Skeleton (cont'd.)

- Appendicular skeleton
  - Upper extremity formed by
    - Scapula (shoulder blade)
    - Clavicle (collarbone)
      - Attached by sternoclavicular joint
    - Humerus
    - Radius and ulna
    - Wrist and hands—27 bones in all

21

- In what part of the body is the humerus? (The humerus is attached to the scapula at its proximal end and articulates with the two bones of the forearm at the elbow joint.)

- In what part of the body are the radius and ulna found? (Bones of the forearm are the radius and ulna.)

- Why is the anatomy of the elbow a good example of how structure is related to function? (Bony process of the ulna, called the olecranon process, fits into the olecranon fossa and makes movement possible.)

Slide 22

Divisions of the Skeleton (cont'd.)

Bones of the Arm, Elbow Joint, and Forearm

22

Slide 23

Divisions of the Skeleton (cont'd.)

- Appendicular Skeleton
  - Lower Extremity
    - Two coxal (pelvic) bones
    - Femur; longest bone in the body
      - Articulates proximally with coxal bone in socket called the *acetabulum*
    - Patella (kneecap)
    - Tibia (shinbone)
    - Fibula (slender bone in the lower leg)
    - Phalanges are composed of metatarsals and tarsals

23

- Coxal bone in infant consists of three separate bones: *ilium, ischium,* and *pubis.*

- The bones of the foot are comparable to the bones of the hand. Each foot contains five metatarsals and seven tarsals, corresponding to the hand's five metacarpals and eight carpals.

- What is the name of the heel bone? (calcaneus)

Thibodeau/Patton

Slide 24

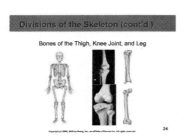

Slide 25

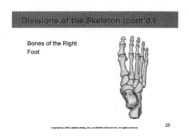

- Compare the names of the foot bones with the names of the hand bones.

Slide 26

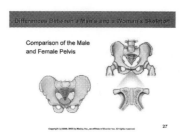

- What are the primary differences between a male and female skeleton? (In general, the female pelvis can accommodate the body of a fetus before birth and allow it to pass through during birth. Male hipbones are generally larger and narrower than the female's.)

Slide 27

- Notice the narrower width of the male pelvis, giving it a more funnel-like shape than the female pelvis.

Slide 28

Joints (Articulations)

- Kinds of joints
  - Synarthrosis (no movement)
    - Fibrous connective tissue grows between articulating bones
    - Example: Sutures of skull
  - Amphiarthrosis (slight movement)
    - Cartilage connects articulating bones
    - Example: Symphysis pubis

- Every bone in the body, except for one, connects to at least one other bone. What is the exception? (The hyoid bone in the neck, to which the tongue anchors.)

- In general, what functions do bone joints serve? (Joints hold the bones together securely and at the same time make it possible for movement to occur between the bones.)

- The joints make it possible to flex forward, sideways, and to rotate.

Slide 29

Joints (Articulations) (cont'd.)

- Diarthrosis (free movement)—most joints belong to this class
  - Structures of freely movable joints—joint capsule and ligaments hold adjoining bones together but permit movement at joint
  - Articular cartilage—covers joint ends of bones and absorbs jolts
  - Synovial membrane—lines joint capsule and secretes lubricating fluid
  - Joint cavity—space between joint ends of bones

- What are three classifications of joints?

  - Synarthroses are joints in which fibrous connective tissue grows between the articulating bones, holding them close together. The joints between cranial bones are synarthroses.

  - Amphiarthroses are joints in which cartilage connects the articulating bones. The joints between the bodies of the vertebrae are amphiarthroses.

  - Diarthroses allow considerable movement; sometimes in many directions and sometimes in only one direction. Most other joints are diarthroses.

- What are the types of freely movable joints? (ball-and-socket, hinge, pivot, saddle, gliding, and condyloid)

Slide 30

Joints (Articulations) (cont'd.)

Joints of the Skeleton

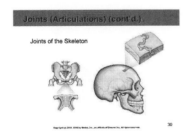

Slide 31

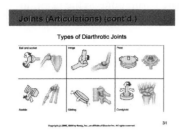

- Ball and socket joints (shoulder and hip) permit the widest range of movement.

- Hinge joints (elbow) allow movement in only two directions: flexion and extension.

- Pivot joints (neck) allow rotation.

- Saddle joints (between thumb and wrist) allow great mobility.

- Gliding joints (between vertebrae) allow limited gliding movements.

- Condyloid joints fit into an elliptical socket. (distal end of radius fits into depressions in carpal bones)

TEACHING FOCUS

Students will have the opportunity to learn about the body's muscular system, including the three major types of muscle tissue and the names, locations, functions, and movements of the major muscle groups. Additionally, students will have the opportunity to explore information about the microscopic structure of a skeletal muscle sarcomere and motor unit, and compare the major types of skeletal muscle contractions.

MATERIALS AND RESOURCES

☐ Copies of Figure 7-3 A (Lesson 7.1)
☐ Copies of Figure 7-6 without the identifying labels (Lesson 7.2)
☐ Index cards (all Lessons)
☐ Paper (Lesson 7.2)
☐ Computer (all Lessons)

LESSON CHECKLIST

Preparations for this lesson include:

- lecture
- demonstration
- review Outline Summary and Review Questions (pp. 178-182)
- guest speakers: physical therapist, sports trainer, medical assistant, nurse
- student performance evaluation of all entry-level skills required for student comprehension and application of principles underlying the structure and function of the muscular system including:
  - the three major types of muscle tissue
  - muscle stimulus and movement
  - the structure and contractions of skeletal muscles, and their major groups

KEY TERMS

abduction (p. 173)
actin (p. 157)
adduction (p. 173)
adductor muscles (p. 171)
aerobic training (p. 164)
all or none (p. 162)
anabolic steroids (p. 17)
antagonist (p. 159)
atrophy (p. 164)
biceps brachii (p. 165)
biceps femoris (p. 171)
bursa (p. 157)
cardiac muscle (p. 156)
carpal tunnel syndrome (p. 164)
diaphragm (p. 170)
disuse atrophy (p. 164)
dorsiflexion (p. 173)
endurance training (p. 164)
extension (p. 172)
external oblique (p. 170)
fatigue (p. 160)
flexion (p. 172)

frontal muscle (p. 165)
gastrocnemius (p. 170)
gluteus maximus (p. 170)
hamstring muscles (p. 171)
hypertrophy (p. 164)
hypervitaminosis (p. 171)
hypothermia (p. 160)
iliopsoas (p. 170)
insertion (p. 157)
intercostal muscles (p. 170)
internal oblique (p. 170)
isometric (p. 162)
isometric contraction (p. 162)
isotonic (p. 162)
latissimus dorsi (p. 165)
masseter (p. 165)
motor neuron (p. 161)
motor unit (p. 161)
muscle fibers (p. 156)
muscles of facial expression (p. 165)
muscles of mastication (p. 165)
myofilaments (p. 157)

ELSEVIER

myosin (p. 157)
neuromuscular junction (p. 161)
orbicularis oris (p. 165)
origin (p. 157)
oxygen debt (p. 160)
paralysis (p. 160)
pectoralis major (p. 165)
peroneus group (p. 171)
peroneus longus (p. 171)
plantar flexion (p. 173)
posture (p. 160)
prime mover (p. 159)
pronation (p. 173)
quadriceps femoris (p. 171)
rectus abdominis (p. 170)
rectus femoris (p. 171)
rotation (p. 173)
sarcomere (p. 157)
semimembranosus (p. 171)
semitendinosus (p. 171)
skeletal muscle (p. 156)
sliding filament model (p. 159)
smooth muscle (p. 156)
sternocleidomastoid (p. 165)

strength training (p. 164)
stimulus (p. 162)
supination (p. 173)
synergist (p. 159)
synovial membrane (p. 157)
temporal (p. 165)
tendon (p. 157)
tendon sheaths (p. 157)
tenosynovitis (p. 164)
testosterone (p. 171)
tetanic contraction (p. 162)
thick myofilaments (p. 157)
thin myofilaments (p. 157)
threshold stimulus (p. 162)
tibialis anterior (p. 171)
tonic contraction (p. 160)
transversus abdominis (p. 170)
trapezius (p. 165)
triceps brachii (p. 165)
twitch (p. 162)
vastus (p. 171)
zygomaticus (p. 165)

ADDITIONAL RESOURCES

AnimationDirect (Book Companion CD)
Instructor's Electronic Resource (IER) (CD)
PowerPoint slides (CD, Evolve)
Test Bank (Evolve)

Legend

ESLR
EVOLVE Student
Learning Resource

EILR TB
EVOLVE Instructor
Learning Resource
Test Bank

AnimationDirect
on Book Companion
CD

PPT
PowerPoint
Slides

SG
Study
Guide

IRM
Instructor's
Resource Manual

Class Activities are indicated in ***bold italic.***

ELSEVIER

Structure & Function of the Body, 13th ed.

Thibodeau/Patton

LESSON 7.1

PRETEST

Study Guide Multiple Choice questions 1-20 (pp. 75-76)

BACKGROUND ASSESSMENT

Question: Voluntary muscular movement is normally accomplished by skeletal muscles working in teams, meaning some muscle groups contract while others relax. This produces a smooth movement free of jerks and tremors. To accomplish this, one muscle becomes the main moving force supported by partner muscles that assist in producing the movement. What are these two muscle groups called, and how do they function together to make movement possible?

Answer: The muscle that is mainly responsible for producing a particular movement is called the *prime mover.* Its partner muscles are called *synergists;* they assist in moving the bones to which they are attached. Other muscles—called *antagonists*—relax, permitting a smooth flow of motion. When antagonist muscles contract, they produce a movement opposite to that produced by the prime movers.

Question: While the muscular system is vitally important to the human body, it cannot function independently. What other body systems contribute to muscle function, and how do they affect both voluntary and involuntary muscle movements?

Answer: A person can have perfectly normal muscles and still be unable to move in a normal fashion. Nervous system disorders including spinal cord injuries, multiple sclerosis, a brain hemorrhage, or brain tumor can shut off necessary impulses to certain skeletal muscles resulting in paralysis. The skeletal system can be affected by diseases such as arthritis. Disturbances in the circulatory system can cause blood supplies to be too insufficient to permit normal muscle function. As with the body in general, the normal function of the muscle system depends on the normal function of many other systems in the body.

CRITICAL THINKING QUESTION

Consider the primary functions of the muscular system. How are these functions critical to survival?

Guidelines: The three primary functions of the muscular system are *movement, posture* or *muscle tone,* and *heat production.* Our ability to survive often depends on our ability to adjust to the changing conditions of the environment. Movements frequently constitute a major part of this adjustment. Good posture means that body parts are held in the positions that optimize their function by distributing weight to minimize strain on the body. Muscle tone maintains posture by counteracting the pull of gravity, which tends to pull the head and trunk down and forward. Survival depends on maintaining body temperature within a narrow range. Contraction of muscle fibers breaks down adenosine triphosphate (ATP) and results in the release of energy. Much of this energy is lost as heat, thus producing most of the heat required to maintain body temperature. Through these three primary functions, the muscular system plays a vital role in survival.

OBJECTIVES	CONTENT	TEACHING RESOURCES
List, locate in the body, and compare the structure and function of the three major types of muscle tissue.	■ Muscle tissue (p. 156)	▨ Slides 5-9 🔖 Muscle Tissue questions 1-10 (p. 70) ✏ Multiple Choice questions 1-4; True or False questions 1-6, 56, 57; Matching questions 2, 6; Short Answer question 1 📕 Matching question 24 (p. 87); Completion questions 30, 33 (p. 88) **Book Resources** Figure 7-1 Muscle tissue (p. 156)

Structure & Function of the Body, 13th ed.

Thibodeau/Patton

OBJECTIVES	CONTENT	TEACHING RESOURCES
		Review questions 1, 2 (p. 181)
		Chapter Test questions 1, 2, 18, 19 (p. 182)
		Quick Check question 1 (p. 159)
		Clear View of the Human Body
		▸ Discuss the differences between the three types of muscle tissue.
		*Class Activity **Divide students into small groups. Ask each group to discuss the three types of muscle tissues:** skeletal, cardiac, **and** smooth. **Have the students discuss the differences between each tissue type and cite examples of each. Discuss the reasons for the structural differences.***

Discuss the microscopic structure of a skeletal muscle sarcomere and motor unit.	■ Structure of skeletal muscle (p. 157)
	  □ Microscopic structure (p. 157)
	■ Functions of skeletal muscle (p. 159)
	  □ Movement (p. 159)
	  □ Posture (p. 160)
	  □ Heat production (p. 160)
	■ Fatigue (p. 160)
	■ Role of other body systems in movement (p. 160)
	■ Motor unit (p. 161)
		Slides 10-23
		
		Skeletal Muscles questions 11-15 (p. 70)
		
		Microscopic Structure questions 16-20 (p. 70)
		
		Functions of Skeletal Muscle questions 21-30 (pp. 70-71)
		
		Fatigue: Role of Body Systems and Motor Unit Muscle Stimulus questions 31-40 (p. 71)
		
		Multiple Choice questions 5-18, 37, 38; True or False questions 7-32, 58; Matching questions 1, 3-5, 7-10; Short Answer questions 2-6
		
		Definition 11 (p. 86); Completion question 34 (p. 88)
		
		Book Resources
		
		Figure 7-2 Attachments of a skeletal muscle (p. 157)
		
		Figure 7-3 Structure of skeletal muscle (p. 158)
		
		Quick Check questions 2, 3 (p. 159)
		
		Quick Check questions 2, 5 (p. 161)
		
		Review questions 3-5 (p. 181)
		
		Critical Thinking questions 16-18 (p. 181)
		
		Chapter Test questions 3-6, 8, 9 (p. 182)
		
		▸ Discuss the roles of the origin and insertion in the attachments of a skeletal muscle.

OBJECTIVES	CONTENT	TEACHING RESOURCES
		▶ Discuss the structure of skeletal muscle, including the function of the sarcomere, referring to Figure 7-3 (p. 158).
		▶ Explain how a motor neuron stimulates a muscle cell. Refer to Figure 7-4 (p. 161).
		*Class Activity **Ask a student to stand in front of the class and volunteer to bend his/her arm as if doing a bicep curl with a weight. Have the other students describe the movement in terms of the prime mover, synergist, and antagonist.***
		*Class Activity **Divide students into small groups and give each group an unlabeled copy of Figure 7-3 A, "Structure of skeletal muscle" (p. 158; available on EILR or IER). Ask each group to label the microscopic structure of a muscle and to discuss the structure of a muscle in both relaxed and contracted states.***

Discuss how a muscle is stimulated and compare the major types of skeletal muscle contractions.	■ Muscle stimulus (p. 161)
	■ Types of skeletal muscle contraction (p. 162)
	  □ Twitch and tetanic contraction (p. 162)
	  □ Isotonic contraction (p. 162)
	  □ Isometric contraction (p. 162)
	■ Effects of exercise on skeletal muscles (p. 164)
		⊠ Slides 24-33
		
		Types of Skeletal Muscle Contraction questions 41-50 (pp. 71-72)
		
		Multiple Choice questions 19-25; True or False questions 33-46, 59-62; Short Answer questions 7-9
		
		Completion questions 1-4 (p. 86); Definitions 7, 9, 10 (pp. 10-11); Completion questions 29, 31 (p. 88)
		
		Types of Skeletal Muscle Contractions
		
		Book Resources
		
		Figure 7-4 Motor neuron (p. 161)
		
		Figure 7-5 Types of muscle contraction (p. 163)
		
		Clinical Application: Carpal Tunnel Syndrome (p. 164).
		
		Review questions 6-10 (p. 181)
		
		Chapter Test questions 7, 10-14 (p. 182)
		
		▶ Discuss the similarities and differences between the two types of muscle contraction. Refer to Figure 7-5 (p. 163).

OBJECTIVES	CONTENT	TEACHING RESOURCES
		Class Activity **Divide the class into groups of three or four students. Ask each group to design both an isotonic and an isometric exercise. Have each group demonstrate the exercises, and explain why they fit into each category.**
		Class Activity **Divide the class into small groups. Ask each group to list the benefits of exercise and to explain the differences between strength and endurance training. Have groups report to the entire class.**
		Class Activity **Have the class explore and discuss the increase in childhood obesity and type II diabetes.**

7.1 Homework/Assignments:

7.1 Teacher's Notes:

Structure & Function of the Body, 13th ed.

Thibodeau/Patton

LESSON 7.2

CRITICAL THINKING QUESTION

We have all heard that exercise is "good for us." While we might think of it in terms of improving our appearance, an exercise program benefits us in other ways as well. In addition to improving muscle tone, posture, heart and lung function, how does exercise specifically benefit our muscles?
Guidelines: Unused muscles can shrink, causing a condition called *disuse atrophy*. Exercise, on the other hand, can strengthen muscles and actually cause an increase in size, called *hypertrophy*. This process is enhanced by strength training, such as weightlifting, or isometric exercise, which increases the myofilaments in muscle fiber. Endurance training (aerobic training) increases the muscle's ability to function for sustained periods. Aerobic activities, such as running, or other isotonic movements increase the number of blood vessels in a muscle, allowing for more efficient delivery of oxygen and glucose to muscle fibers. Aerobic training also allows more adenosine triphosphate (ATP) to be produced in muscles.

OBJECTIVES	CONTENT	TEACHING RESOURCES
Name, identify on a model or diagram, and give the function of the major muscles of the body discussed in this chapter.	■ Skeletal muscle groups (p. 165) ☐ Muscles of the head and neck (p. 169) ☐ Muscles that move the upper extremities (p. 165) ☐ Muscles of the trunk (p. 170) ☐ Muscles that move the lower extremities (p. 170)	▨ Slides 34-41 Skeletal Muscle Groups questions 51-63 (p. 73) *e* Multiple Choice questions 26-29; Matching questions 11-20 Identification questions 1-22 (p. 89) **Book Resources** Figure 7-6 General overview of the body musculature (pp. 166-167) Table 7-1 Principal Muscles of the Body (pp. 168-169) Figure 7-7 Muscles of the head and neck (p. 169) Figure 7-8 Muscles of the trunk (p. 170) Review questions 11-14 (p. 181) Chapter Test questions 20-31 (p. 182) Clear View of the Human Body ▸ Discuss Research, Issues and Trends: Enhancing Muscle Strength (p. 173). Identify examples of anabolic steroids and discuss the use and impact of steroids in sports. *Class Activity Divide students into teams of two. Have each team create flash cards that list the function, insertion, and origin of each muscle. Then ask the students to quiz each other using the flash cards.*

ELSEVIER

OBJECTIVES	CONTENT	TEACHING RESOURCES
		Class Activity **Create a mock game show. Invite three students to act as contestants. Have the other students take turns calling out the name of a muscle. The first contestant to correctly describe that muscle's function receives one point. The game ends when the first contestant reaches ten points.**
		Class Activity **Divide students into small groups and give each group an unlabeled copy of Figure 7-6 (pp. 167-178; available on EILR or IER). Ask each group to complete the labels.**
List and explain the most common types of movement produced by skeletal muscles.	■ Movements produced by skeletal muscle contractions (p. 173)	Slides 42-45
		Movements Produced by Skeletal Muscle Contractions questions 64-69 (p. 73)
		Applying What You Know questions 70-72 (p. 74)
		Word Find (p. 74)
		Multiple Choice questions 30-36; True or False questions 47-55; Short Answer question 10
		Definitions 5, 6, 8, 12, 13 (pp. 86-87); Matching questions 15-23 (p. 87); Completion questions 27, 28, 32 (p. 88)
		Movement Produced by Skeletal Muscle Contractions
		Book Resources
		Figure 7-9 Flexion and extension of the elbow (p. 173)
		Figure 7-10 Flexion and extension of the knee (p. 173)
		Figure 7-11 Examples of body movements (p. 174)
		Table 7-2 Muscles Grouped According to Function (p. 175)
		Review question 15 (p. 181)
		Chapter Test questions 15-17 (p. 182)
		▶ Discuss flexion and extension movements, including the movements of the elbow described in Figure 7-9 (p. 173) and the movements of the knee described in Figure 7-10 (p. 173).

OBJECTIVES	CONTENT	TEACHING RESOURCES
		Class Activity **On individual slips of paper, write down the seven terms that describe body movements. Have each student select a movement to demonstrate for the class.**
Performance Evaluation		*e* Chapter 7 Computerized Test Bank questions
		Classroom Application questions; Lab Activities; Practical/Creative Learning Activities; Student Assignment questions 1; Identification questions
		e Student Post-Test questions
		Book Resource
		Chapter Test (pp. 182-183)

7.2 Homework/Assignments:

7.2 Teacher's Notes:

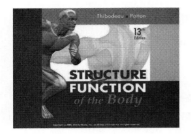

Slide 1

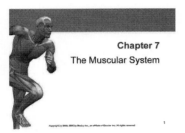

Chapter 7

The Muscular System

Slide 2

Learning Objectives

- List, locate in the body, and compare the structure and function of the three major types of muscle tissue
- Discuss the microscopic structure of a skeletal muscle sarcomere and motor unit
- Discuss how a muscle is stimulated and compare the major types of skeletal muscle contractions

---

Slide 3

Learning Objectives (cont'd.)

- Name, identify on a model or diagram, and give the function of the major muscles of the body discussed in this chapter
- List and explain the most common types of movement produced by skeletal muscles

Thibodeau/Patton

Slide 4

Chapter 7
Lesson 7.1

Slide 5

Introduction

- Muscular tissue enables the body and its parts to move
  - Movement is caused by ability of muscle cells, called fibers, to shorten or contract
  - Muscle cells shorten by converting chemical energy obtained from food into mechanical energy, which causes movement
  - Three types of muscle tissue exist in the body

- What causes movement of the body? (skeletal muscle contraction)

- What stimulates muscle tissue to contract? (nerves)

Slide 6

Muscle Tissue

- Types of muscle tissue
  - Skeletal muscle—also called *striated* or *voluntary muscle*
    - Represents 40% to 50% of body weight
    - Attached to bones
    - Microscope reveals crosswise stripes or striations
    - Contractions can be voluntarily controlled

- What are the three types of muscle tissue? (skeletal, cardiac, and smooth)

- If someone weighs 120 pounds, about 50 pounds of the body weight comes from the skeletal muscles.

Slide 7

Muscle Tissue (cont'd.)

- Types of muscle tissue
  - Cardiac muscle—composes bulk of heart
    - Cardiac muscle cells branch frequently
    - Characterized by unique dark bands called *intercalated disks*
    - Interconnected nature of cardiac muscle cells allows heart to contract efficiently as a unit

- What is the value of the interconnected nature of the cardiac muscle? Recall that structure determines function. (It increases the efficiency of the heart muscle in pumping blood.)

ELSEVIER

Slide 8

Muscle Tissue (cont'd.)

- Types of muscle tissue
  - Nonstriated muscle or involuntary muscle—also called *smooth* or *visceral muscle*
    - Lacks cross stripes or striation when seen under a microscope; appears smooth
    - Found in walls of hollow visceral structures, such as digestive tract, blood vessels, and ureters
    - Contractions not under voluntary control; movement caused by contractions is involuntary
  - Function—all muscle cells specialize in contraction (shortening)

8

Slide 9

Muscle Tissue (cont'd.)

9

Slide 10

Structure of Skeletal Muscle

- Skeletal muscle—an organ composed mainly of skeletal muscle cells and connective tissue
- Extend from one bone across a joint to another bone

10

Slide 11

Structure of Skeletal Muscle (cont'd)

- Parts of a skeletal muscle:
  - Origin—attachment to the bone that remains relatively fixed when movement at the joint occurs
  - Insertion—point of attachment to the bone that moves when a muscle contracts
  - Body—main part of the muscle

11

● What are the *origin* and the *insertion point*, and what are their roles in movement of the body? (*Origin* refers to the portion of the muscle attached to the more stationary bone. The *insertion* refers to the portion of the muscle attached to the movable bone. In a given movement, the *insertion* moves towards the *origin*.)

Thibodeau/Patton

Slide 12

Structure of Skeletal Muscle (cont'd)

- Muscles attach to the bone by *tendons*—strong cords of fibrous connective tissue
- Some tendons are enclosed in synovial-lined tubes and lubricated by synovial fluid
- Bursae—small synovial-lined sacs containing a small amount of synovial fluid

12

- Tendons do not tear or pull away from bone easily, yet emergency room physicians and nurses frequently see torn or severed tendon injuries.

- Small, fluid-filled sacs called *bursae* lie between some tendons and the bones beneath them.

- What is the role of bursae? (Bursae make it easier for a tendon to slide over a bone when the muscle shortens.)

Slide 13

Structure of Skeletal Muscle (cont'd)

Attachments of a Skeletal Muscle

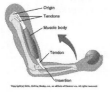

13

Slide 14

Structure of Skeletal Muscle (cont'd)

- Microscopic structure
  - Muscle tissue consists of specialized contractile cells called *fibers*
  - Each fiber contains two kinds of very fine, threadlike structures:
    - Thick myofilaments
    - Thin myofilaments

14

- What are thick and thin myofilaments composed of? (thick myofilaments formed from protein myosin; thin myofilaments composed of actin)

Slide 15

Structure of Skeletal Muscle (cont'd)

- Sarcomere: basic functional (contractile) unit
  - Separated from each other by dark bands called *Z lines*
  - Sliding filament model explains mechanism of contraction
    - Thick and thin myofilaments slide past each other as a muscle contracts

15

- As the osteon (Haversian system) serves as basic building block in compact bone, the sarcomere serves that function in muscle.

- What is required for contraction? (calcium and energy-rich ATP molecules)

Structure & Function of the Body, 13th ed.

Thibodeau/Patton

Slide 16

Functions of Skeletal Muscle

- Movement
  - Muscles produce movement
  - As muscle contracts, it pulls the insertion bone closer to the origin bone
  - Movement occurs at the joint between the origin and the insertion

16

- Describe how muscles produce movement.

Slide 17

Functions of Skeletal Muscle (cont'd.)

- Movement
  - Groups of muscles usually contract to produce a single movement
    - Prime mover—contraction is mainly responsible for producing a movement
    - Synergist—contractions help the prime mover produce a movement
    - Antagonist—actions oppose the action of a prime mover in a movement

17

- When a muscle group produces movement, what are the components of the group called? (prime mover, synergist, antagonist)

- When antagonist muscles contract, roles are reversed and they produce opposite movement.

- Voluntary movement is normally smooth and free of jerks, because skeletal muscles work in coordinated teams, not separately.

Slide 18

Functions of Skeletal Muscle (cont'd.)

- Posture
  - *Tonic contraction:* specialized muscle contraction that enables us to maintain body position
    - Only a few of a muscle's fibers shorten at one time
    - Tonic contractions produce no movement
  - Tonic contractions maintain muscle tone called *posture*

18

- Good posture means that body parts are held in positions that favor best function.

- Bad posture causes fatigue and may lead to deformity.

Slide 19

Functions of Skeletal Muscle (cont'd.)

- Heat production
  - Survival depends on the ability to maintain constant body temperature
    - **Fever:** An elevated body temperature; often a sign of illness
    - **Hypothermia:** A reduced body temperature
  - Contraction of muscle fibers produces most of the heat required to maintain normal body temperature

19

- Heat is produced by the breakdown of adenosine triphosphate (ATP) during contractions.

ELSEVIER

Structure & Function of the Body, 13th ed.

Thibodeau/Patton

Slide 20

Fatigue

- Reduced strength of muscle contraction
- Caused by repeated muscle stimulation
- Repeated muscular contraction depletes cellular ATP store and outstrips the ability of the blood supply to replenish oxygen and nutrients

20

- What can cause a decrease in the strength of muscle contraction? (muscle cells being repeatedly stimulated without adequate rest)

Slide 21

Fatigue (cont'd.)

- Contraction in the absence of adequate oxygen produces lactic acid, which contributes to muscle soreness
- **Oxygen debt:** The continued metabolic effort required to burn excess lactic acid that may accumulate during prolonged periods of exercise

21

- Labored breathing is required to help the body pay the oxygen debt—an example of homeostasis at work.

- What is the body attempting to do on the cellular level during labored breathing following exercise? (to return the cells' energy and oxygen reserves to pre-exercise levels)

Slide 22

Role of Other Body Systems in Movement

- Muscle functioning depends on the functioning of many other parts of the body
- Respiratory, circulatory, nervous, muscular, and skeletal systems play essential roles in producing normal movements

22

- Normal function of one body part depends on the normal function of all other parts.

- What are some examples of pathologic conditions that might affect movement of the body? (skeletal system disorders, multiple sclerosis, brain hemorrhage, and spinal cord injury)

Slide 23

Motor Unit

- Stimulation of a muscle by a nerve impulse is required to produce movement
  - **Motor neuron:** Specialized nerve that transmits an impulse to a muscle, causing contraction
  - **Neuromuscular junction:** Specialized point of contact between a nerve ending and the muscle fiber it innervates
  - **Motor unit:** The combination of a motor neuron with the muscle cell(s) it innervates

23

- Specialized chemicals are released by the motor neuron in response to a nerve impulse.

ELSEVIER

Thibodeau/Patton

Slide 24

- A muscle will contract only if an applied stimulus reaches a certain level of intensity
  - **Threshold stimulus:** Minimal level of stimulation required to cause a muscle fiber to contract
- Once stimulated by a threshold stimulus, a muscle fiber will contract completely, a response called *all or none*

24

- What is a threshold stimulus? (Minimal level of stimulation required to cause a muscle fiber to contract.)

Slide 25

- Different fibers in a muscle are controlled by different motor units with different threshold-stimulus levels
  - Although individual muscle fibers always respond all or none to a threshold stimulus, the muscle as a whole does not

25

- How is a graded response of a muscle accomplished? (Different motor units responding to different threshold stimuli permit a muscle as a whole to execute contractions of graded force.)

Slide 26

- Twitch and tetanic contractions
  - **Twitch contractions:** A quick, jerky response to stimulus
    - Single contraction of muscle fibers caused by a single threshold stimulus
  - **Tetanic contractions**—sustained, steady muscular contractions
    - Caused by a series of stimuli bombarding a muscle in rapid succession

26

- About 30 stimuli per second evoke tetanic contractions in certain types of skeletal muscles.

- Are twitch contractions significant for normal activity? (no)

Slide 27

- Isotonic contractions
  - Contraction of a muscle that produces movement at a joint
  - The muscle changes length, causing the insertion end of the muscle to move relative to the point of origin
  - Most types of body movements such as walking and running are isotonic contractions

27

- What is an isotonic contraction? (muscle contractions that produce movement at a joint)

Structure & Function of the Body, 13th ed.

Thibodeau/Patton

Slide 28

Types of Skeletal Muscle Contraction (cont'd.)

- Isometric contractions
  - Muscle contractions that do not produce movement
    - The muscle as a whole does not shorten
  - No movement occurs during isometric contractions, but tension within the muscle increases

Copyright (c) 2008, 2005 by Mosby, Inc., an affiliate of Elsevier Inc. All rights reserved.   28

- What is an isometric contraction? (muscle contractions that do not produce movement)

- What are the differences between isotonic and isometric contractions? (Isotonic—muscles change size and movement is produced; isometric—only muscle tension increases and there is no movement.)

- Pushing against a wall is an example of an isometric contraction.

Slide 29

Types of Skeletal Muscle Contraction (cont'd.)

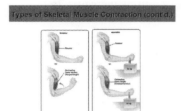

Copyright (c) 2008, 2005 by Mosby, Inc., an affiliate of Elsevier Inc. All rights reserved.   29

Slide 30

Effects of Exercise on Skeletal Muscles

- Regular, properly practiced exercise improves muscle tone and posture
- Results in more efficient heart and lung functioning
- Reduces fatigue
- Helps muscle tissue develop
- Helps maintain a healthy weight

Copyright (c) 2008, 2005 by Mosby, Inc., an affiliate of Elsevier Inc. All rights reserved.   30

- What are some of the health benefits of regular exercise? (Weight management, improved circulation, sense of well-being)

Slide 31

Effects of Exercise on Skeletal Muscles (cont'd.)

- Effects of exercise on skeletal muscles
  - Prolonged inactivity causes disuse, or *atrophy*
  - Regular exercise increases muscle size, called *hypertrophy*

Copyright (c) 2008, 2005 by Mosby, Inc., an affiliate of Elsevier Inc. All rights reserved.   31

- What type of changes do muscles undergo relative to the amount of work they normally do? (Disuse causes atrophy; hypertrophy is an increase in size.)

Slide 32

Effects of Exercise on Skeletal Muscles (cont'd.)

- **Strength training:** Exercise involving contractions of muscles against heavy resistance
  - Increases number of myofilaments in each muscle fiber
  - Total mass of the muscle increases
  - Does not increase the number of muscle fibers

32

- What are examples of strength training? (isometric exercises and weightlifting)

Slide 33

Effects of Exercise on Skeletal Muscles (cont'd.)

- **Endurance training:** Exercise that increases a muscle's ability to sustain moderate exercise over long periods
  - Sometimes called *aerobic training*
  - Allows more efficient delivery of oxygen and nutrients to a muscle via increased blood flow
  - Increases the number of blood vessels in a muscle
  - Does not usually result in muscle hypertrophy

33

- What are the differences between strength training and endurance training? (In strength training, mass of muscle increases. In endurance exercises, there is usually no increase in muscle mass.)

Slide 34

**Chapter 7
Lesson 7.2**

34

Slide 35

Skeletal Muscle Groups

- Muscles of the head and neck
  - Facial muscles
    - Orbicularis oculi, orbicularis oris, zygomaticus
  - Muscles of mastication
    - Masseter, temporal
  - **Sternocleidomastoid:** Flexes head
  - **Trapezius:** Elevates shoulders and extends head

35

- What are the names of the "kissing muscle" and the "smiling muscle"? (Orbicularis oculi is the kissing muscle, and zygomaticus is the smiling muscle.)

- Mastication muscles are among the strongest muscles in the body.

Structure & Function of the Body, 13th ed.

Thibodeau/Patton

Slide 36

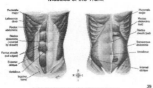

- Many muscles have names similar to bones.

Slide 37

Skeletal Muscle Groups (cont'd.)

- Muscles that move the upper extremities
  - **Pectoralis major:** Flexes upper arm
  - **Latissimus dorsi:** Extends upper arm
  - **Deltoid:** Abducts upper arm
  - **Biceps brachii:** Flexes forearm
  - **Triceps brachii:** Extends forearm

- The upper extremity is attached to the thorax by the pectoralis major.

- What is the name of the "boxer's muscle"? (triceps brachii)

Slide 38

Skeletal Muscle Groups (cont'd.)

- Muscles of the trunk
  - Abdominal muscles
    - Rectus abdominis
    - External oblique
    - Internal oblique
    - Transversus abdominis
  - Respiratory muscles
    - Intercostal muscles
    - Diaphragm

- Rectus abdominis flexes the spinal column.

- Which muscles change the size of the chest during respiration? (respiratory muscles)

Slide 39

Skeletal Muscle Groups (cont'd.)

Muscles of the Trunk

Slide 40

Skeletal Muscle Groups (cont'd.)

- Muscles that move the lower extremities
  - **Iliopsoas:** Flexes thigh
  - **Gluteus maximus:** Extends thigh
  - **Adductor muscles:** Adduct thighs
  - **Hamstring muscles:** Flex lower leg
    - Semimembranosus
    - Semitendinosus
    - Biceps femoris

40

- Iliopsoas normally flexes the thigh but can flex the trunk if the thigh is fixed/immovable as in sit-ups.

Slide 41

Skeletal Muscle Groups (cont'd.)

- Muscles that move the lower extremities
  - **Quadriceps femoris group:** Extend lower leg
    - Rectus femoris
    - Vastus muscles
  - **Tibialis anterior:** Dorsiflexes foot
  - **Gastrocnemius:** Plantar flexes foot
  - **Peroneus group:** Flex foot

41

- Gastrocnemius is sometimes called the *toe dancer's muscle.*

Slide 42

Types of Movements Produced by Skeletal Muscle Contractions

- **Flexion:** Decreases the angle between two bones at their joint: *bending*
- **Extension:** Increases the angle between two bones at their joint: *straightening*
- **Abduction:** Movement of a part away from the midline of the body
- **Adduction:** Movement of a part toward the midline of the body
- **Rotation:** Movement around a longitudinal axis

42

- What are examples of the types of movements listed here?

  - Flexion: Bending elbow or knee

  - Extension: Straightening elbow or knee

  - Abduction: Extending the arm outward to the side

  - Adduction: Moving the arm towards the midline of the body

  - Rotation: Shaking head "no"

Slide 43

Types of Movements Produced by Skeletal Muscle Contractions (cont'd.)

Flexion and Extension of the Elbow

43

Slide 44

Types of Movements Produced by
Skeletal Muscle Contractions (cont'd.)

- **Supination and pronation:** Hand positions from
  rotation of the forearm
  - **Supination:** Palm turned to the anterior position
  - **Pronation:** Palm faces posteriorly
- Dorsiflexion and plantar flexion: Foot movements
  - **Dorsiflexion:** Elevation of the dorsum or top of the
    foot
  - **Plantar flexion:** Bottom of the foot is directed
    downward

44

- What are the origins of the words *supination* and *pronation*?
  (supine and prone)

Slide 45

Types of Movements Produced by
Skeletal Muscle Contractions (cont'd.)

Examples of Body Movements

45

ELSEVIER

8 Lesson Plan
The Nervous System

TEACHING FOCUS

In this chapter, the student will be introduced to the organs and divisions of the nervous system and to a description of the generalized functions of the system as a whole. The student will be exposed to the major types of cells in the nervous system and the function of each. In addition, the student will have the opportunity to learn to identify the major anatomical components of a three-neuron reflex arc, and to learn to compare and contrast the propagation of the nerve impulse along a nerve fiber and across a synaptic cleft. The student will be exposed to the major anatomical components of the brain and spinal cord, and the function of each. In addition, the student will have the opportunity to learn about the spinal and cranial nerves, and the anatomical and functional characteristics of two divisions of the autonomic nervous system.

MATERIALS AND RESOURCES

☐ Ice pack or other irritant (Lesson 8.1)
☐ Model of the brain (Lesson 8.2)
☐ Model of the spine (Lesson 8.2)
☐ Quizzes and activities from Evolve (Lesson 8.2)
☐ Photocopies of the unlabeled cerebrum in the Study Guide (p. 101) (Lesson 8.2)
☐ Photocopies of the unlabeled cranial nerves in the Study Guide (p. 99) (Lesson 8.2)
☐ Photocopies of the unlabeled patellar neural pathway map in the Study Guide (p. 100) (Lesson 8.1)

☐ Photocopies of a sagittal section of the brain in the Study Guide (p. 102) (Lesson 8.2)
☐ Photocopies of the neuron in the Study Guide (p. 98) (Lesson 8.1)
☐ Photocopies of the unlabeled neuron pathways map in the Study Guide (p. 103) (Lesson 8.2)
☐ Rubber hammer for reflex test (Lesson 8.2)
☐ Brief descriptions of the effect of an autonomic function on visceral effectors, as shown in Table 8-3, Autonomic Functions (p. 215)
☐ Computer (all Lessons)

LESSON CHECKLIST

Preparations for this lesson include:
- lecture
- discussion
- demonstration
- student performance evaluation of all entry-level skills required for student comprehension and application of anatomical and physiological principles of the nervous system including:
  ○ anatomical and functional components of a three-neuron reflex arc
  ○ cell structure and physiology
  ○ components of the brain and spinal cord and their functions
  ○ general functions of the nervous system as a whole

KEY TERMS

acetylcholine (p. 195)
action potential (p. 191)
adrenergic fiber (p. 216)
afferent neuron (p. 187)
anesthesia (p. 205)
antidiuretic hormone (ADH) (p. 197)
arachnoidea mater (p. 205)
ascending tract (p. 203)
astrocytes (p. 187)
autonomic or visceral effector (p. 211)
autonomic nervous system (ANS) (p. 187)
axon (p. 187)
blood–brain barrier (p. 189)
brainstem (p. 196)
catecholamines (p. 196)
cell body (p. 187)
central nervous system (CNS) (p. 186)
central or connecting neuron (p. 187)
cerebral nuclei (p. 201)
cerebrospinal fluid (CSF) (p. 206)
cerebrovascular accident (CVA) (p. 201)
cerebrum (p. 199)
cholinergic fiber (p. 215)
choroid plexus (p. 206)
corpus callosum (p. 199)
cranial and spinal nerves (p. 208)
craniosacral system (p. 215)
dendrite (p. 187)
dermatome (p. 210)
descending tract (p. 203)
diencephalon (p. 197)
dopamine (p. 196)
dura mater (p. 205)
effector (p. 192)
efferent neuron (p. 187)
endoneurium (p. 190)
endorphins (p. 196)
enkephalins (p. 196)
epineurium (p. 190)
fascicle (p. 190)
fight-or-flight response (p. 215)
ganglia (p. 211)
ganglion (p. 191)
glia (p. 187)
glioma (p. 187)
gray matter (p. 189)
gyri (p. 199)
herpes zoster, or shingles (p. 217)
hydrocephalus (p. 206)
hypothalamus (p. 197)

interneuron (p. 187)
limbic system (p. 216)
lumbar puncture (p. 208)
medulla oblongata (p. 196)
meninges (p. 196)
microglia (p. 189)
midbrain (p. 196)
motor neuron (p. 187)
multiple sclerosis (MS) (p. 192)
myelin (p. 187)
myelinated fiber (p. 187)
nerve (p. 189)
neurilemma (p. 187)
neuron (p. 187)
neuron pathway (p. 191)
neurotransmitter (p. 195)
nitric oxide (p. 196)
node of Ranvier (p. 187)
norepinephrine (p. 196)
oligodendrocyte (p. 189)
paralysis (p. 205)
parasympathetic nervous system (p. 211)
perineurium (p. 190)
peripheral nervous system (PNS) (p. 186)
pia mater (p. 205)
plexus (p. 208)
pons (p. 196)
posterior (dorsal) root ganglion (p. 191)
postganglionic neuron (p. 211)
postsynaptic neuron (p. 193)
preganglionic neuron (p. 211)
presynaptic neuron (p. 193)
receptor (p. 191)
reflex (p. 192)
reflex arc (p. 191)
reticular formation (p. 196)
saltatory conduction (p. 193)
Schwann cell (p. 189)
sensory neuron (p. 187)
serotonin (p. 187)
spinal tract (p. 203)
sulci (p. 199)
sympathetic chain ganglia (p. 214)
sympathetic nervous system (p. 211)
sympathetic preganglionic neuron (p. 213)
sympathetic postganglionic neuron (p. 214)
synapse (p. 192)
synaptic cleft (p. 193)
synaptic knob (p. 193)
thalamus (p. 199)

Thibodeau/Patton

ADDITIONAL RESOURCES

AnimationDirect (Book Companion CD)
Instructor's Electronic Resource (IER) (CD)
PowerPoint slides (CD, Evolve)
Test Bank (Evolve)

Legend

ESLR
EVOLVE Student
Learning Resource

EILR TB
EVOLVE Instructor
Learning Resource
Test Bank

AnimationDirect
on Book Companion
CD

PPT
PowerPoint
Slides

SG
Study
Guide

IRM
Instructor's
Resource Manual

Class Activities are indicated in *bold italic.*

Structure & Function of the Body, 13th ed.
Thibodeau/Patton

LESSON 8.1

PRETEST

Study Guide Multiple Choice questions 1-10 (pp. 92-93)

BACKGROUND ASSESSMENT

Question: What are the differences between the central nervous system and the peripheral nervous system?
Answer: The central nervous system consists of the *brain* and *spinal cord.* The nerves connecting the brain and spinal cord to other parts of the body constitute the peripheral nervous system. This system includes cranial and spinal nerves that connect the brain and spinal cord, respectively, to peripheral structures such as the skin surface and the skeletal muscles.

Question: Describe the transmission of signals across the synapse.
Answer: When a nerve impulse arrives at the synaptic knob, neurotransmitter molecules are released from the vesicles into the synaptic cleft. The plasma membrane of a postsynaptic neuron has protein molecules embedded in it opposite each synaptic knob. These molecules serve as receptors to which the neurotransmitter molecules bind. This binding can initiate an impulse in the postsynaptic neuron, and the neurotransmitter activity is rapidly terminated.

CRITICAL THINKING QUESTION

Mr. Collins is a 60-year-old patient who was in a car accident earlier in the day. After an examination, the physician determines that Mr. Collins sustained no physical injuries, although the patient's blood pressure and heart rate are elevated. Mr. Collins reports that at the time of the accident, he felt a high level of fear, and he noticed that he had developed goose bumps and was sweating profusely. Currently, he reports feeling constipated. Explain the mechanics of Mr. Collins's physiologic reaction to the stressful experience of an automobile accident, and describe the division of the autonomic nervous system that is responsible for Mr. Collins's symptoms.
Guidelines: The stressful event of the automobile accident activated Mr. Collins's sympathetic nervous system, producing widespread changes throughout the body. In response to the event, Mr. Collins's heart rate increased; most of his blood vessels constricted, thereby increasing his blood pressure; the sweat and adrenal glands secreted more abundantly; and the digestive tract became sluggish, hampering digestion. Mr. Collins experienced a typical response to stress: the fight-or-flight response.

OBJECTIVES	CONTENT	TEACHING RESOURCES
List the organs and divisions of the nervous system and describe the generalized functions of the system as a whole.	■ Organs and divisions of the nervous system (p. 186)	Slides 5, 6 Organs and Divisions of the Nervous System, Cells of the Nervous System, and Nerves questions 1-10 (p. 80) Multiple Choice question 1; True or False questions 1, 66, 67 Divisions of the Nervous System **Book Resource** Clear View of the Human Body ***Class Activity Ask small groups to create a diagram of the organs and divisions of the nervous system.***

OBJECTIVES	CONTENT	TEACHING RESOURCES
Identify the major types of cells in the nervous system and discuss the function of each.	■ Cells of the nervous system (p. 187) □ Neurons (p. 187) □ Glia (p. 187)	Slides 7-11 Cells of the Nervous System questions 11-20 (p. 80) Multiple Choice questions 2-11, 36-38; True or False questions 2-12, 68-73; Matching questions 2, 3, 7-9; Short Answer questions 1, 2 Multiple Choice questions 1, 7 (p. 105) **Book Resources** Figure 8-1 Divisions of the nervous system (p. 186) Figure 8-2 Neuron (p. 188) Figure 8-3 Glia (p. 189) Quick Check questions 1-3 (p. 189) *Class Activity **Form groups of three and give each group a photocopy of the neuron illustration from the Study Guide (p. 89). Ask each group to label the illustration.***
Identify the anatomical and functional components of a three-neuron reflex arc.	■ Nerves (p. 189) ■ Reflex arcs (p. 190)	Slides 12-16 Reflex Arcs questions 21-30 (p. 81) Multiple Choice questions 12-15, 39, 40; True or False questions 13-20, 74; Matching question 4; Short Answer questions 3, 4 Completion question 21 (p. 106) **Book Resources** Figure 8-4 The nerve (p. 190) Figure 8-5 Patellar reflex (p. 191) Clinical Application: Multiple Sclerosis (MS) (p. 192) ▶ Discuss multiple sclerosis, characterized by myelin loss and destruction, including its definition, etiology, symptoms, and treatment options. *Class Activity **Ask a student to volunteer and perform a reflex test using the rubber hammer. Then use an ice pack or other irritant to demonstrate a three-neuron reflex. (Refer to pp. 191-192.)***

ELSEVIER

OBJECTIVES	CONTENT	TEACHING RESOURCES
		Class Activity **Divide the class into three groups, representing sensory neurons, interneurons, and motor neurons. Have each group discuss their neuron's role in a three-neuron reflex arc. Have one representative of each group describe and act out a reflex arc for the class.**
		Class Activity **Hand out copies of the patellar neural pathway picture from the Study Guide (p. 100), and have students fill in the names of the parts of the neural pathway of the patellar reflex.**
Compare and contrast the propagation of a nerve impulse along a nerve fiber and across a synaptic cleft.	■ Nerve impulses (p. 193) ■ The synapse (p. 193)	⊠ Slides 17-22 📖 Nerve Impulses and The Synapse questions 31-40 (p. 81) ✐ Multiple Choice questions 16-20, 26; True or False questions 21-31, 75, 76; Matching questions 1, 5, 6; Short Answer questions 5-7 📕 Multiple Choice question 8 (p. 105); Completion questions 22, 23 (p. 106) ⊙ Nerve Impulse **Book Resources** Quick Check questions 1-4 (p. 193) Figure 8-6 Conduction of nerve impulses (p. 194) Figure 8-7 Components of a synapse (p. 195) Quick Check questions 1-4 (p. 196) Health and Well-Being: Suppressing Pain During Exercise (p. 196)

8.1 Homework/Assignments:

8.1 Teacher's Notes:

LESSON 8.2

CRITICAL THINKING QUESTION

Mr. Stevens comes to your office complaining that he is frequently losing his balance. He says that he feels like a drunken man when he walks and cannot even draw a straight line. Mr. Stevens will have to undergo testing before the physician determines a diagnosis, but what part of his brain do you think might be involved based on the symptoms he reports?

Guidelines: The cerebellum is the part of the brain that controls normal movement. A physician might consider it possible that a tumor on his cerebellum is causing his lack of coordination. Patients who have such tumors often complain of loss of balance and frequent falling, clumsiness, and poor muscle coordination. Based on scientific observation of patients with cerebellum diseases and animals with their cerebellum removed, the cerebellum's key general function is to create smooth, coordinated movements, sustain physical equilibrium, and maintain normal posture.

OBJECTIVES	CONTENT	TEACHING RESOURCES
Identify the major anatomical components of the brain and spinal cord and briefly comment on the functions of each.	■ Central nervous system (p. 196) 　□ Divisions of the brain (p. 196) 　　– Brainstem (p. 196) 　　– Diencephalon (p. 197) 　　– Cerebellum (p. 199) 　　– Cerebrum (p. 199) 　□ Spinal cord (p. 202) 　　– Structure (p. 202) 　　– Functions (p. 204) 　□ Coverings and fluid spaces of the brain and spinal cord (p. 205)	Slides 24-35 Central Nervous System and Divisions of the Brain questions 41-55 (pp. 82-83) Spinal Cord questions 56-62 (p. 84) Coverings and Fluid Spaces of Brain and Spinal Cord questions 63-67 (p. 84) Multiple Choice questions 21-25, 27-31, 41-44; True or False questions 32-41, 44-51, 77-84; Matching questions 10-20, 26; Short Answer questions 8-16 Multiple Choice questions 2-4, 9, 31, 32 (pp. 105-107); Completion questions 24-26, 29, 30 (p. 106) Areas of the Brain that Control Body Functions **Book Resources** Figure 8-8 The nervous system (p. 197) Figure 8-9 Major regions of the central nervous system (p. 198) Figure 8-10 The cerebrum (p. 200) Table 8-1 Functions of Major Divisions of the Brain (p. 201) Quick Check questions 1-4 (p. 202) Figure 8-11 Spinal cord and spinal nerves (p. 203) Figure 8-12 Spinal cord (p. 204) Figure 8-13 Spinal cord (p. 205)

Structure & Function of the Body, 13th ed.

Thibodeau/Patton

OBJECTIVES	CONTENT	TEACHING RESOURCES
		Figure 8-14 Fluid spaces of the brain (p. 206)
		Figure 8-15 Flow of cerebrospinal fluid (p. 207)
		Quick Check questions 1-4 (p. 208)
		Critical Thinking question 21 (p. 222)
		▸ Discuss Research, Issues and Trends: Parkinson's Disease (p. 202). Ask students if they are aware of other research or proposed treatments for Parkinson's disease.
		▸ Discuss Clinical Application: Lumbar Puncture (p. 208). Use this as an opportunity to review the origins and function of cerebrospinal fluid and the disorders for which a lumbar puncture would be required as part of the diagnosis.
		Class Activity Form groups of three and give each group a photocopy of the sagittal section picture of the brain from the Study Guide (p. 102). Ask each group to label the illustration.
		Class Activity Ask pairs to create a drawing of the cerebrum and label the lobes.
		Class Activity Ask students to discuss areas of research with spinal cord injuries. Divide the class into small groups, and ask the groups to come up with a list of spinal cord and nervous system issues they remember hearing about in the news. Have the groups present their findings to the class.
Compare and contrast spinal and cranial nerves.	■ Peripheral nervous system (p. 208) □ Cranial nerves (p. 208) □ Spinal nerves (p. 208) – Structure (p. 208) – Functions (p. 209)	⊠▤ Slides 36-39 🔖 Peripheral Nervous System: Cranial Nerves question 68 (p. 85) 🔖 Cranial Nerves and Spinal Nerves questions 69-76 (p. 86) ✐ True or False questions 52-54; Matching questions 21-24, 26, 27; Short Answer question 17 ⊙ Cranial Nerves **Book Resources** Figure 8-16 Cranial nerves (p. 209) Table 8-2 Cranial Nerves (p. 210) Quick Check questions 1-3 (p. 210)

Thibodeau/Patton

OBJECTIVES	CONTENT	TEACHING RESOURCES
		Critical Thinking question 22 (p. 222)
		Class Activity Hand out copies of the cranial nerves picture from the Study Guide (p. 99) and have students label the parts.
		Class Activity Divide the class into three groups and have each group choose a contestant for a game show. Display an illustration of the cranial nerves. Ask the three contestants to identify each of the numbered nerves. If a contestant gives an incorrect answer, the team must present a new contestant. The team with the most correct answers wins.
		Class Activity Have two or more competing teams create a table listing the 12 cranial nerves, the areas to which they conduct impulses, and the functions of the cranial nerve. The first team with the most complete and accurate table wins.
		Class Activity Have students demonstrate the actions of the cranial nerves (e.g., blinking, smiling, chewing, etc.)
Discuss the anatomical and functional characteristics of the two divisions of the autonomic nervous system.	■ Autonomic nervous system (p. 210) □ Functional anatomy (p. 211) □ Autonomic conduction paths (p. 212) □ Sympathetic nervous system (p. 213) – Structure (p. 213) – Functions of the sympathetic nervous system (p. 214) □ Parasympathetic nervous system (p. 215) – Structure (p. 215) – Functions of the parasympathetic nervous system (p. 215) □ Autonomic neurotransmitters (p. 215) □ Autonomic nervous system as a whole (p. 216)	Slides 40-52 Autonomic Nervous System questions 77-82 (p. 86) Sympathetic and Parasympathetic Nervous System questions 83-98 (pp. 86-87) Autonomic Neurotransmitters and Autonomic Nervous System as a Whole questions 99-104 (p. 88) Multiple Choice questions 32-35, 45; True or False questions 55-65; Matching questions 25, 28-40; Short Answer questions 18-20 Multiple Choice questions 5, 6, 10 (pp. 105-106); Completion question 27 (p. 106) **Book Resources** Figure 8-17 Dermatomes (p. 211) Figure 8-18 Innervation of the major target organs by the autonomic nervous system (p. 212) Figure 8-19 Autonomic conduction paths (p. 213)

OBJECTIVES	CONTENT	TEACHING RESOURCES
		Table 8-3 Autonomic Functions (p. 214)
		Figure 8-20 Autonomic neurotransmitters (p. 215)
		Quick Check questions 1-4 (p. 217)
		Clinical Application: Herpes Zoster or Shingles (p. 216)
		Critical Thinking question 23 (p. 222)
		▶ Discuss drugs that act as selective serotonin reuptake inhibitors (SSRIs). How does the drug's action increase the amount of serotonin present in the synaptic cleft, and how would this affect an individual with depression?
		▶ Discuss antidepressants that inhibit the enzymes that naturally break down serotonin at the synaptic cleft. Explain how this might reduce the symptoms of depression.
		*Class Activity **Make copies of the word find activity (SG p. 115) for students to complete during class.***
		*Class Activity **Make copies of the crossword puzzle (SG p. 95) for students to complete during class.***
		*Class Activity **Hand out copies of the neuron pathways picture from the Study Guide (p. 103), and have students label the parts.***
		*Class Activity **Have small groups create a diagram showing the autonomic conduction paths. Ask a group to volunteer to present their diagram and to describe the anatomical and functional characteristics of the two divisions of the autonomic nervous system. Have the class offer improvements.***
		*Class Activity **Divide the class into two competing teams. Give them a series of brief descriptions on the effect of an autonomic function on visceral effectors, and ask them to categorize it as being a result of sympathetic or parasympathetic control. The team with the most correct answers wins.***
Performance Evaluation		𝒆 Chapter 8 Computerized Test Bank questions
		📖 Multiple Choice (pp. 105-106)
		𝒆 Student Post-Test questions

Copyright © 2008, 2005 by Mosby, Inc., an affiliate of Elsevier Inc.

Thibodeau/Patton

OBJECTIVES	CONTENT	TEACHING RESOURCES
		Book Resources
		Review questions (p. 222)
		Critical Thinking questions (p. 222)
		Chapter Test (pp. 223-224)

8.2 Homework/Assignments:

8.2 Teacher's Notes:

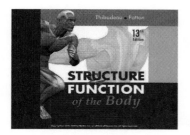

Slide 1

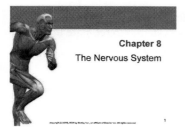

Chapter 8
The Nervous System

Slide 2

Learning Objectives

- List the organs and divisions of the nervous system and describe the generalized functions of the system as a whole
- Identify the major types of cells in the nervous system and discuss the function of each
- Identify the anatomical and functional components of a three-neuron reflex arc. Compare and contrast the propagation of a nerve impulse along a nerve fiber and across a synaptic cleft

Slide 3

Learning Objectives (cont'd.)

- Identify the major anatomical components of the brain and spinal cord and briefly comment on the function of each
- Compare and contrast spinal and cranial nerves.
- Discuss the anatomical and functional characteristics of the two divisions of the autonomic nervous system

ELSEVIER

Structure & Function of the Body, 13th ed.
Thibodeau/Patton

Slide 4

Chapter 8
Lesson 8.1

Slide 5

Organs and Divisions of the Nervous System

- **Central nervous system (CNS):** Brain and spinal cord
- **Peripheral nervous system (PNS):** All nerves
  - Autonomic nervous system (ANS)

- What are the two principal divisions of the nervous system? (the central nervous system and the peripheral nervous system)

- What is the function of the autonomic nervous system, a subdivision of the peripheral nervous system? (to regulate the body's autonomic or involuntary functions)

Slide 6

Divisions of the Nervous System

Slide 7

Cells of the Nervous System

- Neurons
  - Consist of three main parts
    - Dendrites
    - Cell body
    - Axon
  - Classified according to function
    - Sensory
    - Motor
    - Interneurons

- What are the two types of cells found in the nervous system? (*neurons,* or nerve cells, and *glia,* specialized connective tissue cells)

- What is the direction of neural transmission from sensory neurons and motor neurons? (Sensory neurons transmit towards the CNS, motor neurons carry impulses away from the CNS.)

- What are interneurons? (Interneurons are those that connect impulses from sensory to motor neurons.)

Structure & Function of the Body, 13th ed.

Thibodeau/Patton

Slide 8

Neuron

- Ask students to identify parts of the neuron.

Slide 9

Cells of the Nervous System (cont'd.)

- Schwann cells form myelin sheaths of axons in the peripheral nervous system (PNS).

- What is myelin? (Myelin is a white, fatty substance.)

- What are nodes of Ranvier? (Nodes of Ranvier are indentations between adjacent Schwann cells.)

- The outer cell membrane of a Schwann cell is called the *neurilemma*. Axons in the brain and spinal cord have no *neurilemma;* therefore, the potential for regeneration in the brain and spinal cord is less than in the PNS.

Slide 10

Cells of the Nervous System (cont'd.)

- Glia (neuroglia)
  - Support cells, bringing the cells of nervous tissue together structurally and functionally
  - Three main types of glial cells of the CNS
    - Astrocytes
    - Microglia
    - Oligodendrocytes

- What is the function of glia cells? (Glia cells [Greek for *glue*] hold the functioning neurons together, protect them, and regulate neuron function.)

- How are the three types of glia different? (Astrocytes are star shaped and form the blood–brain barrier; microglia are small and usually stationary and can assist with phagocytosis; oligodendorcytes help hold nerve fibers together and produce myelin.)

Slide 11

Cells of the Nervous System (cont'd.)

Glia

- Have students identify the different types of glial cells.

Thibodeau/Patton

Slide 12

Nerves

- **Nerve:** Bundle of peripheral axons
  - Tract of central axons
  - **White matter:** Tissue composed primarily of myelinated axons (nerves or tracts)
  - **Gray matter:** Tissue composed primarily of cell bodies and unmyelinated fibers

12

- What is white matter composed of? (Nerve fibers usually have a myelin sheath and myelin is white.)

- What is *gray matter* composed of? (Tissue composed of cell bodies and unmyelinated axons and dendrites is called *gray matter* because of its characteristic gray appearance.)

Slide 13

Nerves (cont'd.)

- **Nerve coverings:** Fibrous connective tissue
  - **Endoneurium:** Surrounds individual fibers within a nerve
  - **Perineurium:** Surrounds a group (fascicle) of nerve fibers
  - **Epineurium:** Surrounds the entire nerve

13

- Ask students to describe the coverings that surround an axon.

Slide 14

The Nerve

14

- Each nerve contains axons bundled into fascicles.

- A connective tissue epineurium wraps the entire nerve.

- Perineurium surrounds each fascicle.

Slide 15

Reflex Arcs

- Nerve impulses are conducted from receptors to effectors over neuron pathways or reflex arcs
- Conduction by a reflex arc results in a reflex, either contraction by a muscle or secretion by a gland

15

- What is the difference between a neuron pathway and a reflex arc? (A neuron pathway is the route traveled by a nerve impulse. The reflex arc is a specialized path of the neuron pathway, allowing impulse conduction in only one direction)

ELSEVIER

Structure & Function of the Body, 13th ed.

Thibodeau/Patton

Slide 16

Reflex Arcs (cont'd.)

- Simplest reflex arcs are two-neuron arcs; they consist of sensory neurons synapsing in the spinal cord with motor neurons
- Three-neuron arcs consist of sensory neurons synapsing in the spinal cord with interneurons that synapse with motor neurons

- What is a two-neuron arc? (The simplest type of reflex arc consisting of only two types of neurons: sensory neurons and motor neurons.)

- What is a three-neuron arc? (It consists of three different types of neurons: *sensory neurons, motor neurons,* and *interneurons.*)

- What is an *effector,* and how does it relate to the reflex arc? (An effector is an organ that puts nerve signals "into effect". The impulse conduction by a reflex arc causes the effector to react.)

Slide 17

Nerve Impulses

- Self-propagating waves of electrical disturbances that travel along the surface of a neuron membrane

- Where does impulse conduction originate? (It normally starts in receptors, the beginnings of dendrites of sensory neurons.)

- The end of the sensory neuron's axon synapses first with an interneuron before chemical signals are sent across a second synapse, resulting in conduction through the motor neuron.

- For example, application of an irritating stimulus to the skin of the thigh initiates a three-neuron reflex response that causes contraction of muscles to pull the leg away from the irritant.

Slide 18

Nerve Impulses (cont'd.)

- Mechanism
  - Stimulus triggers the opening of Na+ channels in the plasma membrane of the neuron
  - Inward movement of positive sodium ions leaves a slight excess of negative ions outside at a stimulated point
    - Marks beginning of a nerve impulse

- What are some types of stimuli that initiate nerve impulses? (pressure, temperature, and chemical changes)

- What is saltatory conduction? (If the traveling impulse encounters a section of membrane covered with insulating myelin, it simply "jumps" across the myelin. Called *saltatory conduction,* this type of impulse travels much faster than what is seen in nonmyelinated sections.)

Slide 19

Conduction of Nerve Impulses

- In an unmyelinated fiber, a nerve impulse is a self-propagating wave of electrical disturbance.

- In a myelinated fiber, the action potential "jumps" around the insulating myelin in a rapid type of conduction called *saltatory conduction.*

Slide 20

The Synapse

- Chemical compounds are released from axon terminals (of a presynaptic neuron) into a synaptic cleft
- Neurotransmitters bind to specific receptor molecules in the membrane of a postsynaptic neuron
  - Open ion channels, stimulate impulse conduction by the membrane

20

- What are the three structures that make up a synapse? (a synaptic knob, a neurotransmitter, and a synaptic cleft)

- How does a nerve impulse travel from one neuron to another? (across a synapse with the assistance of neurotransmitters)

- Ask students to draw a schematic diagram correctly charting the following structures and chemicals: axon terminal, synaptic knob, presynaptic neuron, postsynaptic neuron, neurotransmitter, synaptic cleft, plasma membrane, receptor molecules.

Slide 21

The Synapse (cont'd.)

- Types of neurotransmitters
  - Acetylcholine
  - Catecholamines (norepinephrine, dopamine, and serotonin)
  - Other compounds

21

- What is a neurotransmitter and how many are there? (Neurotransmitters are chemicals by which neurons communicate. At least 30 different compounds have been identified as neurotransmitters.)

- Name some of the neurotransmitters.

  - Acetylcholine is released at some of the synapses in the spinal cord and at neuromuscular junctions.

  - Norepinephrine, dopamine, and serotonin belong to a group of compounds called *catecholamines,* which may play a role in sleep, motor function, mood, and pleasure recognition.

  - Two morphine-like neurotransmitters called *endorphins* and *enkephalins* are natural painkillers.

Slide 22

Components of a Synapse

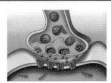

22

- The diagram shows the synaptic knob or axon terminal of the presynaptic neuron, the plasma membrane of a postsynaptic neuron, and a synaptic cleft.

- Describe how signals are transmitted across the synapse. (Signals are transmitted from neuron to neuron across a synapse with the help of neurotransmitters.)

ELSEVIER

Structure & Function of the Body, 13th ed.

Thibodeau/Patton

Slide 23

Chapter 8
Lesson 8.2

Slide 24

Central Nervous System

- Divisions of the brain
  - Brainstem
    - Medulla oblongata
    - Pons
    - Midbrain

- What are the three main parts of the brainstem? (the medulla oblongata, pons, and midbrain)

- Structure—white matter with bits of gray matter scattered through it.

- What is the function of the brainstem? (This structure is responsible for basic vital life functions such as breathing, heartbeat, and blood pressure.)

Slide 25

Central Nervous System (cont'd.)

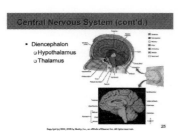

- Diencephalon
  - Hypothalamus
  - Thalamus

- What are the structure and function of the hypothalamus? (pea sized structure that makes some hormones and is also responsible for regulating body temperature)

- What are the structure and function of the thalamus? Dumbbell-shaped section of gray matter; helps produce sensations, associates sensation with emotions, and plays a part in the alerting mechanism.

Slide 26

Central Nervous System (cont'd.)

- Cerebellum
  - Second largest part of the human brain
  - Helps control muscle contractions to produce coordinated movements so that we can maintain balance, move smoothly, and sustain posture

- What is the cerebellum and what are its primary functions? (second largest part of the brain underneath the cerebrum; functions in balance and coordination of body movements)

- Have students refer to Figure 8-9 in the text.

ELSEVIER

Structure & Function of the Body, 13th ed.

Thibodeau/Patton

Slide 27

- Cerebrum
  - Largest part of the human brain
  - Outer layer of gray matter is the cerebral cortex, composed mainly of dendrites and cell bodies of neurons
  - Interior of the cerebrum composed mainly of white matter (nerve fibers arranged in bundles called *tracts*)

27

- What is the cerebrum and what are its primary lobes? (largest uppermost part of the brain; lobes include frontal, parietal, temporal and occipital)

- What are some of the main functions of the cerebrum? (consciousness, thinking, memory, sensations, emotion, and willed movements)

- Have students refer to Figure 8-10 in the text.

Slide 28

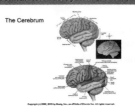

Major Regions of the Central Nervous System

28

- Ask students to identify the major regions of the central nervous system.

Slide 29

The Cerebrum

29

- The lobes of the cerebrum and the functional regions of the cerebral cortex.

Slide 30

Central Nervous System (cont'd.)

TABLE 8-1
Functions of Major Divisions of the Brain

30

- Summarize the functions of the major divisions of the brain.

Structure & Function of the Body, 13th ed.
Thibodeau/Patton

Slide 31

Central Nervous System (cont'd.)

- Spinal cord
  - Outer part composed of white matter made up of many bundles of axons called *tracts*
  - Interior is composed of gray matter made up mainly of neuron dendrites and cell bodies
  - Functions as the center for all spinal cord reflexes
    - Sensory tracts conduct impulses to the brain
    - Motor tracts conduct impulses from the brain

31

- Typically, how long is the spinal cord? (about 17 to 18 inches long)

- Distinguish between the spinal cord and the spinal column. (The spinal cord lies inside the spinal column in the spinal cavity.)

- Tracts are functional organizations: all axons composing one tract serve a general function.

- Other ascending tracts transmit sensations of touch and pressure to the brain.

Slide 32

Central Nervous System (cont'd.)

Spinal Cord and
Spinal Nerves

32

- The spinal cord is viewed from behind (posterior aspect).

Slide 33

Central Nervous System (cont'd.)

- Coverings and fluid spaces of the brain and spinal cord
  - Coverings
    - Cranial bones and vertebrae
    - Cerebral and spinal meninges—dura mater, arachnoid mater, and pia mater
  - Fluid spaces—subarachnoid spaces of meninges, central canal inside cord, and ventricles in the brain

33

- Nerve tissue needs to be protected, so the brain and spinal cord are surrounded by a tough, fluid-containing membrane called the *meninges*.

- The meninges are surrounded by bone. The spinal meninges form a tubelike covering around the spinal cord and line the bony vertebral foramen of the vertebrae that surround the cord. There are three layers of meninges with spaces between each layer.

- What are the three layers of the spinal meninges? (dura, arachnoid, and pia)

- What are the spaces between the meninges called? (epidural, subdural, and subarachnoid)

Slide 34

Central Nervous System (cont'd.)

Fluid Spaces of the Brain

34

- Ask students to identify the ventricles in the left lateral view.

ELSEVIER

Thibodeau/Patton

Slide 35

Central Nervous System (cont'd.)

Flow of Cerebrospinal Fluid

- What is the pathway through which the cerebrospinal fluid flows? (choroid plexus to ventricles to subarachnoid space.)

- What is the function of CSF? (acts as a shock absorber for CNS)

- Discuss lumbar puncture.

Slide 36

Peripheral Nervous System

- Cranial nerves
  - Structure—12 pairs are attached to the undersurface of the brain
  - Function—conducts impulses between the brain and structures in the head and neck and in the thoracic and abdominal cavities

- What are some of the structures included in the peripheral nervous system? (includes cranial and spinal nerves that connect the brain and spinal cord, respectively, to peripheral structures such as the skin surface and the skeletal muscles)

Slide 37

Peripheral Nervous System (cont'd.)

- Spinal nerves
  - Structure—contains dendrites of sensory neurons and axons of motor neurons
  - Functions—conducts impulses necessary for sensations and voluntary movements

- Other structures in the autonomic nervous system are considered part of the peripheral nervous system; they connect the brain and spinal cord to various glands in the body and to the cardiac and smooth muscles in the thorax and abdomen.

Slide 38

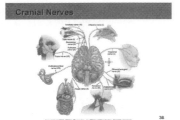

Cranial Nerves

- How many pairs of cranial nerves are there? (12)

Structure & Function of the Body, 13th ed.
Thibodeau/Patton

Slide 39

Cranial Nerves (cont'd.)

● Summarize the functions of the cranial nerves.

Slide 40

Autonomic Nervous System

- Motor neurons that conduct impulses from the central nervous system to cardiac muscle, smooth muscle, and glandular epithelial tissue
- Regulates the body's autonomic or involuntary functions

● Motor nerves that control the voluntary actions of skeletal muscles are sometimes called the *somatic nervous system*.

● What are the two divisions of the autonomic nervous system (ANS)? (sympathetic nervous system, parasympathetic nervous system)

Slide 41

Autonomic Nervous System (cont'd.)

Innervation of the Major Target Organs by the Autonomic Nervous System

● Sympathetic and parasympathetic pathways are highlighted.

Slide 42

Autonomic Nervous System (cont'd.)

- Autonomic neurons
  - Preganglionic autonomic neurons conduct from spinal cord or brainstem to autonomic ganglia
  - Postganglionic neurons conduct from autonomic ganglia to cardiac muscle, smooth muscle, and glandular epithelial tissue

● Spinal nerves conduct impulses between the spinal cord and parts of the body not supplied by cranial nerves.

● Spinal nerves function to make possible sensations and movements.

ELSEVIER

Structure & Function of the Body, 13th ed.
Thibodeau/Patton

Slide 43

Autonomic Nervous System (cont'd.)

- Autonomic or visceral effectors
  - Tissues to which autonomic neurons conduct impulses
- Autonomic conduction paths
  - Consist of two-neuron relays

43

- What are autonomic effectors? (tissues to which autonomic neurons conduct impulses—cardiac and smooth muscle and glandular epithelial tissue)

- Autonomic paths to visceral effectors consist of two-neuron relays. Impulses travel over preganglionic neurons from the spinal cord or brainstem to autonomic ganglia. There they are relayed across synapses to postganglionic neurons, which then conduct the impulses from the ganglia to visceral effectors.

- In contrast, somatic motor neurons conduct all the way from the spinal cord or brainstem to somatic effectors with no intervening synapses.

Slide 44

Autonomic Nervous System (cont'd.)

- Sympathetic nervous system
  - Structure
    - Sympathetic preganglionic neurons have dendrites and cell bodies in gray matter of thoracic and upper lumbar segments of the spinal cord
    - Sympathetic postganglionic neurons have dendrites and cell bodies in sympathetic ganglia

44

- What are the two divisions of the autonomic nervous system (ANS)? (sympathetic and parasympathetic)

- What is the structure of the sympathetic nervous system? (consists of preganglionic and postganglionic neurons)

Slide 45

Autonomic Nervous System (cont'd.)

- Sympathetic nervous system:
  - Functions
    - Serves as the emergency or stress system
    - Group of changes induced by sympathetic control is called the *fight-or-flight response*

45

- What are the functions of the sympathetic nervous system? (to respond to emergency or stress conditions)

- What physiologic changes are associated with the fight-or-flight response? (enlarged pupils, increased heart rate, dilated skeletal blood vessels)

- The sympathetic nervous system controls visceral effectors during strenuous exercise and strong emotions, such as anger, fear, hate, or anxiety.

Slide 46

Autonomic Nervous System (cont'd.)

- Parasympathetic nervous system:
  - Structure
    - Parasympathetic preganglionic neurons have dendrites and cell bodies in the gray matter of brainstem and sacral segments of the spinal cord
    - Parasympathetic preganglionic neurons terminate in parasympathetic ganglia located in the head and the thoracic and abdominal cavities close to visceral effectors

46

- Where are the dendrite and cell bodies of the parasympathetic preganglionic neurons located? (brainstem and sacral portion of spinal cord)

Slide 47

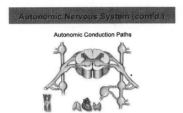

Autonomic Nervous System (cont'd.)

- Parasympathetic nervous system
  - Function
    - Dominates control of many visceral effectors under normal, everyday conditions

47

- What are the functions of the parasympathetic nervous system, and how do they differ from the functions of the sympathetic nervous system? (The parasympathetic system slows heart rate and increases peristalsis and the secretion of digestive juices. It dominates in normal, everyday activities. The sympathetic system has the opposite effect and dominates in emergency situations.)

Slide 48

Autonomic Nervous System (cont'd.)

Autonomic Conduction Paths

48

- What is the minimum number of autonomic motor neurons required for conduction from the spinal cord to any visceral effector? (at least two autonomic motor neurons—a preganglionic and a postganglionic neuron)

Slide 49

Autonomic Nervous System (cont'd.)

- Autonomic neurotransmitters:
  - Cholinergic fibers
    - Preganglionic axons of parasympathetic and sympathetic systems and parasympathetic postganglionic axons
    - Release acetylcholine

49

- What are neurotransmitters? (chemicals released from the axons of automatic neurons)

- Ask students to offer examples of neurotransmitters associated with the ANS, including the division of the ANS associated with each neurotransmitter.

- Three axons—the sympathetic preganglionic axon, the parasympathetic preganglionic axon, and the parasympathetic postganglionic axon—release acetylcholine. These axons are classified as cholinergic fibers.

- *Cholingeric=aCetylCholine-"C" the point!*

Slide 50

Autonomic Nervous System (cont'd.)

- Autonomic neurotransmitters
  - Adrenergic fibers
    - Axons of sympathetic postganglionic neurons
    - Release norepinephrine (noradrenaline)

50

- Only one type of autonomic axon releases the neurotransmitter norepinephrine; this is the axon of a sympathetic postganglionic neuron, and such neurons are classified as adrenergic fibers.

- The organ's response is dependent on the neurotransmitter it receives. Parasympathetic and sympathetic divisions use different neurotransmitters in order to stimulate the desired response.

- What determines the nature of an organ's response to stimulation by the autonomic nervous system?

- Adrenergic=SympAthetic=norAdrenaline. You got an A!!

Slide 51

Autonomic Nervous System (cont'd.)

Autonomic Neurotransmitters

51

- Autonomic neurotransmitters are the chemical compounds released from the axon terminals of autonomic neurons.

Slide 52

Autonomic Nervous System (cont'd.)

- Autonomic nervous system as a whole
  - Regulates the body's autonomic functions in ways that maintain or quickly restore homeostasis

52

- What is the primary function of the autonomic nervous system? (restore homeostasis)

- How can emotions affect the autonomic nervous system? (Anger and fear can lead to increased sympathetic activity, while meditation deceases sympathetic activity.)

- Many organs are doubly innervated by the ANS; in other words, they receive fibers from both the parasympathetic and sympathetic divisions.

- Parasympathetic and sympathetic impulses continually bombard the organs and influence their function in opposite or antagonistic ways but achieve a balance (homeostasis).

ELSEVIER

Structure & Function of the Body, 13th ed.
Thibodeau/Patton

Lesson Plan

9 | The Senses

TEACHING FOCUS

In this chapter, the student will have the opportunity to distinguish between special and general sense organs. The student will have the opportunity to learn how a stimulus is converted into a sensation, as well as how general sense organs and their components function. The student will be exposed to the structure of the eye and the anatomy of the ear, including its sensory function in hearing and equilibrium. Students also will have the opportunity to learn about chemical receptors and their functions.

MATERIALS AND RESOURCES

- ☐ Blindfolds (Lesson 9.2)
- ☐ Index cards (Lesson 9.1)
- ☐ Model of the ear (Lesson 9.2)
- ☐ Computer (all Lessons)

- ☐ Sensory stimuli, including a tape of sounds, foods, seasoning to taste, materials to touch, and so on (all Lessons)
- ☐ Tuning fork (Lesson 9.2)

LESSON CHECKLIST

Preparations for this lesson include:

- lecture
- demonstration
- field trip: local optometrist's office
- guest speaker: ear specialist or otologist
- student performance evaluation of all entry-level skills required for comprehension and application of the senses including:
  - o the structure of the eye and the functions of its components
  - o the anatomy of the ear and its sensory function in hearing and equilibrium
  - o the general sense organs and their functions
  - o chemical receptors and their functions
  - o common terms used to describe the senses

ELSEVIER

Thibodeau/Patton

KEY TERMS

aqueous humor (p. 235)
auricle (p. 236)
cataract (p. 234)
chemoreceptor (p. 241)
choroid (p. 231)
cochlea (p. 239)
conjunctiva (p. 231)
crista ampullaris (p. 239)
endolymph (p. 239)
glaucoma (p. 235)
gustatory cells (p. 241)
lacrimal gland (p. 231)
lens (p. 233)
macular degeneration (p. 234)

mechanoreceptor (pp. 230, 235)
organ of Corti (p. 240)
ossicles (p. 238)
papillae (p. 241)
perilymph (p. 239)
photoreceptor (p. 235)
presbyopia (p. 233)
proprioception (p. 230)
pupil (p. 232)
retina (pp. 231, 234)
sclera (pp. 231, 234)
semicircular canals (p. 239)
tympanic membrane (p. 236)
vitreous humor (p. 235)

ADDITIONAL RESOURCES

AnimationDirect (Book Companion CD)
Instructor's Electronic Resource (IER) (CD)
PowerPoint slides (CD, Evolve)
Test Bank (Evolve)

Legend

ESLR
EVOLVE Student
Learning Resource

EILR TB
EVOLVE Instructor
Learning Resource
Test Bank

AnimationDirect
on Book Companion
CD

PPT
PowerPoint
Slides

SG
Study
Guide

IRM
Instructor's
Resource Manual

Class Activities are indicated in ***bold italic.***

Structure & Function of the Body, 13th ed.
Thibodeau/Patton

LESSON 9.1

PRETEST

Study Guide Multiple Choice questions 1-10 (pp. 105-106)

BACKGROUND ASSESSMENT

Question: At a doctor visit, 44-year-old Mrs. Jones mentions that she is finding it harder to read and is planning on making an appointment with an ophthalmologist. What can you tell her about her condition?
Answer: Presbyopia, or "oldsightedness," occurs as we grow older. The lens of the eye lies directly behind the pupil and is held in place by a ligament attached to the ciliary muscle. When we look at distant objects, the ciliary muscle is relaxed, but when we focus on near objects, the ciliary muscle must contract. Most of us become more farsighted as we grow older, partly because our lenses lose some of their elasticity and can no longer bulge enough to bring near objects into focus.

Question: It's Thanksgiving and 9-year-old Sam is suffering from a bad cold. He tells his mother that he cannot taste anything, not even her great stuffing. Why is it difficult for Sam to taste his dinner?
Answer: Most flavors result from a combination of taste bud and olfactory receptor stimulation, meaning that most of the tastes we recognize are actually tastes and odors. For this reason, a cold that interferes with the stimulation of the olfactory receptors by odors from foods in the mouth markedly dulls taste sensations.

CRITICAL THINKING QUESTION

Mr. Scialello, a computer programmer, is suffering from presbyopia. He finds reading glasses inconvenient and wants to know if surgery will improve his condition.
Guidelines: A surgical technique to treat myopia (nearsightedness) without the use of eyeglasses or contact lenses has been available for 25 years. The procedure, called *radial keratotomy*, involves the surgical placement of six or more radial slits (incisions) in a spokelike pattern around the cornea. As a result, the cornea flattens, and the ability to focus improves. Another procedure, called *automated lamellar keratoplasty* (ALK), uses a special surgical device called a *microkeratome* to cut a thin cap off the corneal surface and then shave and reshape the underlying tissue. At the end of the procedure, the corneal cap is replaced and will heal without the need for sutures. ALK is used to treat both nearsightedness and farsightedness.

OBJECTIVES	CONTENT	TEACHING RESOURCES
Classify sense organs as special or general, and explain the basic differences between the two groups.	■ Introduction (p. 227) ■ Classification of sense organs (p. 227)	🖳 Slides 5-7 📖 Classification of Sense Organs, Converting a Stimulus into a Sensation, General Sense Organs questions 1-5 (p. 100) *e* True or False questions 1, 56-59; Short Answer questions 1, 2 *Class Activity Allot board space to "general sense organs" and "special sense organs." As students name the organs that fall under each category, jot them down. Ask students to also name the organs' functions and their locations in the body. Then have students define and list the six types of encapsulated nerve endings found in Table 9-1 on pp. 229-230.*

OBJECTIVES	CONTENT	TEACHING RESOURCES
Discuss how a stimulus is converted into a sensation.	■ Converting a stimulus into a sensation (p. 230)	Slide 8 True or False questions 2, 60 *Class Activity Divide the class into two teams and have them compete in correctly identifying different sensory stimuli. For example, bring in a tape of different sounds and see how easily they can name them. Put blindfolds on students and have them touch and then name different materials, including foods. Do the same to test their skill in identifying taste. When is it easier to identify a given stimuli: using one or multiple sense organs?*
Discuss the general sense organs and their functions.	■ General sense organs (p. 230)	Slide 9 Multiple Choice questions 1-6, 36, 37; True or False questions 3-11, 61; Short Answer question 3 **Book Resources** Table 9-1 General sense organs (pp. 228-229) Figure 9-1 General sense receptors (p. 231) Quick Check questions 1-3 (p. 230) Clear View of the Human Body *Class Activity Using Tables 9-1 and 9-2, have students make two sets of flash cards. Both sets should include cards with the name of a sense organ on one side. The sets should either have the sense organ's main location or organs' general senses on the reverse side. Have pairs of students quiz each other using the flash cards.*

9.1 Homework/Assignments:

9.1 Teacher's Notes:

LESSON 9.2

CRITICAL THINKING QUESTION

How does a cochlear implant help a person to hear better?

Guidelines: The organ of hearing, which lies in the snail-shaped cochlea, is the organ of Corti. Specialized hair cells on the organ of Corti generate nerve impulses when they are bent by the movement of endolymph set in motion by sound waves. If the hairs on the organ of Corti are damaged, nerve deafness results, even if the vestibulocochlear nerve is healthy. A surgically implanted device known as a *cochlear implant* can improve this form of hearing loss by eliminating the need for the sensory hairs. A transmitter just outside the scalp sends external sound information to a receiver under the scalp (behind the auricle). The receiver transmits the information into an electrical code that is relayed down an electrode to the cochlea. The electrode, wired to the organ of Corti, stimulates the vestibulocochlear nerve endings directly, and sound can be perceived.

OBJECTIVES	CONTENT	TEACHING RESOURCES
Describe the structure of the eye and the functions of its components.	■ Special sense organs (p. 231) □ The eye (p. 231) – Visual pathway (p. 235)	Slides 11-13 Eye diagram (p. 107) Eye questions 6-18 (pp. 100-101) Multiple Choice questions 7-17, 38, 39; True or False questions 12-34, 62-66; Matching questions 1-10; Short Answer questions 4-7 Process of Seeing **Book Resources** Table 9-2 Special Sense Organs (p. 230) Figure 9-2 Horizontal section through the left eyeball (p. 232) Clinical Application: Refractive Eye Surgery (p. 233) Clinical Application: Visual Acuity (p. 234) Clinical Application: Finding Your Blind Spot (p. 234) Figure 9-3 Corneal transplant (p. 232) Research, Issues and Trends: Corneal Stem Cell Transplants (p. 237) Figure 9-4 Cells of the retina (p. 235) Clinical Application: Focusing Problems (p. 236) Clinical Application: Color Blindness (p. 237) Quick Check questions 1-3 (p. 235) Critical Thinking question 19 (p. 247)

Structure & Function of the Body, 13th ed.

Thibodeau/Patton

OBJECTIVES	CONTENT	TEACHING RESOURCES
		Class Activity Have students visit a local optometrist's office to observe and discuss various models, diagrams, and tests. What are the most common tests for evaluating eyesight? What are the most common eye ailments, and how are they generally treated? Have students try out various acuity tests. *Class Activity Have students fill in the diagram of the eye featured in the Study Guide, p. 114.*
Discuss the anatomy of the ear and its sensory function in hearing and equilibrium.	☐ The ear (p. 235) – External ear (p. 236) – Middle ear (p. 238) – Inner ear (p. 239)	▧ Slides 14-17 📖 Ear questions 19-36 (p. 102) 💾 Multiple Choice questions 18-28; True or False questions 35-50, 67, 68; Matching questions 11-20; Short Answer questions 8-12 💿 Pathway of Sound Waves **Book Resources** Figure 9-5 The ear (p. 238) Figure 9-6 The inner ear (p. 239) Figure 9-7 Effect of sound waves on cochlear structures (p. 241) Health and Well-Being: Swimmer's Ear (p. 241) Clinical Application: Cochlear Implants (p. 242) Quick Check questions 1-4 (p. 241) *Class Activity Bring in an ear specialist, or otologist, to field questions from students concerning the structure and function of the ear, as well as tests for hearing. What are common problems and remedies for hearing loss, buzzing, and other ailments of the ear? If possible, have the physician demonstrate hearing tests on students.* *Class Activity Use a model of the ear to teach the different structures. Pass the model around the room to allow students to look at it closely.* *Class Activity Assign student groups and place various objects into a shoebox. Have students shake the shoebox and attempt to guess its contents from the sounds made.*

ELSEVIER

Structure & Function of the Body, 13th ed.
Thibodeau/Patton

OBJECTIVES	CONTENT	TEACHING RESOURCES
		Class Activity **Bring in tuning forks and have students experiment with different tones at various distances. Then have students fill in the diagram of the ear featured in the Study Guide, p. 115.**
Discuss the chemical receptors and their functions.	☐ The taste receptors (p. 241) ☐ The smell receptors (p. 243)	Slides 18-19 Taste Receptors, Smell Receptors questions 37-41 (p. 102) Multiple Choice questions 29-35, 40, 41; True or False questions 51-55; Short Answer questions 13-16 How the Brain Interprets Odors **Book Resources** Figure 9-8 The tongue (p. 242) Figure 9-9 Olfactory structures (p. 243) Quick Check questions 1-3 (p. 244) Science Applications: The Senses (p. 244) Critical Thinking questions 17-18 (p. 247) *Class Activity* **Have students wear blindfolds and taste various "mystery" foods and seasonings. Can they name them correctly? Have them smell and then touch the products. How do the senses work together to help students determine the right answer? Do students agree on taste and smell sensations? Have them share which ones are pleasant or unpleasant to them.**
Performance Evaluation		Chapter 9 Computerized Test Bank questions Chapter Test Student Post-Test questions **Book Resource** Chapter Test (pp. 248-249)

Structure & Function of the Body, 13th ed.

Thibodeau/Patton

9.2 Homework/Assignments:

9.2 Teacher's Notes:

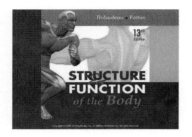

Slide 1

Chapter 9

The Senses

1

Slide 2

Learning Objectives

- Classify sense organs as special or general and explain the basic differences between the two groups
- Discuss how a stimulus is converted into a sensation
- Discuss the general sense organs and their functions

2

Slide 3

Learning Objectives (cont'd.)

- Describe the structure of the eye and the functions of its components
- Discuss the anatomy of the ear and its sensory function in hearing and equilibrium
- Discuss the chemical receptors and their functions

3

Slide 4

Chapter 9
Lesson 9.1

Slide 5

Classification of the Sense Organs

- General sense organs
  - Often exist as individual cells or receptor units
  - Widely distributed throughout the body
- Special sense organs
  - Large and complex organs
  - Localized grouping of specialized receptors

- Where do general sense organs reside in the body? (skin, muscles, tendons, joints)

- What are the general senses responsible for? (pain, temperature, touch, and pressure)

- What are the special sense organs responsible for? (smell, taste, vision, hearing, and equilibrium)

Slide 6

Classification of the Sense Organs (cont'd.)

- Classified by presence or absence of covering capsule
  - Encapsulated
  - Unencapsulated ("free" or "naked")

- Where might encapsulated receptor cells be found? (skin)

Slide 7

Classification of the Sense Organs (cont'd.)

- Classification made by type of stimuli required to activate receptors
  - Photoreceptors (light)
  - Chemoreceptors (chemicals)
  - Pain receptors (injury)
  - Thermoreceptors (temperature changes)
  - Mechanoreceptors (movement or deforming of capsule)
  - Proprioceptors (position of body parts or changes in muscle length or tension)

- Reaction to stimulation is almost instantaneous.

- It is the specialized form and function of different receptor cells that allow them to respond to different stimuli.

- For example, mechanoreceptors are activated by mechanical stimuli that change the position or shape of the receptor.

Structure & Function of the Body, 13th ed.
Thibodeau/Patton

Slide 8

Converting a Stimulus into a Sensation

- All sense organs have common functional characteristics
  - All are able to detect a particular stimulus
  - A stimulus is converted into a nerve impulse
  - A nerve is perceived as a sensation in the CNS

8

- Three things are necessary to experience a sensation: stimulus, nerve impulse, and intact CNS to percieve the sensation.

Slide 9

General Sense Organs

- Distribution is widespread; single-cell receptors are common
- Examples
  - Free nerve endings: Sensitive to pain and crude touch
  - Meissner's corpuscles: Responsive to fine touch and vibration
  - Ruffini's corpuscles: Sensitive to touch and pressure
  - Krause's end-bulbs: Touch or cold
  - Golgi tendon receptors: Proprioception
  - Muscle spindles: Proprioception

9

- Where are proprioceptors located? (between tendons and muscles and deep within skeletal muscle tissue)

- What is the function of proprioceptors? Provides information on position or movement of the different parts of the body.

Slide 10

Chapter 9
Lesson 9.2

10

Slide 11

Special Sense Organs

- The eyeball
  - Three layers of the eyeball
    - Sclera
    - Choroid
    - Retina

11

- What is sometimes called the "window" of the eye? (the cornea)

- What does the middle layer of the eyeball, the choroid, contain? (a dark pigment to prevent the scattering of incoming light rays)

- What involuntary muscles make up the front part of the choroid? (iris and the ciliary muscle)

- What is the sclera? (tough outer coat [of eyeball], white of eye; includes cornea)

Slide 12

- **Conjunctiva:** Mucous membrane covering the front surface of the sclera and lining the eyelid
- **Lens:** Transparent body behind the pupil; focuses light rays on the retina
- **Eye fluids**
  - **Aqueous humor:** Watery fluid in the anterior chamber in front of the lens
  - **Vitreous humor:** Jellylike fluid in the posterior chamber behind the lens

12

- What is the function of the ciliary muscle? (helps dilate or constrict pupils.)

- What is presbyopia? (Old sightedness) Myopia? (Near sightedness) Hyperopia? (Far sightedness)

- What does long-term exposure to ultraviolet light do to the eye? (Can cause cataracts)

- What is glaucoma? (Increased intraocular pressure)

Slide 13

- **Visual pathway**
  - Innermost layer of retina contains rods and cones
  - Impulse travels from the rods and cones through the bipolar and ganglionic layers of retina
  - Nerve impulse leaves the eye through the optic nerve; the point of exit is free of receptors and is therefore called a blind spot
  - Visual interpretation occurs in the visual cortex of the cerebrum

13

- Discuss the different types of refractive eye surgery—RK, ALK, LASIK, and CK.

- Discuss what is new in transplant surgery.

- What is a cataract? (opacity of the lens)

Slide 14

- The ear
  - The ear functions in hearing, equilibrium, and balance.
    - Receptors for hearing and equilibrium are mechanoreceptors.

14

- The ear is divided into the following anatomical areas: the *external ear*, the *middle ear*, and the *inner ear*, which is internal.

Slide 15

- Divisions of the ear
  - External ear
    - Auricle (pinna)
    - External auditory canal
      - Curving canal or tube 2.5 cm (1 inch) in length
      - Contains ceruminous glands producing ear wax
      - Ends at the tympanic membrane or eardrum

15

- What is another name for ear wax? (cerumen)

- What is the function of the tympanic membrane? (vibrates to help transmit sounds)

- What common technology uses the same principle as the eardrum? (telephone)

Slide 16

❑ Middle ear
  ○ Houses ear bones or ossicles—malleus, incus, and stapes
  ○ Ends in the oval window
  ○ The auditory (eustachian) tube connects the middle ear to the throat
  ○ Inflammation called "otitis media"

16

- The temporal bone houses the middle ear in a cavity less than 1 inch long.

- What are the shapes of the three ossicles? (malleus, hammer-shaped; the incus, anvil-shaped; the stapes, stirrup-shaped)

- Describe the sequence of events as sound moves through the middle ear.

Slide 17

❑ Inner ear
  ○ The bony labyrinth is filled with fluid called *perilymph*
  ○ The labyrinth is divided into the vestibule, semicircular canals, and cochlea
  ○ Membranous labyrinth is filled with endolymph
  ○ Receptors for balance in the semicircular canals are called *cristae ampullaris*
  ○ Specialized hair cells on the organ of Corti respond when bent by the movement of surrounding endolymph set in motion by sound waves

17

- Three spaces in the temporal bone and the adjacent bony labrynth of structures comprise the inner ear.

- What is the organ of Corti? (the organ of hearing)

Slide 18

• The taste receptors
  ▪ Receptors are chemoreceptors called *taste buds*
  ▪ Cranial nerves VII and IX carry gustatory impulses
  ▪ Six kinds of "primary" taste sensations—sweet, sour, bitter, salty, metallic, and umami (meaty)
  ▪ Gustatory and olfactory senses work together

18

- What is another name for the chemoreceptors? (gustatory cells)

- What are the papillae? (taste buds)

- Where are most of the taste buds located? (circumvallate papillae, located at the back of the tongue)

Slide 19

• The olfactory (smell) receptors
  ▪ Receptors for fibers of olfactory or cranial nerve lie in olfactory mucosa of nasal cavity
  ▪ Olfactory receptors are extremely sensitive but easily fatigued
  ▪ Odor-causing chemicals initiate a nervous signal that is interpreted as a specific odor by the brain

19

- Where are the chemoreceptors located? (in the epithelial tissue located in the upper part of the nasal cavity)

- What must happen for the olfactory receptors to detect odors? (Chemicals must be dissolved in the watery mucus that lines the nasal cavity.)

10 Lesson Plan
The Endocrine System

TEACHING FOCUS

In this chapter, students will have the opportunity to learn about the functions of endocrine glands and the hormones they secrete. These hormones regulate such body activities as metabolism, growth and development, and reproduction. Students will also have the opportunity to learn the important roles that hormones play in homeostasis, normalcy, and abnormalities such as dwarfism, gigantism, sterility, and the survival of humans. Students will also be introduced to diseases of the endocrine glands, including tumors that result from hypersecretion and hyposecretion.

MATERIALS AND RESOURCES

- ☐ Computer (all Lessons)
- ☐ Flash cards (Lesson 10.1)

LESSON CHECKLIST

Preparations for this lesson include:

- lectures
- demonstration
- guest speaker: endocrinologist, diabetic patients, diabetic educators
- student performance evaluation of all entry-level skills required for student comprehension and application of the endocrine system including:
  - ○ description of primary endocrine glands and the hormones produced in each gland
  - ○ knowledge of mechanisms of steroid and nonsteroid hormone action
  - ○ identification of negative and positive feedback mechanisms that regulate the secretion of hormones
  - ○ knowledge of conditions that may result from hyposecretion or hypersecretion

KEY TERMS

acromegaly (p. 259)
Addison's disease (p. 267)
adrenal cortex (p. 263)
adrenal medulla (p. 266)
adrenocorticotropic hormone (p. 258)
aldosterone (p. 264)
androgens (p. 266)
anterior pituitary gland (p. 258)
antidiuretic hormone (p. 259)
atrial natriuretic hormone (p. 272)
calcitonin (p. 261)
chorion (p. 271)
chorionic gonadotropins (p. 271)
corpus luteum (p. 271)
corticoids (p. 263)
cortisol (p. 264)
cretinism (p. 264)
Cushing's syndrome (p. 267)
cyclic AMP (p. 255)
diabetes insipidus (p. 259)
diabetes mellitus (p. 268)
dwarfism (p. 259)
endocrine glands (p. 251)

endocrine system (p. 251)
epinephrine (p. 266)
exocrine glands (p. 251)
follicle-stimulating hormone (p. 258)
gigantism (p. 258)
glucagon (p. 268)
glucocorticoids (p. 265)
gluconeogenesis (p. 265)
glycogenolysis (p. 268)
glycosuria (p. 269)
growth hormone (p. 258)
hormone (p. 252)
hydrocortisone (p. 264)
hypercalcemia (p. 261)
hyperglycemia (p. 259)
hypersecretion (p. 252)
hyperthyroidism (p. 264)
hypoglycemia (p. 259)
hyposecretion (p. 252)
hypothyroidism (p. 264)
inhibiting hormones (p. 261)
insulin (p. 268)
islets of Langerhans (p. 268)

Thibodeau/Patton

leptin (p. 272)
liver glycogenolysis (p. 268)
luteinizing hormone (p. 258)
melatonin (p. 271)
mineralocorticoids (p. 263)
myxedema (p. 264)
negative feedback (p. 256, 257)
nonsteroid hormones (p. 252)
norepinephrine (p. 266)
ova (p. 271)
ovarian follicles (p. 271)
oxytocin (p. 259)
pancreatic islets (p. 268)
parathyroid glands (p. 261)
parathyroid hormone (p. 261)
pituitary gland (p. 258)
positive feedback (p. 257)
posterior pituitary gland (p. 258)
prolactin (p. 259)

prostaglandins (p. 257)
releasing hormones (p. 261)
second messenger mechanism (p. 255)
sex hormones (p. 265)
signal transduction (p. 255)
simple goiter (p. 264)
sperm (p. 271)
steroid hormones (p. 252)
target organ cell (p. 252)
testosterone (p. 271)
thymosin (p. 271)
Thyroid gland (p. 261)
thyroid-stimulating hormone (p. 258)
thyroxine or T_4 (p. 261)
triodothyronine or T_3 (p. 261)
tropic hormone (p. 258)
type 1 diabetes mellitus (p. 268)
type 2 diabetes mellitus (p. 268)

ADDITIONAL RESOURCES

AnimationDirect (Book Companion CD)
Instructor's Electronic Resource (IER) (CD)
PowerPoint slides (CD, Evolve)
Test Bank (Evolve)

Legend

ESLR
EVOLVE Student
Learning Resource

EILR TB
EVOLVE Instructor
Learning Resource
Test Bank

AnimationDirect
on Book Companion
CD

PPT
PowerPoint
Slides

SG
Study
Guide

IRM
Instructor's
Resource Manual

Class Activities are indicated in ***bold italic.***

ELSEVIER

Structure & Function of the Body, 13th ed.

Thibodeau/Patton

LESSON 10.1

PRETEST
Study Guide Multiple Choice questions 1-10 (pp. 117-118)

BACKGROUND ASSESSMENT
Question: The posterior pituitary hormone secretes a hormone during pregnancy known as *oxytocin.* What does this hormone do?

Answer: Oxytocin stimulates contraction of the pregnant uterus and is believed to initiate and maintain labor. This is why physicians sometimes prescribe oxytocin to induce or increase labor. Oxytocin also causes the glandular cells in the breasts to release milk into ducts to breastfeed the baby.

Question: What are some abnormalities that result from hyposecretion and hypersecretion of growth hormones?

Answer: Hypersecretion of growth hormones early in life produces a condition known as gigantism. Hyposecretion of growth hormones produces pituitary dwarfism. If the anterior pituitary gland secretes too much growth hormone after the normal growth years, acromegaly develops. Characteristics of acromegaly are enlargement of the bones of the hands, feet, jaws, and cheeks. People with acromegaly also have a prominent forehead, a large nose, and large, widened pores.

CRITICAL THINKING QUESTION
At her last visit, Mrs. Westfall complained of recent weight gain and an overall feeling of sluggishness. Her blood work indicates that she has myxedema. What can you tell her about this condition?

Guidelines: Myxedema is also known as *hypothyroidism.* Usually occurring later in life, deficient thyroid function can result in a decrease of production of the thyroid hormones T_3 and T_4. Because these hormones regulate the body's metabolism, deficient production causes the body to use energy more slowly than it should, leading to the disease known as *myxedema.* The condition is characterized by lessened mental and physical vigor, weight gain, loss of hair, and swelling of tissues. The condition is treated with thyroid replacement therapy. If left untreated, cardiogenic shock can result.

OBJECTIVES	CONTENT	TEACHING RESOURCES
Distinguish between endocrine and exocrine glands and define the terms *hormone* and *prostaglandin*.	■ Introduction (p. 251) ■ Mechanisms of hormone action (p. 252)	Slide 5 Multiple Choice question 1 (p. 117) Multiple Choice questions 1, 2; True or False questions 1-5, 57-60; Short Answer questions 1-2 **Book Resources** Figure 10-1 Location of the endocrine glands (p. 252) Table 10-1 Endocrine Glands, Hormones, and Their Functions (pp. 253-254) Review questions 1, 2 (p. 276) Chapter Test questions 1-4 (p. 277) *Class Activity* ***Choose an endocrine gland and have students identify where in the body it is located.***

OBJECTIVES	CONTENT	TEACHING RESOURCES
		Class Activity Ask groups of three to develop definitions of endocrine and exocrine glands and the terms hormone and prostaglandin. Pick a group and have them share their definitions with the class. Have the class offer improvements.
Describe the mechanisms of steroid and nonsteroid hormone action.	☐ Nonsteroid hormones (p. 252) ☐ Steroid hormones (p. 255)	⊠▪ Slides 6, 7 🅔 Multiple Choice questions 3-7, 36-38; True or False questions 6-13, 61; Short Answer questions 3, 4 📓 Completion question 30 (p. 138) **Book Resources** Figure 10-2 Mechanism of nonsteroid hormone action (p. 255) Figure 10-3 Mechanism of steroid hormone action (p. 256) Quick Check questions 1-3 (p. 256) Review questions 3, 4 (p. 276) Critical Thinking question 18 (p. 276) Chapter Test questions 5, 6 (p. 277) ▶ Discuss some differences between nonsteroid and steroid hormones. Besides estrogen, what is an example of a steroid hormone? *Class Activity Divide the class into small groups. Have each group create a diagram that explains the second messenger mechanism, including the lock-and-key model of chemical activity. Then have groups present their diagrams and explanations to the class.* *Class Activity Have groups of four develop a description of the mechanisms of steroid and nonsteroid hormone action. Pick a group to share their description with the class. Have the class offer improvements.*

OBJECTIVES	CONTENT	TEACHING RESOURCES
Explain how negative and positive feedback mechanisms regulate the secretion of endocrine hormones.	■ Regulation of hormone secretion (p. 256)	Slides 8, 9 *e* Multiple Choice question 8; True or False questions 14-18; Short Answer questions 5, 6 **Book Resources** Figure 10-4 Negative feedback (p. 257) Review questions 5, 6 (p. 276) Critical Thinking question 19 (p. 276) *Class Activity Have small groups develop a description of how negative and positive feedback mechanisms regulate the secretion of endocrine hormones. Ask them to cite examples of both mechanisms. Pick a group to share their descriptions with the class. Have the class offer improvements*
Distinguish between endocrine and exocrine glands and define the terms *hormone* and *prostaglandin*.	■ Prostaglandins (p. 257)	Slides 10, 11 Mechanisms of Hormone Action, Regulation of Hormone Secretion, and Prostaglandins question 7 (p. 110) Check Your Knowledge question 3 (p. 118) *e* True or False questions 19-21, 62, 63; Short Answer question 7 Multiple Choice question 8 (p. 136) **Book Resources** Quick Check question 2 (p. 258) Review question 7 (p. 276) Chapter Test question 7 (p. 277) ▸ Discuss why prostaglandins are considered tissue hormones. *Class Activity Ask students to create a written explanation describing why prostaglandins are called* tissue hormones. *Students can then read their explanations, and the class can discuss the distinction between a tissue hormone and a typical hormone.* *Class Activity Have students look up an NSAID (nonsteroidal antiinflammatory drug) such as ibuprofen. Have them discuss the action of the drug and its relationship to prostaglandins*

10.1 Homework/Assignments:

10.1 Teacher's Notes:

LESSON 10.2

CRITICAL THINKING QUESTION

Mrs. Armstrong has a 6-year-old son who was recently diagnosed with type 1 diabetes. She says that he stays inside a lot lately, and that she is afraid to let him play outside, because he might have a hypoglycemic reaction. What can you tell her about the importance of exercise for diabetic patients?

Guidelines: Type 1 diabetes is characterized by high blood-glucose concentrations, because a lack of insulin prevents glucose from entering the cells. Exercise physiologists have found that aerobic training increases the number of insulin receptors in target cells and the insulin affinity (attraction) of the receptors. This allows a small amount of insulin to have a greater effect than usual. Thus, exercise reduces the severity of the diabetic condition. Of course, Mrs. Armstrong's concerns about hypoglycemia are warranted. The physician will likely discuss the importance of testing her son before prolonged exercise and making sure that a source of sugar (glucose tablets, a juice box, or cake icing) is available in case hypoglycemia does occur.

OBJECTIVES	CONTENT	TEACHING RESOURCES

Identify and locate the primary endocrine glands and list the major hormones produced by each gland.	■ Pituitary gland (p. 258)
	   □ Anterior pituitary gland hormones (p. 258)
	   □ Posterior pituitary gland hormones (p. 259)
	■ Hypothalamus (p. 260)
	■ Thyroid gland (p. 261)
	■ Parathyroid glands (p. 261)
	■ Adrenal glands (p. 263)
	   □ Adrenal cortex (p. 263)
	   □ Adrenal medulla (p. 266)
		⊠ Slides 13-29
		
		Pituitary Gland and Hypothalamus questions 18-42 (pp. 110-112)
		
		Thyroid and Parathyroid Glands questions 43-52 (p. 113)
		
		Adrenal Glands questions 53-69 (p. 113)
		
		Applying What You Know question 93 (p. 115)
		
		Multiple Choice questions 1-10 (pp. 117-118)
		
		Multiple Choice questions 9-26, 39-43; True or False questions 22-48, 64-72; Short Answer questions 8-12, 15
		
		Identification question 31 (p. 138)
		
		Thyroid Secretion
		
		Adrenal Function
		
		Book Resources
		
		Figure 10-5 Pituitary hormones (p. 260)
		
		Quick Check questions 1-4 (p. 261)
		
		Figure 10-6 Thyroid and parathyroid glands (p. 262)
		
		Figure 10-7 Thyroid gland tissue (p. 262)
		
		Figure 10-8 Regulation of blood calcium levels (p. 263)
		
		Quick Check questions 1-3 (p. 263)

ELSEVIER

Structure & Function of the Body, 13th ed.

Thibodeau/Patton

OBJECTIVES	CONTENT	TEACHING RESOURCES
		Figure 10-9 The adrenal gland (p. 265)
		Figure 10-10 Stress responses induced by high concentrations of glucocorticoids in blood (p. 266)
		Quick Check questions 1-3 (p. 267)
		Review questions 8-17 (p. 276)
		Critical Thinking questions 20, 21 (p. 276)
		Chapter Test questions 8-25 (pp. 277-278)
		Clear View of the Human Body
		Class Activity Using Table 10-1 (p. 252), have students make flash cards with the glands on one side and the secreted hormones and their functions on the other side. Divide the class into two teams to see which team can most often match the hormones and functions with the correct endocrine glands. Assign points to determine a winner.
		Class Activity Have an endocrinologist address issues associated with thyroid disorders, such as problems with energy levels, muscle strength, emotions, weight control, and tolerating heat or cold. How can patients manage thyroid growths, thyroid cancer, or swollen thyroid glands?
		Class Activity Distribute an unlabeled copy of Figure 10-5 and have students fill in the blanks with the appropriate anterior and posterior pituitary gland hormones.
Define *diabetes insipidus, diabetes mellitus, gigantism, goiter, cretinism,* and *glycosuria.*	■ Pancreatic islets (p. 268)	⊞ Slides 30-33
		ℰ Multiple Choice questions 27-29, 44; True or False questions 49-53, 73-75; Short Answer question 13
		Multiple Choice question 7 (p. 136)
		Book Resources
		Figure 10-11 Pancreas (p. 269)
		Quick Check questions 1-3 (p. 269)
		Figure 10-12 Diabetes mellitus (p. 270)
		Class Activity Have an endocrinologist discuss problems associated with diabetes, including problems in the eyes, kidneys, and nerves that can lead to blindness, dialysis, or amputation. How is diabetes treated with diet and medications, including insulin? Discuss how to control blood sugar levels.

ELSEVIER

Structure & Function of the Body, 13th ed.

Thibodeau/Patton

OBJECTIVES	CONTENT	TEACHING RESOURCES
		Class Activity Divide the class into six groups and assign a term (as listed in the objective) to each of them. Have them collaborate on a description of the term. Pick a representative from each group to present the description to the class. Have the class offer improvements.
		Class Activity Have students bring in various food labels. Discuss the amount of servings, calories, carbohydrates, fats, and proteins listed. Are they surprised? Have students offer ideas for patients who need to control their dietary intake.
		Class Activity Invite a speaker from a local hospital or support group to discuss diabetes mellitus and current technologies (insulin pumps, nasal insulin, transplants, etc.)
Identify the principal functions of each major endocrine hormone and describe the conditions that may result from hyposecretion or hypersecretion.	■ Female sex glands (p. 271) ■ Male sex glands (p. 271) ■ Thymus (p. 271) ■ Placenta (p. 271) ■ Pineal gland (p. 271) ■ Other endocrine structures (p. 271)	⊠ Slides 34-42 Pancreatic Islets, Sex Glands, Thymus, Placenta, and Pineal Gland questions 70-86 (p. 114) Applying What You Know questions 92, 93 (p. 115) *e* Multiple Choice questions 30-35, 45; True or False questions 54-56; Short Answer question 14 Completion questions 28, 29 (p. 138) **Book Resources** Quick Check questions 1-3 (p. 272) ***Class Activity Infertility is a problem for many couples. Have an endocrinologist discuss how to diagnose and treat hormonal imbalances that can cause infertility. How does hormone replacement work? Students also might want to inquire about menopause symptoms, irregular periods, endometriosis, polycystic ovary syndrome, premenstrual syndrome, and impotence.***
Performance Evaluation		*e* Chapter 10 Computerized Test Bank questions Multiple Choice questions 1-10; Matching questions 11-20; Completion questions 21-30; Identification question 31 (pp. 136-138) *e* Student Post-Test questions

Thibodeau/Patton

OBJECTIVES	CONTENT	TEACHING RESOURCES
		Book Resources
		Review questions (p. 276)
		Critical Thinking questions (p. 276)
		Chapter Test (pp. 277-278)

10.2 Homework/Assignments:

10.2 Teacher's Notes:

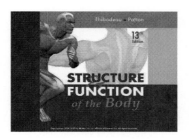

Slide 1

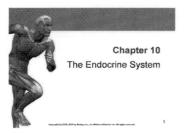

Chapter 10

The Endocrine System

Slide 2

Learning Objectives

- Distinguish between endocrine and exocrine glands and define the terms *hormone* and *prostaglandins*
- Identify and locate the primary endocrine glands and list the major hormones produced by each gland
- Describe the mechanisms of steroid and nonsteroid hormone action

2

Slide 3

Learning Objectives (cont'd)

- Explain how negative and positive feedback mechanisms regulate the secretion of endocrine hormones
- Identify the principal functions of each major endocrine hormone and describe the conditions that may result from hyposecretion or hypersecretion
- Define *diabetes insipidus, diabetes mellitus, gigantism, goiter, cretinism,* and *glycosuria*

3

Thibodeau/Patton

Slide 4

Chapter 10
Lesson 10.1

Slide 5

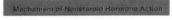

The Endocrine System

- Performs the same general functions as the nervous system
  - Communication
  - Control
- Provides slower, longer-lasting control by **hormones** secreted into and circulated by the blood

- ● What are endocrine glands? (ductless glands that secrete *hormones* into intracellular spaces.)

- ● What is a target-organ cell? (a cell that has receptors for a specific hormone)

Slide 6

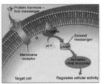

Mechanism of Nonsteroid Hormone Action

- ● What are the two major classes of hormones? (nonsteroid and steroid hormones)

- ● How do nonsteroid and steroid hormones differ? (Nonsteroid hormones are whole proteins, chains of amino acids, or simply versions of single amino acids. These hormones provide communication between endocrine glands and target organs. Steroids hormones are lipid soluble and pass directly through the plasma membrane of the target cell.)

- ● What is a second messenger mechanism? (chemical that provides communication within a hormone's target cell)

Slide 7

Mechanism of Steroid Hormone Action

- ● What are steroid hormones? (hormones that can pass through the target cell's membrane to the nucleus, where they bind with a receptor to form a hormone-receptor complex)

- ● Give an example of a steroid hormone. (Estrogen)

Slide 8

Regulation of Hormone Secretion

- Hormone secretion is controlled by homeostatic feedback
  - **Negative feedback:** Mechanisms that reverse the direction of a change in a physiologic system
  - **Positive feedback:** (Uncommon) mechanisms that amplify physiologic changes

- Give an example of positive feedback. (During labor, muscle contractions become stronger by means of a positive feedback mechanism that regulates the secretion of oxytocin.)

- Give an example of negative feedback. (As blood sugar normalizes, insulin secretion decreases.)

Slide 9

Negative Feedback: Insulin

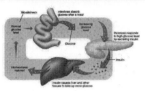

- How does insulin work as a negative feedback mechanism? (It lowers blood sugar levels.)

Slide 10

Prostaglandins

- **Prostaglandins** (or tissue hormones) are powerful substances found in a wide variety of body tissues
- A prostaglandin is often produced in a tissue and diffuses only a short distance to act on cells in that tissue

- Do prostaglandins meet the definition of a typical hormone? (no)

- How do prostaglandins differ from most hormones? (Prostaglandins only influence the activities of neighboring cells.)

Slide 11

Prostaglandins (cont'd.)

- Several classes of prostaglandins include prostaglandin A, prostaglandin E, and prostaglandin F
- Prostaglandins influence many body functions, including respiration, blood pressure, gastrointestinal secretions, and reproduction

- What research is being conducted with prostaglandins? (the role of prostaglandins in the treatment of high blood pressure, asthma, and ulcers)

ELSEVIER

Slide 12

Chapter 10
Lesson 10.2

12

Slide 13

Pituitary Gland

- Anterior pituitary gland (adenohypophysis)
  - Major hormones
    - Thyroid-stimulating hormone (TSH)
    - Adrenocorticotropic hormone (ACTH)
    - Follicle-stimulating hormone (FSH)
    - Luteinizing hormone (LH)
    - Growth hormone (GH)
    - Prolactin hormone (PH)

13

- Why is the anterior gland sometimes called the master gland? (It controls the thyroid gland, the adrenal cortex, the ovarian follicles, and the corpus luteum.)

- What do the major hormones do? (ACTH stimulates the adrenal cortex, causing it to increase in size and secrete larger amounts of its hormones.)

Slide 14

Pituitary Gland (cont'd.)

- Functions of major hormones
  - TSH
    - Stimulates growth of the thyroid gland
    - Stimulates it to secrete thyroid hormone
  - ACTH
    - Stimulates growth of the adrenal cortex
    - Stimulates thyroid to secrete glucocorticoids and mineralocorticoids

14

Slide 15

Pituitary Gland (cont'd.)

- FSH
  - Initiates growth of ovarian follicles each month in the ovary and stimulates one or more follicles to develop to the stage of maturity and ovulation
  - Stimulates estrogen secretion by developing follicles
  - Stimulates sperm production in the male

15

ELSEVIER

Structure & Function of the Body, 13th ed.
Thibodeau/Patton

Slide 16

Pituitary Gland (cont'd.)

- ☐ **LH**
  - ◦ Acts with FSH to stimulate estrogen secretion and follicle growth to maturity
  - ◦ Causes ovulation
  - ◦ Causes luteinization of the ruptured follicle and stimulates progesterone secretion by corpus luteum
  - ◦ Causes interstitial cells in the testes to secrete testosterone in the male

16

- ● How does the pituitary gland relate to fertility? (controls the actions of ovaries and testes)

Slide 17

Pituitary Gland (cont'd.)

- ☐ **GH**
  - ◦ Stimulates growth by accelerating protein anabolism
  - ◦ Accelerates fat catabolism and slows glucose catabolism
  - ◦ By slowing glucose catabolism, tends to increase blood glucose to higher than normal level (hyperglycemia)

17

- ● How do growth hormones promote normal growth? (They speed up the movement of amino acids out of the blood and into the cells, which accelerates the cells' anabolism of amino acids to form tissue proteins. Children experiencing a growth spurt will often have elevated blood sugars.)

Slide 18

Pituitary Gland (cont'd.)

- ☐ **Prolactin or lactogenic hormone**
  - ◦ Stimulates breast development during pregnancy and secretion of milk after the delivery of the baby

18

Slide 19

Posterior Pituitary Gland Hormones

- • **Antidiuretic hormone (ADH)**
  - ▪ Accelerates water absorption from urine in the kidney tubules into the blood, thereby decreasing urine secretion
- • **Oxytocin**
  - ▪ Stimulates the pregnant uterus to contract
  - ▪ May initiate labor
  - ▪ Causes glandular cells of the breast to release milk into ducts

19

- ● What does the hyposecretion of ADH cause? (diabetes insipidus, which results in excessive urine secretion)

- ● How are dehydration and electrolyte imbalances treated? (with injections or nasal sprays containing ADH)

Slide 20

Hypothalamus

- Actual production of ADH and oxytocin occurs in the hypothalamus
- After production in the hypothalamus, hormones pass along axons into the pituitary gland
- The secretion and release of posterior pituitary hormones are controlled by nervous stimulation

20

- In addition to oxytocin and ADH, what substances does the hypothalamus produce? (releasing and inhibiting hormones that travel to the anterior pituitary gland)

- The hypothalamus regulates many body functions related to homeostasis. Give some examples. (body temperature, appetite, and thirst)

Slide 21

Thyroid and Parathyroid Glands

21

- Where is the thyroid located? (in the neck just below the larynx)

Slide 22

Thyroid Gland Hormones

- Thyroxine (T₄)
  - Most abundant
  - To be produced in adequate amounts, diet must contain sufficient iodine
- Triiodothyronine (T₃)
  - More potent
  - Considered by physiologists to be the principal thyroid hormone

22

- How do T3 and T4 influence body cells? (They speed up the release of energy from foods.)

- How does calcitonin help maintain homeostasis of blood calcium? (It decreases blood calcium concentrations.)

Slide 23

Thyroid Gland Hormones (cont'd)

- Calcitonin
  - Decreases the blood calcium concentration by inhibiting breakdown of bone, which would release calcium into the blood

23

Structure & Function of the Body, 13ᵗʰ ed.
Thibodeau/Patton

Slide 24

Parathyroid Gland

- **Parathyroid hormone (PTH)**
  - Increases blood calcium concentration by increasing the breakdown of bone with the release of calcium into the blood
  - Has opposite effect of calcitonin, because PTH acts to increase calcium

- How does PTH increase calcium? (It stimulates bone-resorbing cells to increase their breakdown of bone's hard matrix, which frees the calcium stored there.)

Slide 25

Adrenal Glands

- **Adrenal cortex**
  - Three cell layers (zones) secrete hormones
    - Outer layer secretes **mineralocorticoids**
    - Middle layer secretes **glucocorticoids**
    - Inner layer secretes **sex hormones**, small amounts of male hormones (androgens) secreted by adrenal cortex of both sexes

- Where is the adrenal gland? (It curves over the top of each kidney.)

- What are hormones secreted by the adrenal cortex called? (corticoids)

- What are the adrenal cortex and the adrenal medulla? (The adrenal cortex is the outer part of an adrenal gland, the medulla is its inner part.)

Slide 26

Mineralocorticoids

- Increase blood sodium
- Decrease body potassium concentrations by accelerating kidney tubule reabsorption of sodium and excretion of potassium

- What is the chief mineralocorticoid? (aldosterone)

- What does aldosterone do? (increases the amount of sodium and decreases potassium in the blood)

Slide 27

Glucocorticoids

- Maintain normal blood glucose concentration by increasing gluconeogenesis, the formation of "new" glucose from amino acids produced by the breakdown of proteins, mainly those in muscle tissue cells

- Secretion of glucocorticoid quickly increases when the body is under stress.

Slide 28

Glucocorticoids (cont'd.)

- Play an essential part in maintaining normal blood pressure
- Make it possible for epinephrine and norepinephrine to maintain a normal degree of vasoconstriction, a condition necessary for maintaining normal blood pressure
- Act with epinephrine and norepinephrine to produce an antiinflammatory effect to bring about normal recovery from inflammation of various kinds
- Produce antiimmunity, antiallergy effects

28

- During periods of prolonged stress, glucocorticoids may have harmful side effects because they are antiinflammatory and cause blood vessels to constrict

- Glucocorticoids can cause increased blood sugar levels

Slide 29

Adrenal Glands

- **Adrenal medulla**
  - Hormones
    - Epinephrine (adrenaline)
    - Norepinephrine
  - Help the body resist stress by intensifying and prolonging the effects of sympathetic stimulation
  - An increased epinephrine secretion is the first endocrine response to stress

29

- Increased secretion by the adrenal medulla occurs rapidly, because nerve impulses conducted by sympathetic nerve fibers stimulate the adrenal medulla.

- Fight-or-flight response!

Slide 30

Pancreatic Islets

- Hormones
  - **Glucagon** is secreted by alpha cells
    - It increases the blood glucose level by accelerating liver glycogenolysis (conversion of glycogen to glucose)

30

- How do endocrine glands differ from pancreatic islets? (Endocrine glands are much larger than pancreatic islets.)

Slide 31

Pancreatic Islets (cont'd)

- **Insulin** is secreted by beta cells.
  - It decreases the blood glucose by accelerating the movement of glucose out of the blood into cells, which increases glucose metabolism by cells.

31

- What happens if the pancreatic islets do not secrete enough insulin? (Blood glucose increases.)

Structure & Function of the Body, 13th ed.

Thibodeau/Patton

Slide 32

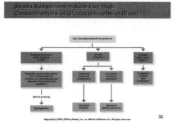

- What is liver glycogenolysis? (a chemical process by which glycogen is converted to glucose)

- What does it mean that insulin and glucagons are antagonists? (Insulin decreases blood-glucose concentrations, and glucagon increases.)

Slide 33

- How are most screening tests for diabetes mellitus done? (with a drop of blood)

- Testing for sugar in the urine is another common screening procedure.

Slide 34

Female Sex Glands

- The ovaries contain two structures that secrete hormones
  - **The ovarian follicles**
    - Little pockets in which egg cells, or ova, develop
    - Secrete estrogen, the "feminizing hormone"
  - **The corpus luteum**

- All egg cells in females are present at birth. They develop at puberty.

Slide 35

Female Sex Glands (cont'd)

- Effects of estrogen
  - Development and maturation of breasts and external genitals
  - Development of adult female body contours
  - Initiation of menstrual cycle

- Menarche: name give to first menstrual cycle.

- Menopause: name given to the cessation of estrogen production.

Slide 36

Male Sex Glands

- The interstitial cells of the testes secrete the male hormone testosterone
- Effects of testosterone
  - Maturation of external genitals
  - Beard growth
  - Voice changes at puberty
  - Development of musculature and body contours typical of the male

36

- The cells of the testes produce what? (Sperm production is ongoing after puberty.)

- The interstitial cells in the testes secrete what male sex hormone directly into the blood? (testosterone)

Slide 37

Thymus

- Hormone: **Thymosin**
  - This hormone plays an important role in the development and function of the body's immune system

37

- Where is the thymus located? (the mediastinum)

Slide 38

Placenta

- Hormones
  - **Chorionic gonadotropins**: tropic hormones secreted by cells of the chorion, the outermost membrane that surrounds the baby during development in the uterus
  - **Estrogens**
  - **Progesterone**

38

- These hormones maintain the corpus luteum during pregnancy.

- What fact led to the development of the early pregnancy test? (During the earliest weeks of pregnancy, the kidneys excrete chorionic gonadotropins into the urine.)

Slide 39

Pineal Gland

- The **pineal gland** is a small gland near the roof of the third ventricle of the brain
  - Glandular tissue predominates in children and young adults
  - Tissue becomes fibrous and calcified with age
  - Called third eye because its influence on secretory activity is related to the amount of light entering the eyes

39

- Why is this gland named *pineal?* (Because it resembles a pine nut.)

ELSEVIER

Structure & Function of the Body, 13th ed.
Thibodeau/Patton

Slide 40

Pineal Gland (cont'd)

- Pineal Gland
  - Secretes melatonin, which
    - Inhibits ovarian activity
    - Regulates the body's internal clock

40

- Some controversy exists regarding melatonin's value for insomnia.

Slide 41

Other Endocrine Structures

- Other organs (stomach, intestines, and kidneys) produce endocrine hormones
  - **Atrial natriuretic hormone (ANH)**
    - Secreted by atrial wall of the heart
    - Stimulates sodium loss from the kidneys

41

- Nearly every organ and system has an endocrine function.

Slide 42

Other Endocrine Structures (cont'd)

- **Leptin**
  - Newly discovered hormone
  - Secreted by fat-storing cells
  - Controls how full or hungry we feel

42

- Leptin is still being studied as a possible weight loss substance.

11 Lesson Plan
Blood

TEACHING FOCUS

In this chapter, the student will have the opportunity to learn the primary functions of blood, the characteristics of blood plasma, and the functions of the formed elements of blood. The student will also have the opportunity to discuss anemia, as well as to provide an explanation of the steps involved in blood clotting. Additionally, the student will be given the opportunity to describe ABO and Rh blood typing and define a number of medical terms associated with blood.

MATERIALS AND RESOURCES

- ☐ Computer (Lesson 11.1)
- ☐ Copy of Table 11-1 (Lesson 11.1)
- ☐ Flash cards (developed by instructor) that focus on medical conditions associated with blood (Lesson 11.2)
- ☐ Microscope (Lesson 11.1)

LESSON CHECKLIST

Preparations for this lesson include:

- lecture
- demonstration
- guest speaker: hematologist or representative from a local blood bank
- student performance evaluation of all entry-level skills required for student comprehension and application of principles related to blood including:
  - ○ functions of blood
  - ○ blood clotting
  - ○ blood typing
  - ○ medical terms associated with blood

KEY TERMS

anemia (p. 285)
antibodies (p. 291)
antigens (p. 291)
basophil (p. 288)
buffy coat (p. 287)
carbaminohemoglobin (p. 285)
embolism (p. 291)
embolus (p. 291)
eosinophil (p. 287)
erythroblastosis fetalis (p. 294)
erythrocyte (p. 283)
fibrin (p. 289)
fibrinogen (p. 289)
hematocrit (p. 286)
hemoglobin (p. 284)
heparin (p. 288)
leukopenia (p. 288)
leukemia (p. 289)

leukocyte (p. 283)
leukocytosis (p. 288)
lymphocyte (p. 288)
monocyte (p. 288)
neutrophil (pp. 287, 288)
oxyhemoglobin (p. 284)
pernicious anemia (p. 285)
phagocyte (p. 288)
plasma (p. 281)
plasma protein (p. 282)
polycythemia (p. 286)
prothrombin (p. 289)
prothrombin activator (p. 289)
serum (p. 282)
thrombin (p. 289)
thrombocyte (p. 283)
thrombosis (p. 291)
thrombus (p. 291)

ADDITIONAL RESOURCES

AnimationDirect (Book Companion CD)
Instructor's Electronic Resource (IER) (CD)
PowerPoint slides (CD, Evolve)
Test Bank (Evolve)

Legend

ESLR
EVOLVE Student
Learning Resource

EILR TB
EVOLVE Instructor
Learning Resource
Test Bank

AnimationDirect
on Book Companion
CD

PPT
PowerPoint
Slides

SG
Study
Guide

IRM
Instructor's
Resource Manual

Class Activities are indicated in ***bold italic.***

Structure & Function of the Body, 13th ed.

Thibodeau/Patton

LESSON 11.1

PRETEST
Study Guide Multiple Choice questions 1-27 (pp. 122-125)

BACKGROUND ASSESSMENT
Question: What is the significance of the Rh factor in blood?

Answer: If a person has Rh-positive blood, his or her red blood cells contain the Rh factor. In the United States, the Rh factor is seen in 85% of Caucasians and 88% of African Americans. People with Rh-negative blood do not have the Rh factor in their red blood cells. If blood cells that contain the Rh factor are introduced into the blood of a person with Rh-negative blood, anti-Rh antibodies will appear in the blood plasma.

Question: What is the hereditary disease known as *sickle cell anemia?*

Answer: Sickle cell anemia, a disease caused by an abnormal type of hemoglobin, is severe and sometimes fatal. In people with sickle cell disease, the red blood cells contain a small amount of hemoglobin that is less soluble than normal. Solid crystals form when blood oxygen is low, causing the red blood cells to become distorted. If a person inherits two defective genes—one from each parent—even more defective hemoglobin is produced, and the red blood cell distortion is more severe. Stroke is one of the most devastating side effects of sickle cell anemia. The risk of stroke can be reduced by removing abnormal cells (electrophoresis) or by administering frequent blood transfusions.

CRITICAL THINKING QUESTION
Mrs. Wilson is brought into the ER after a car accident. A major artery in her leg has been damaged, and she had lost an undetermined amount of blood before EMTs arrived and were able to stop the bleeding. What dangers might Mrs. Wilson be facing? How might she be treated?

Guidelines: Most adults have between 4 to 6 liters of blood. If too much blood is lost, Mrs. Wilson's body will go into shock because of a lack of blood pressure. In this case, Mrs. Wilson might receive plasma and other fluids to maintain blood pressure. Furthermore, blood loss can reduce the number of red blood cells in the blood to dangerous levels. Because red blood cells deliver oxygen to the body's cells, a large loss could result in Mrs. Wilson's cells not receiving enough oxygen to function. In this case, Mrs. Wilson will likely receive packed red blood cells.

OBJECTIVES	CONTENT	TEACHING RESOURCES
Describe the primary functions of blood.	■ Introduction (p. 281)	*e* True or False question 51 *Class Activity Go around the room and ask students to state one fact about blood. Write the facts on the board.*
Describe the characteristics of blood plasma.	■ Blood composition (p. 281) □ Blood plasma (p. 282)	Slide 5 Blood Composition questions 1, 2, 22 (pp. 122, 124) *e* Multiple choice questions 1-5, 36, 37; True or False questions 1-6, 27, 52-54; Short Answer question 1 Classroom Application questions 1, 2 (p. 147); Multiple Choice questions 14, 15 (p. 149)

ELSEVIER

OBJECTIVES	CONTENT	TEACHING RESOURCES
		Book Resources
		Figure 11-1 Components of blood (p. 283)
		Review Question 1 (p. 298)
List the formed elements of blood and identify the most important function of each.	☐ Formed elements (p. 283)	Slides 6-8
		Blood Composition questions 3-5, 16-18 (pp. 122-124)
		Multiple Choice questions 6-11, 38-43; True or False questions 7-18, 55-57
		Multiple Choice questions 16, 20 (p. 150)
		Book Resources
		Quick Check questions 1, 2 (p. 284)
		Table 11-1 Classes of Blood Cells (p. 283)
		Review questions 2-5 (p. 298)
		*Class Activity **Using slides that show the classes of blood cells listed in Table 11-1 (p. 284), allow the students to view slides of the various types of cells and identify them. A copy of Table 11-1 should be posted nearby to aid in identification.***
		*Class Activity **Students are assigned a blood cell type from Table 11-1. When it is their turn, they will explain their cell type's role in the body and answer questions about their type of cell.***
Discuss anemia in terms of red blood cell numbers and hemoglobin content.	☐ Red blood cells (p. 284) ☐ White blood cells (p. 287)	Slides 9-12
		Blood Composition questions 6-11, 14, 15, 19-21, 23-25 (pp. 122-124)
		Multiple Choice questions 12-24, 44, 45; True or False questions 19-26, 28-33, and 58-62; Matching questions 11-20; Short Answer questions 2-4
		Classroom Application questions 3, 4 (p. 147); Multiple Choice questions 12, 18, 19, 21, 22 (p. 150)
		Red Blood Cells
		White Blood Cells
		Book Resources
		Figure 11-2 RBCs (p. 285)

Thibodeau/Patton

OBJECTIVES	CONTENT	TEACHING RESOURCES
		Figure 11-3 Hematocrit tubes showing normal blood, anemia, and polycythemia (p. 286)
		Figure 11-4 Leukocytes in human blood smears (p. 287)
		Figure 11-5 Phagocytosis (p. 288)
		▶ Discuss Clinical Application: Bone Marrow Transplants (p. 284)
		Class Activity Have students dialogue about the controversies surrounding stem cell use.
		Class Activity After discussing sickle cell disease, ask students to pair up. One student will take the role of the patient and one of the medical assistant. The medical assistant will explain sickle cell disease to a patient in lay terms. The other student will critique the explanation and add any pertinent facts that were omitted.
		Class Activity Have students devise a diet that is rich in iron for the patient with low hemoglobin. Have students explore Internet sites for this information.

11.1 Homework/Assignments:

11.1 Teacher's Notes:

LESSON 11.2

CRITICAL THINKING QUESTION

Mrs. Emery is pregnant. Her blood type is O negative and her husband's blood type is O positive. She has been told that she will need to receive RhoGAM during her pregnancy (between 26 and 28 weeks) and again at delivery, if the baby has O positive blood. She feels that it is important to receive as few medications as possible during her pregnancy. How should you consult her?

Guidelines: The red blood cells of a person with Rh-negative blood do not contain the Rh factor. Plasma never contains anti-Rh antibodies naturally. However, if Rh-positive blood cells are introduced into the Rh-negative person's body, anti-Rh antibodies will soon appear. This can happen if a woman with Rh-negative blood is carrying a fetus with Rh-positive blood, or if a person with Rh-negative blood received a transfusion of Rh-positive blood. In the case of a pregnancy, if Rh-positive blood mixes with the Rh-negative blood, the mother's body will form anti-Rh antibodies. Then, if she later carries another Rh-positive fetus, the fetus may develop a disease called erythroblastosis fetalis, caused by the mother's Rh antibodies reacting with the baby's Rh-positive cells. For this reason, all Rh-negative mothers who carry an Rh-positive baby must be treated with RhoGAM, which stops the mother's body from forming anti-Rh antibodies.

OBJECTIVES	CONTENT	TEACHING RESOURCES
Explain the steps involved in blood clotting.	☐ Platelets and blood clotting (p. 289)	Slide 13 Blood Composition questions 12, 13, 26, 27 (pp. 123, 125) Multiple Choice questions 25-30; True or False questions 34-41; Short Answer questions 5-7 Multiple Choice questions 13, 17 (pp. 148-149) **Book Resources** Quick Check question 3 (p. 291) Figure 11-6 Blood clotting (p. 290) Review questions 12, 13 (p. 298) Critical Thinking questions 16, 17 (p. 298) ▸ Discuss Clinical Application: Anticoagulant Therapy (p. 289). *Class Activity Go around the room and ask students to state one new fact that they have learned about blood. Write the new facts on the board and summarize at the end.* *Class Activity Using Figure 11-6 as a tool, ask a student volunteer to explain the process of blood clotting to the class.*

OBJECTIVES	CONTENT	TEACHING RESOURCES
Describe ABO and Rh blood typing.	■ Blood types (p. 291) □ ABO system (p. 291) □ Rh system (p. 293)	⊠🖥 Slides 15-17 📘 Blood Types Rh Factor questions 28-35 (p. 125) 📖 Multiple Choice questions 31-35, 46; True or False questions 42-50, 63; Matching questions 1-10; Short Answer questions 8-11 📖 Multiple Choice questions 11, 23 (pp. 149-150); Completion questions 24-33 (p. 151) 🔘 Blood Grouping **Book Resources** Figure 11-7 Results of different combinations of donor and recipient blood (p. 292) Figure 11-8 Erythroblastosis fetalis (p. 295) Quick Check questions 1, 2 (p. 294) Review questions 13, 14 (p. 298) Critical Thinking question 18 (p. 298) ▸ Discuss Health and Well-Being: Blood Doping (p. 293). ▸ Discuss Research, Issues and Trends: Artificial Blood (p. 294). *Class Activity Break the class into three groups, and assign the following topics:* **surgical glue, artificial blood,** *and* **erythropoietin.** *If an Internet connection is available, ask students to use it to research their topic and present their findings to the class.* *Class Activity: Invite a representative from a blood bank to discuss issues with blood typing and answer students' questions about blood.*
Define the following medical terms associated with blood: *hematocrit, leukocytosis, leukopenia, polycythemia, sickle cell, phagocytosis, acidosis,*	(Throughout chapter. See also the Key Terms of this lesson plan for the locations of these terms in the chapter.)	📖 Matching questions 1-10 (p. 149) *Class Activity Divide the class into two teams and split up the flash cards that focus on medical conditions associated with blood. Each team takes a turn holding up a flash card for the other team to answer with the correct hormone and its function. A team wins one point for a correct answer or for the opposing team's wrong answer.*

OBJECTIVES	CONTENT	TEACHING RESOURCES
thrombosis, erythroblastosis fetalis, serum, fibrinogen, Rh factor, anemia.		*Class Activity Have students play medical terminology bingo. Create various "bingo cards" with the terms listed in the objectives. Randomly select the definitions of the terms from cards previously prepared. Recite the definitions and have students place a mark on their bingo card if they have a match. The first person to get a bingo wins. You can also add terms from previous chapters to play "a cover-all card."*
Performance Evaluation		Chapter 11 Computerized Test Bank questions Student Assignment questions 1-33 (pp. 150-151) Student Post-Test questions **Book Resources** Review questions 1-15 (p. 298) Chapter Test questions 1-21 (p. 299)

11.2 Homework/Assignments:

11.2 Teacher's Notes:

Structure & Function of the Body, 13th ed.

Thibodeau/Patton

Slide 1

Chapter 11

Blood

1

Slide 2

Learning Objectives

- Describe the primary functions of blood
- Describe the characteristics of blood plasma
- List the formed elements of blood and identify the most important function of each
- Discuss anemia in terms of red blood cell numbers and hemoglobin content

2

Slide 3

Learning Objectives (cont'd.)

- Explain the steps involved in blood clotting
- Describe ABO and Rh blood typing
- Define the following medical terms associated with blood: *hematocrit, leukocytosis, leukopenia, polycythemia, sickle cell, phagocytosis, acidosis, thrombosis, erythroblastosis fetalis, serum, fibrinogen, Rh factor, anemia*

3

ELSEVIER

Structure & Function of the Body, 13th ed.

Thibodeau/Patton

Slide 4

Chapter 11
Lesson 11.1

Slide 5

Blood Composition

- Blood plasma
  - Definition—blood minus its cells
  - Composition—water containing many dissolved substances (for example, foods, salts, and hormones)
  - Amount of blood—varies with a person's size and sex; average is about 4 to 6 L (about 7% to 9% of body weight)

- What is hematology? (study of the blood)

- Is blood a fluid tissue? (Yes)

- What percent of blood is comprised of plasma? (Approximately 55%)

- What is suspended in the plasma? (proteins, water, and solutes)

- What is the difference between blood plasma and blood serum? (Plasma contains clotting factors, serum does not.)

Slide 6

Blood Composition (cont'd.)

- Formed elements
  - RBCs (erythrocytes)
  - WBCs (leukocytes)
    - Granular leukocytes: Neutrophils, eosinophils, and basophils
    - Nongranular leukocytes: Lymphocytes and monocytes
  - Platelets or thrombocytes

- What is the formation of new blood cells called? *(hemopoiesis)*

- What is myeloid tissue better known as? *(red bone marrow)*

- Where is red bone marrow produced? (chiefly in the sternum, ribs, and hip bones)

- Approximately how many RBCs, WBCs, and platelets are in one mm^3? (RBC = 5 million, WBC = 7500, Platelets = 250,000)

Slide 7

Blood Composition (cont'd.)

- Formed elements
  - Numbers
    - RBCs: 4.5 to 5 million per mm³ of blood
    - WBCs: 5,000 to 10,000 per mm³ of blood
    - Platelets: 300,000 per mm³ of blood
  - Formation
    - Red bone marrow, or myeloid tissue, forms all blood cells except some lymphocytes and monocytes, which are formed by lymphatic tissue in the lymph nodes, thymus, and spleen

- How long do erythrocytes circulate before they break apart and move into the liver? (approximately four months)

- What is the lifespan of granular leukocytes? (only a few days)

- What is the lifespan of nongranular leukocytes? (six months or more)

Structure & Function of the Body, 13th ed.

Thibodeau/Patton

Slide 8

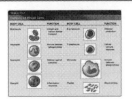

Blood Composition (cont'd.)

Slide 9

Blood Composition (cont'd.)

- RBCs
  - Structure
    - Disk-shaped, without nuclei
  - **Anemia:** Inability of blood to carry adequate oxygen to tissue; often caused by
    - Inadequate RBC numbers
    - Deficiency of hemoglobin or iron
    - **Pernicious anemia:** Deficiency of the intrinsic factor

- Because of the large number of RBCs and their unique shape, their total surface area is enormous. If they were laid out flat, the total surface of the RBCs in the body would be larger than a football field.

- What are some of the functions of RBCs? (They transport oxygen and carbon dioxide to and from cells.)

- What is sickle cell anemia, and how does it affect the body? (Sickle cell anemia is a hereditary disease in which the RBC is abnormally shaped (S curved) and cannot hold enough hemoglobin to properly oxygenate the body.)

- Pernicious anemia is due to absence of the intrinsic factor that allows for the absorption of B_{12}.

Slide 10

Blood Composition (cont'd.)

- RBCs
  - **Hematocrit:** Medical test in which a centrifuge is used to separate whole blood into formed elements and liquid fraction
    - Buffy coat is WBC and platelet fraction
    - Normal RBC level is about 45%
    - **Polycythemia:** Abnormally high RBC count

- What happens to RBCs during the hematocrit procedure? (RBCs are forced to the bottom of the tube.)

- What happens to the RBC count in a patient with anemia? (The RBC is less than normal.)

- What is *blood doping*? (Blood doping involves the removal and freezing of some RBC and reinjecting them at a later date. Adding these additional RBC is thought to increase the oxygen capacity of the blood.)

Slide 11

Blood Composition (cont'd.)

- WBCs
  - Neutrophils and monocytes carry out phagocytosis
  - Lymphocytes produce antibodies (B-lymphocytes) or directly attack foreign cells (T-lymphocytes)
  - Eosinophils protect against parasitic irritants that cause allergies
  - Basophils produce heparin, which inhibits clotting

- What are the functions of WBCs? (phagocytosis, antibody production, protection from allergies, and anticoagulation)

- What is phagocytosis? (condition in which neurophils and monoctyes digest microbes)

- Eosinophils are granulocytic WBCs. They are also capable of phagocytosis.

- Basophils also function in allergic reactions.

ELSEVIER

Structure & Function of the Body, 13th ed.

Thibodeau/Patton

Slide 12

Blood Composition (cont'd.)

- WBCs
  - Clinical conditions related to blood
    - **Leukopenia:** Abnormally low WBC count
    - **Leukocytosis:** Abnormally high WBC count
    - **Leukemia:** Elevated WBC count; cells do not function properly, cells are immature

12

- AIDS, acquired immune deficiency syndrome, is one example of a disease characterized by marked leukopenia.

- Which of these conditions almost always accompanies infections? (leukocytosis)

Slide 13

Blood Composition (cont'd.)

- Platelets and blood clotting
  - Platelets play an essential role in blood clotting
  - Blood clot formation
    - Clotting factors released at the injury site produce prothrombin activator
    - Prothrombin activator and calcium convert prothrombin to thrombin
    - Thrombin triggers formation of fibrin, which traps RBC to form a clot

13

- What does thrombin combine with to form fibrin? (fibrinogen)

- When does clotting become dangerous? (Clots are dangerous when they occlude normal blood flow.)

- What is an embolism? (This is a clot that has moved from the site of formation.)

- What is a thrombus? (This is a stationary clot.)

Slide 14

Chapter 11
Lesson 11.2

14

Slide 15

Blood Types

- ABO system
  - **Type A blood:** Type A self-antigens in RBCs; anti-B-type antibodies in plasma
  - **Type B blood:** Type B self-antigens in RBCs; anti-A-type antibodies in plasma
  - **Type AB blood:** Type A and type B self-antigens in RBCs; no anti-A or anti-B antibodies in plasma
  - **Type O blood:** No type A or type B self-antigens in RBCs; both anti-A and anti-B antibodies in plasma

15

- What are antigens and antibodies, and how do they relate to each other? (Antigens are substances that can react with antibodies. Antibodies are substances which can react with antigens which are labeled as "foreign" to the body.)

- What can happen if a patient receives a blood transfusion with a blood type not compatible with her own? (illness and/or death)

- Which type is known as the universal donor? (type O blood)

- What is the universal recipient? (type AB blood)

ELSEVIER

Structure & Function of the Body, 13th ed.

Thibodeau/Patton

Slide 16

- **Rh system**
  - Rh-positive blood
    - Rh factor antigen present in RBCs
  - Rh-negative blood
    - No Rh factor present in RBCs
    - No anti-Rh antibodies present naturally in plasma
    - Anti-Rh antibodies appear in the plasma of Rh-negative people if Rh-positive RBCs have been introduced into their bodies

16

- Where did the term "Rh" come from? (Rh was discovered in a rhesus monkey, thus its name.)

- What is an antigen in blood typing? What is an antibody? (An antigen is a substance that can activate the immune system. An antibody is the substance made in response to the stimulation of an antigen.)

- What happens when many antibodies react with their antigens? (Agglutination can occur and lead to death. Crossmatching of blood is essential to avoid agglutination.)

Slide 17

- **Rh system**
  - **Erythroblastosis fetalis:** May occur when Rh-negative mother carries a second Rh-positive fetus; caused by mother's Rh antibodies reacting with baby's Rh-positive cells

17

- What is the trade name of the protein usually given to all Rh-negative mothers who carry an Rh-positive baby? (RhoGAM)

- What does this protein do? (It stops the mother's body from forming anti-Rh antibodies.)

- Discuss Research, Issues & Trends: Artificial Blood.

12 Lesson Plan
The Circulatory System

TEACHING FOCUS

In this chapter, the student will have the opportunity to discuss the location, size, and position of the heart in the thoracic cavity and identify the heart chambers, sounds, and valves. The student will have the opportunity to trace blood through the heart and compare the functions of the heart chambers on the right and left sides. The student will have the opportunity to explain the relationship between blood vessel structure and function; trace the path of blood through the systemic, pulmonary, hepatic portal, and fetal circulations; and identify the primary factors involved in the generation and regulation of blood pressure.

MATERIALS AND RESOURCES

- ☐ Blood pressure cuff (Lesson 12.2)
- ☐ ECG reading (Lesson 12.1)
- ☐ Model of the heart (Lesson 12.1)
- ☐ Stethoscope (Lesson 12.2)
- ☐ Computer (all Lessons)

LESSON CHECKLIST

Preparations for this lesson include:
- lecture
- demonstration
- guest speaker: an ECG technician, cardiologist, coronary care nurse, nurse practitioner
- student performance evaluation of all entry-level skills required for student comprehension and application of the circulatory system principles including:
  - o the structure and function of the heart and blood vessels
  - o systemic, pulmonary, hepatic portal, and fetal circulations
  - o blood pressure and pulse

KEY TERMS

angina pectoris (p. 307)
apex (p. 302)
arteriole (p. 311)
artery (p. 311)
atrioventricular (AV) valve (p. 305)
atrium (p. 302)
bicuspid valve (p. 305)
blood pressure (p. 325)
capillary (p. 311)
cardiac output (p. 308)
cardiopulmonary resuscitation (CPR) (p. 302)
coronary bypass surgery (p. 307)
coronary circulation (p. 307)
ductus arteriosus (p. 319)
ductus venosus (p. 319)
electrocardiogram (ECG) (p. 310)
endocarditis (p. 302)
endocardium (p. 302)
epicardium (p. 305)
foramen ovale (p. 319)

hepatic portal circulation (p. 317)
mitral valve (p. 305)
myocardial infarction (p. 307)
myocardium (p. 302)
P wave (p. 310)
pacemaker (p. 310)
pericardium (p. 305)
pulmonary circulation (pp. 307, 315)
pulse (p. 326)
Purkinje fibers (p. 310)
QRS complex (p. 310)
semilunar valve (p. 305)
sinoatrial (SA) node (p. 310)
systemic circulation (pp. 307, 315)
T wave (p. 310)
tricuspid valve (p. 305)
umbilical (p. 319)
vein (p. 313)
ventricle (p. 302)

ADDITIONAL RESOURCES

AnimationDirect (Book Companion CD)
Instructor's Electronic Resource (IER) (CD)
PowerPoint slides (CD, Evolve)
Test Bank (Evolve)

Legend

ESLR
EVOLVE Student
Learning Resource

EILR TB
EVOLVE Instructor
Learning Resource
Test Bank

AnimationDirect
on Book Companion
CD

PPT
PowerPoint
Slides

SG
Study
Guide

IRM
Instructor's
Resource Manual

Class Activities are indicated in ***bold italic.***

Structure & Function of the Body, 13th ed.

Thibodeau/Patton

LESSON 12.1

PRETEST

Study Guide questions (select from pp. 134-149)

BACKGROUND ASSESSMENT

Question: What is a cardiac cycle? What takes place during each cardiac cycle?
Answer: The beating of the heart is a regular and rhythmic process. Each complete heartbeat is called a *cardiac cycle* and includes the contraction (systole) and relaxation (diastole) of atria and ventricles. Each cycle takes about 0.8 seconds to complete, if the heart is beating at an average rate of about 72 beats per minute.

Question: What four factors influence blood pressure?
Answer: The factors that affect blood pressure include the volume of blood in the veins and arteries, the strength of each heart contraction, heart rate, and the thickness of blood.

CRITICAL THINKING QUESTION

Mrs. Haas comes to your office for her annual checkup, and you note that her blood pressure is very low. She tells you that her blood pressure has always been a bit low, and that she has been told that low blood pressure is actually a good thing. What should you tell her?
Guidelines: Both high blood pressure and low blood pressure are bad for circulation. High blood pressure may cause rupture of one or more blood vessels. But low blood pressure can also be dangerous; if arterial pressure falls low enough, circulation and life cease. Massive hemorrhage, which dramatically reduces blood pressure, kills in this way. Mrs. Haas needs further evaluation.

OBJECTIVES	CONTENT	TEACHING RESOURCES

Discuss the location, size, and position of the heart in the thoracic cavity, and identify the heart chambers, sounds, and valves.	■ Heart (p. 303)
	
	□ Location, size, and position (p. 302)
	
	□ Anatomy (p. 302)
	
	  – Heart chambers (p. 302)
	
	  – Covering sac or pericardium (p. 305)
	
	  – Heart action (p. 305)
	
	  – Heart valves (p. 305)
	
	□ Heart sounds (p. 305)
		⊠▀ Slides 4-8
		
		▨ Heart questions 2-4, 7, 14, 15, 18, 19, 25, 26 (p. 134)
		
		⚡ Multiple Choice questions 1-9, 38-41; True or False questions 1-13, 59-64; Matching 1-10, 12, 17; Short Answer questions 1-3
		
		◉ Location of the Heart
		
		◉ Chambers of the Heart
		
		Book Resources
		
		Quick Check questions 1-3 (p. 308)
		
		Figure 12-1 The heart (p. 303)
		
		Figure 12-2 An internal view of the heart (p. 304)
		
		Review questions 1-6 (p. 332)
		
		Clear View of the Human Body
		
		Class Activity Using a plastic model of the heart, point to a part of the heart and ask students to identify and describe it.

OBJECTIVES	CONTENT	TEACHING RESOURCES
		Class Activity Distribute to students the diagram of the heart found on p. 166 of the IM, and have them label the structures of the heart.
		Class Activity Have students make flash cards of terms associated with heart anatomy (pp. 302-305), writing terms on one side and definitions on the other. Have pairs of students quiz each other on the terminology.
		Class Activity Have students search the Internet to find additional diagrams of the heart. Keep a list of the Web sites.
Trace blood through the heart and compare the functions of the heart chambers on the right and left sides.	☐ Blood flow through the heart (p. 305) ☐ Blood supply to the heart muscle (p. 307) ☐ Cardiac cycle (p. 307)	Slides 9-15 Blood Vessels: Circulation questions 27-35, 39 (pp. 135-136) Multiple Choice questions 10-15, 42; True or False questions 14-19, 65, 66; Matching questions 14, 19, 20, 31-42; Short Answers question 4 **Book Resources** Figure 12-3 Heart action (p. 306) Figure 12-4 Blood flow through the circulatory system (p. 308) Quick Check question 4 (p. 308) Figure 12-5 Coronary circulation (p. 309) Figure 12-6 Coronary bypass (p. 309) Review questions 7, 8 (p. 332) Clear View of the Human Body *Class Activity Divide the class into groups, one that researches the blood flow through the circulatory system and another that researches coronary circulation. Have them make presentations to the class, using Figures 12-4 and 12-5.* *Class Activity Arrange the class in a circle, and have them act as a part of the heart, describing the blood flow. (e.g., "I am the left ventricle, I have just received the oxygenated blood from the left atrium after it passed through the mitral valve.")*

OBJECTIVES	CONTENT	TEACHING RESOURCES
List the anatomical components of the heart conduction system and discuss the features of a normal electrocardiogram.	□ Conduction system of the heart (p. 310) □ Electrocardiogram (pp. 310, 312)	Slides 16-19 Applying What You Know question 67 (p. 138) Conduction System of the Heart diagram (p. 144) Multiple Choice questions 16-21; True or False questions 21-33; Matching questions 11, 13, 15, 16, 18; Short Answer questions 5-7 **Book Resources** Figure 12-7 Conduction system of the heart (p. 311) Quick Check questions 1, 2 (p. 311) Figure 12-8 Events represented by the electrocardiogram (ECG) (p. 312) Health and Well-Being: Changes in Blood Flow During Exercise (p. 313) Critical Thinking question 17 (p. 332) Review questions 9, 10 (p. 332) *Class Activity Tape several copies of an ECG to the wall in different places throughout the room. Have students go up to the ECGs and analyze them. When they return to their seats, they can compare results. Repeat the process with an ECG that shows different results.* *Class Activity An ECG technician can give a presentation to the class explaining the reasons for this type of testing and answering students' questions.* *Class Activity Distribute to students the diagram of the conduction system of the heart, found on p. 166 of the IM, and have them label the appropriate structures.*

12.1 Homework/Assignments:

12.1 Teacher's Notes:

LESSON 12.2

CRITICAL THINKING QUESTION

Mrs. Owens comes to your office for a visit. Her blood pressure is usually in the normal range. However, last week while she was waiting for a prescription at the local pharmacy, she tested her blood pressure on a machine that was recently installed there and found it to be 145/100 mm Hg. Today, her reading is 120/80 mm Hg. What would account for the different reading?

Guidelines: Of course, it is possible that the machine in Mrs. Owens' pharmacy is not accurate. However, you should also point out to her that no one's blood pressure stays the same all the time, and that it fluctuates even in healthy people. Not only is this fluctuation normal, but the increased blood pressure serves a good purpose; it increases circulation to bring more blood to muscles each minute and supplies them with more oxygen and food for more energy.

OBJECTIVES	CONTENT	TEACHING RESOURCES
Explain the relationship between blood structure and function.	■ Blood vessels (p. 311) □ Types (p. 311) □ Structure (p. 313) □ Functions (p. 315)	Slides 21-24 Blood Vessels—Circulation questions 36-38, 45 (pp. 135-136) Check Your Knowledge question 10 (p. 142) Multiple Choice questions 22-27, 43-44; True or False questions 20, 34-36, 38-40, 67-68; Matching questions 21, 23, 25, 27, 29, 30; Short Answer questions 8, 9 **Book Resources** Figure 12-9 Artery and vein (p. 314) Quick Check questions 1-3 (p. 315) Review questions 11, 12 (p. 332) *Class Activity Have students make flash cards of terms associated with blood vessels (see pp. 311-315), writing definitions of terms on the reverse side of cards. Have pairs of students quiz each other on the terminology.* *Class Activity Have students discuss the effects of arteriosclerosis and atherosclerosis on blood vessels.*
Trace the path of blood through the systemic, pulmonary, hepatic portal, and fetal circulations.	■ Circulation (p. 315) □ Systemic and pulmonary circulation (p. 315) □ Hepatic portal circulation (p. 317) □ Fetal circulation (p. 319)	Slides 25-27 Blood Vessels: Circulation questions 39-43 (p. 136) Check Your Knowledge question 10 (p. 142) Fetal Circulation diagram (p. 145) Hepatic Circulation diagram (p. 146)

ELSEVIER

OBJECTIVES	CONTENT	TEACHING RESOURCES
		E Multiple Choice questions 28-32; True or False questions 37, 41-50; Matching questions 24, 26, 28; Short Answer questions 10-11, 17, 18
		⊙ Pulmonary Circulation
		⊙ Systemic Circulation
		Book Resources
		Figure 12-10 Principal arteries of the body (p. 316)
		Table 12-1 The Major Arteries (p. 317)
		Figure 12-11 Principal veins of the body (p. 318)
		Table 12-2 The Major Veins (p. 319)
		Figure 12-12 Main superficial veins of the arm (p. 320)
		Quick Check questions 1-3 (p. 320)
		Critical Thinking questions 18, 19 (p. 332)
		Review question 13 (p. 332)
		Chapter Test questions 20, 21, 23 (pp. 333-334)
		Class Activity Divide the class into three groups. Assign one the task of describing the systemic and pulmonary circulation; the second, the hepatic portal circulation; the third, the fetal circulation. Have the non-presenting groups critique each presentation.
		Class Activity Have students create mnemonics to help them remember the flow of blood in the body.
		Class Activity Divide the class into two teams: the* major arteries *and the* major veins. *Using Tables 12-1 and 12-2, alternately call out the name of a vein or artery and have the appropriate side come up with the correct tissue supplied by the artery or tissue drained by the vein. Give points for correct answers to determine which team wins.

OBJECTIVES	CONTENT	TEACHING RESOURCES

Identify and discuss the primary factors involved in the generation and regulation of blood pressure, and explain the relationships between these factors.	■ Blood pressure (p. 320)
	  □ Defining blood pressure (p. 320)
	  □ Factors that influence blood pressure (p. 321)
	    – Blood volume (p. 321)
	    – Strength of heart contractions (p. 322)
	    – Heart rate (p. 324)
	    – Blood viscosity (p. 325)
	  □ Fluctuations in blood pressure (p. 325)
	■ Pulse (p. 324)
		⊠▤ Slides 28-30
		
		📖 Blood Pressure: Pulse questions 46-60 (p. 137)
		
		📖 Applying What You Know question 69 (p. 138)
		
		e Multiple Choice questions 28-37; True or False questions 51-57, 69, 70; Matching question 22; Short Answer questions 12-16
		
		Book Resources
		
		Figure 12-13 Diagram of blood flow in the circulatory system (p. 321)
		
		Figure 12-14 Hepatic portal circulation (p. 322)
		
		Figure 12-15 The fetal circulation (p. 323)
		
		Figure 12-16 Pressure gradients in blood flow (p. 324)
		
		Figure 12-17 Vasomotor mechanism (p. 325)
		
		Figure 12-18 Pulse points (p. 326)
		
		Clinical Application: Blood Pressure Readings (p. 327)
		
		Quick Check questions 1-4 (p. 328)
		
		Critical Thinking question 20 (p. 332)
		
		Review questions 14-16 (p. 332)
		
		Chapter Test question 22 (p. 333)
		
		*Class Activity **Have the class practice taking each others' blood pressure and pulse and record the results. Discuss what results are in the normal range and which should be checked. When proficient, have students offer a free blood pressure screening in the community.***
		
		*Class Activity **Ask the class to identify the nine major pulse points on the body and rank them in order of strength.***
		
		*Class Activity **Distribute to students the diagram of normal ECG deflections, found on p. 139 of the IM, and have them label the appropriate structures.***

Thibodeau/Patton

OBJECTIVES	CONTENT	TEACHING RESOURCES
Performance Evaluation		Chapter 12 Computerized Test Bank questions
		Student Assignment (pp. 164-166)
		Student Post-Test questions
		Book Resources
		Review questions (p. 332)
		Chapter Test (p. 333)

12.2 Homework/Assignments:

12.2 Teacher's Notes:

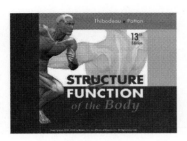

Slide 1

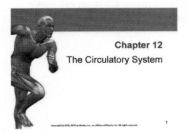

Chapter 12
The Circulatory System

Slide 2

Learning Objectives

- Discuss the location, size, and position of the heart in the thoracic cavity; identify the heart chambers, sounds, and valves
- Trace blood through the heart; compare the functions of the heart chambers on the right and left sides
- List the anatomical components of the heart conduction system; discuss the features of a normal electrocardiogram

Slide 3

Learning Objectives (cont'd.)

- Explain the relationship between blood vessel structure and function
- Trace the path of blood through the systemic, pulmonary, hepatic portal, and fetal circulations
- Identify and discuss the primary factors involved in the generation and regulation of blood pressure, and explain the relationships between these factors

Slide 4

Chapter 12
Lesson 12.1

Slide 5

Heart

- Location, size, position
  - Triangular organ located in mediastinum with two thirds of the mass to the left of the body midline and one third to the right
  - Heart lies between the sternum (in front) and the bodies of the thoracic vertebrae (behind)
  - Cardiopulmonary resuscitation (CPR)

- What part of the heart do healthcare professionals prefer for listening to heart sounds? (apex)

- How does the position of the heart help to make CPR an effective intervention? (Because the heart is located between bony structures, it can be compressed.)

Slide 6

Heart (cont'd.)

- Anatomy
  - Heart chambers
    - Two upper chambers are called *right and left atria* (receiving chambers)
    - Two lower chambers are called *right and left ventricles* (discharging chambers)
    - Wall of each heart chamber is composed of cardiac muscle tissue called *myocardium*
    - **Endocardium:** Smooth lining of heart chambers—inflammation of endocardium is *endocarditis*

- Why are atria called *receiving chambers?* (Peripheral blood returns to the heart and empties into the atria.)

- Why are ventricles referred to as the *discharging chambers* of the heart? (The ventricles pump or *discharge* the blood into vessels.)

- What can happen if the smooth lining of the heart becomes inflamed and abrasive? (A condition called *endocarditis* occurs and predisposes one to the formation of blood clots.)

Slide 7

Heart (cont'd.)

- Covering sac, or pericardium
  - Pericardium is a two-layered fibrous sac with a lubricated space between the two layers
  - Inner layer is the *visceral pericardium,* or *epicardium*
  - Outer layer is the *parietal pericardium*
- Heart action
  - Contraction of the heart is called *systole;* relaxation is *diastole*

- Why is the outer layer of the heart like a loose-fitting sack? (To allow for cardiac movement)

- Why do the two pericardial layers slip against each other without friction? (There is a lubricated space between the two layers.)

ELSEVIER

Thibodeau/Patton

Slide 8

Heart (cont'd.)

- Heart sounds
  - Two distinct heart sounds are in every heartbeat or cycle—"lub-dup".
  - First (lub) sound is caused by the vibration and closure of AV valves during contraction of the ventricles
  - Second (dup) sound is caused by the closure of the semilunar valves during relaxation of the ventricles

8

- Which contracts first, the atria or ventricles? (atria)

- Where do atrial contractions force blood? (into the ventricles)

- Where do ventricular contractions force blood? (The right ventricle forces blood into the pulmonary artery; the left ventricle forces blood into the aorta)

Slide 9

Heart (cont'd.)

- Blood flow through the heart
  - Heart acts as two separate pumps
  - The right atrium and ventricle perform different functions from the left atrium and ventricle

9

- What does the heart muscle (myocardium) require a steady supply of in order to function effectively? (oxygen)

Slide 10

Heart (cont'd.)

- Sequence of blood flow through the heart
  - Venous blood enters the right atrium through the superior and inferior venae cavae
  - Passes from the right atrium through the tricuspid valve to the right ventricle

10

- What are the aorta's first branches? (coronary arteries) *Ask students to think about the reasoning behind the answer. Clue: Structure determines function.*

- What can happen to blood in the aorta that backs up behind the aortic SL valve during ventricular diastole? (The blood can flow into the coronary arteries.)

Slide 11

Heart (cont'd.)

- From the right ventricle blood passes through the pulmonary semilunar valve to the pulmonary artery to the lungs
- Blood moves from the lungs to the left atrium, passing through the bicuspid (mitral) valve to the left ventricle
- Blood in the left ventricle is pumped through the aortic semilunar valve into the aorta and is distributed to the body as a whole

11

- Valves must be "competent," that is, working properly for blood to flow.

Slide 12

Heart (cont'd.)

- Blood supply to the heart muscle
  - Blood, which supplies oxygen and nutrients to the myocardium, flows through the right and left coronary arteries
  - Blockage of blood flow through the coronary arteries is called *myocardial infarction (MI),* or *heart attack*

- What happens to heart muscle cells when a vessel becomes occluded? (The cells become hypoxic, which can lead to an MI.)

- What is the most common cause of death during middle and late adulthood? (heart attack)

Slide 13

Heart (cont'd.)

- **Angina pectoris:** Chest pain caused by inadequate oxygen to the heart
- **Coronary bypass surgery:** Veins from other parts of the body are used to bypass blockages in coronary arteries

- What conditions can disrupt the supply of fresh blood to the heart muscle? (coronary thrombosis and coronary embolism)

- For what does angina pectoris often serve as a warning? (an impending heart attack)

- What is angioplasty? (a procedure in which a device is inserted into a blood vessel to open the channel for blood flow)

Slide 14

Heart (cont'd.)

- Cardiac cycle
  - Heartbeat is regular and rhythmic—each complete beat is called a *cardiac cycle*
  - Each cycle is subdivided into systole (contraction phase) and diastole (relaxation phase)

- How long does each cardiac cycle take to complete, if the heart is beating at an average rate of about 72 beats per minute? (approximately 0.8 seconds)

Slide 15

Heart (cont'd.)

- **Stroke volume:** Volume of blood ejected from one ventricle with each beat
- **Cardiac output:** Amount of blood that one ventricle can pump each minute; average is about 5 L per minute at rest

Slide 16

Heart (cont'd.)

- Conduction system
  - Intercalated disks are electrical connectors that join all the cardiac muscle fibers in a region together so that they receive their impulse, and thus contract, at about the same time
  - **Sinoatrial (SA) node:** The pacemaker located in the wall of the right atrium near the opening of the superior vena cava

- What controls the rate of the cardiac muscle's rhythm? (The autonomic nervous system, the intercalated disks, and the SA node.)

Slide 17

Heart (cont'd.)

- **AV (atrioventricular) node:** Located in the right atrium along the lower part of the interatrial septum
- **AV bundle (bundle of His):** Located in the septum of the ventricle
- **Purkinje fibers:** Located in the walls of the ventricles

- What may physicians implant to treat heart block? (artificial pacemaker)

Slide 18

Heart (cont'd.)

- The visible tracing of these electrical signals is called an *electrocardiogram,* or *ECG*
- A normal ECG has three deflections or waves called the *P wave,* the *QRS complex,* and the *T wave*
  - **P wave:** Associated with depolarization of the ventricles
  - **QRS complex:** Associated with depolarization of the ventricles
  - **T wave:** Associated with repolarization of the ventricles

- To where do the heart's electrical currents spread? (SA node to AV node to bundle of His to purkinje fibers)

- What is an electrocardiogram? (graphic record of heart's electrical activity)

Slide 19

Electrocardiogram

- Specialized conduction system structures generate and transmit the electrical impulses that result in contraction of the heart
- These tiny electrical impulses can be picked up on the surface of the body and transformed into visible tracings by an electrocardiograph

- What does depolarization describe? (describes the electrical activity that triggers contraction of the heart muscle)

- When does repolarization begin? (begins just before the relaxation phase of cardiac muscle activity)

- What do physicians look for in ECG tracings to diagnose heart disease? (P waves, QRS complexes, and T waves)

Slide 20

Chapter 12
Lesson 12.2

20

Slide 21

Blood Vessels

- Types
  - **Arteries:** Carry blood away from the heart into arterioles
  - **Veins:** Carry blood toward the heart
  - **Capillaries:** Carry blood from the arterioles to the venules

21

- What is the largest artery in the body? (aorta)

- What is the difference between the functions of arteries and veins? (Arteries carry oxygenated blood, veins carry deoxygenated blood.)

- Where does the exchange of nutrients and respiratory gases between blood and tissue fluid take place? (capillaries)

Slide 22

Blood Vessels (cont'd.)

- Structure
  - Arteries
    - **Tunica intima:** Inner layer of endothelial cells
    - **Tunica media:** Smooth muscle with some elastic tissue; thick in arteries; important in blood pressure regulation
    - **Tunica adventitia:** Thin layer of elastic tissue

22

- Why is the muscle layer thicker in arteries than in veins? (to maintain blood pressure)

- What feature is present in veins but not in arteries? (valves)

- What is the function of a precapillary sphincter? (controls the amount of blood flow into the capillary)

Slide 23

Blood Vessels (cont'd.)

- **Capillaries:** Microscopic vessels
  - Only layer is the tunica intima
- Veins
  - **Tunica intima:** Inner layer; valves prevent retrograde movement of blood
  - **Tunica media:** Smooth; thin in veins
  - **Tunica adventitia:** Thickest layer in veins

23

- What vessels distribute blood from the heart to capillaries? (arteries and arterioles)

- How do arterioles help keep arterial blood pressure at a normal level? (by constricting or dilating)

ELSEVIER

Thibodeau/Patton

Slide 24

- Functions
    - **Arteries:** Distribute nutrients, gases, etc. with movement of blood under high pressure; assist in maintaining arterial blood pressure
    - **Capillaries:** Serve as exchange vessels for nutrients, wastes, and fluids
    - **Veins:** Collect blood for return to the heart; low-pressure vessels

24

- Why do venules and veins serve as blood reservoirs? (They carry blood that is under low pressure and can expand to hold large volumes of blood.)

- Why are capillaries known as *exchange vessels*? (Exchange of gases and nutrients takes place in the capillaries.)

- What are some of the major arteries? (aorta, carotid, renal, femoral, radial, subclavian)

- What are some of the major veins? (subclavian, femoral, jugular, saphenous)

- Do you see the similarities in some names? (They frequently share names.)

Slide 25

- **Plan of circulation:** refers to the blood flow through the vessels arranged to form a circuit or circular pattern
- Types of circulation
    - Systemic circulation
        - Carries blood throughout the body
        - Path goes from left ventricle through aorta, smaller arteries, arterioles, capillaries, venules, venae cavae, to right atrium

25

- Is the plan of systemic circulation similar in all tissues and organs? (yes)

- In what parts of the body do capillaries host the exchange of nutrients and respiratory gases? (the organ's capillary beds)

Slide 26

- Pulmonary circulation
    - Carries blood to and from the lungs; arteries deliver deoxygenated blood to the lungs for gas exchange
    - Path goes from right ventricle through pulmonary arteries, lungs, pulmonary veins, to left atrium
- Hepatic portal circulation
    - Unique blood route through the liver
    - Vein (hepatic portal vein) exists between two capillary beds
    - Assists with homeostasis of blood glucose levels

26

- What is the function of liver cells in hepatic portal circulation? (maintain homeostasis by storing excess glucose as glycogen and by removing toxins from the blood)

- Why is it important to understand the roles of blood pressure and blood pressure gradient in circulation? (Blood pressure gradients are vitally involved in keeping blood flowing. Gradients are necessary for adequate blood pressures. These pressures ensure that organs are perfused with oxygen and nutrients.)

- What is the function of pulmonary circulation? (to gain oxygen and release carbon dioxide)

- What occurs in hepatic portal circulation? (In hepatic portal circulation, nutrient rich blood flows from the small intestine into the liver.)

Thibodeau/Patton

Slide 27

- Fetal circulation
  - Refers to circulation before birth
  - Modifications required for fetus to efficiently secure oxygen and nutrients from maternal blood
  - Unique structures include the placenta, umbilical arteries and vein, ductus venosus, ductus arteriosus, and foramen ovale

27

- How does the exchange of nutrients and oxygen between fetal and maternal blood occur? (through the placenta)

- What is the role of the *ductus venosus?* (The ductus *venosus* acts like a shunt to allow blood to bypass the immature fetal liver.)

Slide 28

- Blood pressure is the push or force of blood in the blood vessels
- Highest in arteries, lowest in veins
- Blood pressure gradient causes blood to circulate— liquids can flow only from areas of higher pressure to lower pressure

28

- How is the blood pressure gradient for the entire systemic circulation measured? (It is measured by calculating the difference between the average blood pressure in the aorta and the blood pressure at the termination of the vena cava.)

- Why can high blood pressure become a problem in circulation? (High blood pressure can cause the rupture of blood vessels and lead to a stroke.)

- Why can very low blood pressure become a problem in circulation? (With low blood pressure, the organs may not be adequately perfused.)

Slide 29

- Blood volume, heartbeat, and viscosity are main factors that affect blood pressure
- Blood pressure varies within a normal range from time to time
- Venous return of blood to the heart depends on five mechanisms—a strongly beating heart, adequate arterial blood pressure, valves in the veins, pumping action of skeletal muscles as they contract, and changing pressures in the chest cavity caused by breathing

29

- Why is the diameter of the arterioles important? (The diameter determines how much blood can flow into arterioles.)

- What is the relationship between the strength of a heartbeat and blood pressure? (The strength of the heartbeat affects cardiac output which in turn affects blood pressure.)

- What happens if blood is less viscous than normal? (Blood pressure deceases.)

- What happens if blood is more viscous? (Blood pressure increases.)

- What device is used to take blood pressure readings? (sphygmomanometer)

Slide 30

- **Pulse:** alternate expansion and recoil of the blood vessel wall
- Places where you can feel the pulse
  - Superficial temporal artery, facial artery, carotid artery, axillary artery, brachial artery, radial artery, femoral artery, popliteal (posterior to patella), dorsalis pedis

30

- What information can the pulse provide about the heartbeat? (rate, rhythmicity, and strength)

- How many major pulse points are there? (9)

- What are pulse points named after? (named after the associated artery)

- What are the common places to count the pulse? (radial artery, carotid artery)

13 Lesson Plan
The Lymphatic System and Immunity

TEACHING FOCUS

In this chapter, the students will be given the opportunity to learn about the underlying structure and function of the lymphatic system and the concept of immunity. After the relevant organs and their functions are presented, the focus will be on the immune system and the concepts of nonspecific and specific immunity, inherited and acquired immunity, and active and passive immunity. Antibody and complement function are also addressed. Relevant clinical applications to AIDS, allergy, and cancer are also presented.

MATERIALS AND RESOURCES

- ☐ Any anatomical charts, diagrams, or other teaching materials (model of the human body) (all Lessons)
- ☐ Instruction sheet from pregnancy test kit (Lesson 13.2)
- ☐ Lymphangiograms (Lesson 13.1)
- ☐ Computer (all Lessons)

LESSON CHECKLIST

Preparations for this lesson include:

- lecture, discussion
- demonstration
- student performance evaluation of all entry-level skills required for student comprehension and application of lymphatic system and immunity principles including:
  - ○ the structure of the lymphatic system
  - ○ the processes of the immune system and the differences between specific and nonspecific immunity
  - ○ the functions of immune system molecules and cells

KEY TERMS

adenoids (p. 342)
afferent (p. 339)
AIDS (p. 352)
antibodies (p. 346)
antibody-mediated (humoral) immunity
   (p. 346)
antigen (p. 346)
B cells (lymphocytes) (p. 349)
cell-mediated immunity (p. 353)
cisterna chyli (p. 339)
clone (p. 350)
complement (p. 347)
complement cascade (p. 347)
complement-binding sites (p. 347)
efferent (p. 340)
humoral immunity (p. 346)
immune system (p. 344)
inflammatory response (p. 344)
innate immunity (p. 344)
interferon (p. 349)
lingual tonsils (p. 342)

lymph (p. 338)
lymphatic system (p. 337)
lymph nodes (p. 339)
lymphatic vessels (p. 338)
lymphocytes (p. 349)
macrophages (p. 349)
memory cells (p. 352)
monoclonal antibodies (p. 348)
nonspecific immunity (p. 344)
palatine tonsils (p. 342)
phagocytes (p. 346)
pharyngeal tonsils (p. 342)
plasma cells (p. 352)
right lymphatic duct (p. 339)
specific immunity (p. 345)
spleen (p. 342)
T cells (lymphocytes) (p. 342)
thoracic duct (p. 339)
thymus (p. 341)
thymosins (p. 342)
tonsils (p. 342)

ADDITIONAL RESOURCES

AnimationDirect (Book Companion CD)
Instructor's Electronic Resource (IER) (CD)
PowerPoint slides (CD, Evolve)
Test Bank (Evolve)

Legend					
ESLR EVOLVE Student Learning Resource	**EILR TB** EVOLVE Instructor Learning Resource Test Bank	**AnimationDirect** on Book Companion CD	**PPT** PowerPoint Slides	**SG** Study Guide	**IRM** Instructor's Resource Manual

Class Activities are indicated in ***bold italic***.

Structure & Function of the Body, 13th ed.
Thibodeau/Patton

LESSON 13.1

PRETEST

Study Guide Multiple Choice questions 1-10 (pp. 159-160)

BACKGROUND ASSESSMENT

Question: Why does a physician check a person's lymph nodes? What is the physician looking for?
Answer: During both a routine physical examination and a visit prompted by an illness, the physician will check the size of the lymph nodes. If the lymph nodes are swollen beyond their normal size, this is an indication that the body is fighting an infection. Careful palpation of the lymph nodes can alert the physician to the presence of disease.

Question: What is an allergy, and how are allergies related to the immune system?
Answer: An allergy is a hypersensitivity of the immune system to antigens found in the environment, such as pollen, dust mites, or animal dander. These antigens are not irritating to most people, but people with allergies to specific antigens have an antigen–antibody reaction that triggers the release of histamine and other inflammatory substances. This causes the characteristic symptoms—such as runny nose, nasal congestion, conjunctivitis, or hives—often associated with allergies.

CRITICAL THINKING QUESTION

What would happen in the human body if there were no lymphatic system?
Guidelines: The lymphatic system is very similar to the circulatory system, except instead of bringing nutrients and oxygen to the tissues of the body, the lymphatic system filters out particles in the blood, including foreign invaders such as microorganisms and cancerous cells, and then attacks them. If these microorganisms were allowed to continue to flow through the circulatory system, they could proliferate and cause or spread disease. Without the lymph nodes to filter out and annihilate cancerous cells, cancers would be allowed to spread (metastasize) throughout the entire body. Just as the skin is the body's first line of defense, the lymphatic system combats invaders that have already gained access to the bloodstream and tissues.

OBJECTIVES	CONTENT	TEACHING RESOURCES
Describe the generalized functions of the lymphatic system, and list the primary lymphatic structures.	■ The lymphatic system (p. 337) □ Lymph and lymph vessels (p. 337) □ Lymph nodes (p. 339) – Defense function: biological filtration (p. 339) □ Thymus (p. 341) □ Tonsils (p. 342) □ Spleen (p. 342)	Slides 4-14 The Lymphatic System questions 1-8 (p. 152) Thymus, Tonsils, Spleen questions 9-15 (p. 152) Multiple Choice questions 1-13, 33-36; True or False questions 1-20, 51-56; Matching questions 1-10; Short Answer questions 1-7 Critical Thinking questions 15, 16 (p. 176); Classroom Application questions 1-5 (pp. 176-177); Lab Activities 1-4 (p. 177) Lymph and Lymph Vessels Lymph Node Spleen

ELSEVIER

Copyright © 2008, 2005 by Mosby, Inc., an affiliate of Elsevier Inc.

OBJECTIVES	CONTENT	TEACHING RESOURCES
		Book Resources
		Figure 13-1 The lymphatic system (p. 338)
		Figure 13-2 Role of lymphatic system in fluid homeostasis (p. 339)
		Figure 13-3 Lymph node structure and function (p. 340)
		Figure 13-4 Lymph node structure and function (p. 341)
		Figure 13-5 Lymphangiogram (p. 342)
		Figure 13-6 Lymphatic drainage of the breast (p. 343)
		Figure 13-7 Location of the tonsils (p. 341)
		Review questions 1-7 (p. 358)
		Critical Thinking questions 15, 16 (p. 358)
		Clear View of the Human Body
		▶ Discuss Health and Well-Being: Effects of Exercise on Immunity (p. 340). Take an informal poll to see if students who exercise regularly suffer fewer colds or other infections.
		▶ Discuss why nearby lymph nodes are often removed during treatment for breast cancer.
		Class Activity Have students work together in groups of two to three. Ask them to name as many organs of the lymphatic system as they can and write them down. One person acts as resource person and should prompt the other members for any organ listings that have been left out based on the information in Figure 13-1 (p. 338). Afterward, have students try to locate the organs on the diagram of the human body, found on p. 169 of the SG. Have the resource person check the accuracy by consulting Figure 13-1 in the text and confirm or correct the group's response.
		Class Activity Have student groups list differences and similarities between lymphatic capillaries and blood capillaries. How do their differences in structure relate to their functions?
Discuss and compare nonspecific and specific immunity, inherited and	■ The immune system (p. 344) □ Function of the immune system (p. 344) □ Nonspecific immunity (p. 344)	Slides 15-22 The Immune System questions 16-20 (p. 142)

Thibodeau/Patton

OBJECTIVES	CONTENT	TEACHING RESOURCES
acquired immunity, and active and passive immunity.	☐ Specific immunity (p. 345)	*e* Multiple Choice questions 14-20, 37; True/False questions 21-31, 57-59; Matching questions 11, 15, 17, 19; Short Answer question 8

Book Resources

Table 13-1 Specific Immunity (p. 345)

Review Questions 8-10 (p. 358)

▸ Discuss Clinical Application: Allergy (p. 343). Explain the antigen-antibody reaction that occurs with allergies. What symptoms does this reaction cause? Under what circumstances might someone expect to encounter anaphylactic shock in the physician's practice?

▸ Discuss Figure 13-8: Inflammatory Response (p. 344). What happens in terms of the inflammatory response when a cut gets infected? What is responsible for the characteristic signs of inflammation?

▸ Discuss the pros and cons of administering substances that confer artificial passive immunity. Under what circumstances might it be a desirable option?

Class Activity Working in groups of two to three people and referencing Table 13-1 (p. 345), have teams list at least one example for each of the following: **innate immunity, natural acquired immunity, active acquired immunity, passive acquired immunity, artificial active immunity,** *and* **artificial passive immunity.**

Class Activity Have student teams list various techniques for inducing artificial immunity. Explain the principle on which each is based.

Class Activity Have students explore the controversies surrounding the administration of immunizations. What is important for a healthcare worker to know? How would one address patients' concerns?

Class Activity Have students work in small groups and prepare a table to compare allergies and colds. They should list allergies and colds horizontally in the table. At the top of the table, write **Cause, Organs (or Structures) Involved, Lymph Node Involvement, Symptoms,** *and* **Treatment** *as column headers. Fill out the table. Under* **Cause,** *and be sure to note if the cause is*

Thibodeau/Patton

OBJECTIVES	CONTENT	TEACHING RESOURCES
		bacterial, viral, or environmental. If lymph nodes are involved, state which lymph nodes. For the treatments listed, indicate if the treatment will "cure" the disorder or simply alleviate symptoms. For symptoms that are the same for both conditions, indicate what other factors should be considered in order to make the correct diagnosis.

13.1 Homework/Assignments:

13.1 Teacher's Notes:

LESSON 13.2

CRITICAL THINKING QUESTION

A patient being treated for AIDS comes to the office for a follow-up visit. The patient tested positive for the disease several months ago but has had no real symptoms of the disease up to this time. At the last visit, the physician prescribed a "cocktail" of several antiviral drugs. When asked about his compliance with the drug regimen, the patient replies that he has stopped taking the drugs, because he does not feel bad and does not think he needs the drugs. How would you explain to the patient the importance of taking the prescribed medication?

Guidelines: Explain to the patient that although he does not have any symptoms of the disease, a blood test has verified that the virus is indeed present. Some individuals show no symptoms for months or even years. These individuals are fortunate, because their immune systems are strong enough to hold infection at bay for this period of time. However, the disease is still present in the body, and it is important to combat it before it takes over and causes symptoms. This is why the physician has prescribed certain drugs to take, even though the patient does not feel ill. Studies have shown that certain drugs can further inhibit the disease by blocking reproduction of the virus in the infected cells. Other drugs can greatly reduce the number of viruses circulating in the blood. In any case, instruct the patient to always call the office before he stops taking any prescribed drugs. The physician can answer any questions or prescribe another drug if the patient is experiencing severe side effects. Also, some drugs should not be stopped abruptly. The body needs to be weaned gradually away from some medications, or severe side effects could result. The physician is the best person to advise the patient about his condition and the drugs he is taking. A pharmacist can also provide advice about prescription medications.

OBJECTIVES	CONTENT	TEACHING RESOURCES
Discuss the major types of immune system molecules and indicate how antibodies and complements function.	■ Immune system molecules (p. 346) ☐ Antibodies (p. 346) – Definition (p. 346) – Functions (p. 344) ☐ Complement proteins (p. 347)	Slides 24-27 Immune System Molecules questions 21-35 (p. 153) Multiple Choice questions 21-25, 38; True or False questions 32-39, 60; Matching questions 12, 14, 20; Short Answer questions 9, 10 **Book Resources** Figure 13-9 Antibody function (p. 346) Figure 13-10 Complement cascade (p. 347) Quick Check questions 1, 2 (p. 348) Review questions 11, 12 (p. 358) ▶ Discuss Research, Issues and Trends: Monoclonal Antibodies (p. 348). Explain monoclonal antibodies and their significance for medical applications. ▶ Discuss where complement proteins are found and how they work to combat foreign cells. What is a *complement cascade?*

OBJECTIVES	CONTENT	TEACHING RESOURCES
		▶ Discuss the two defining characteristics of antibodies. How do antibodies produce humoral, or antibody-mediated, immunity? ▶ Discuss the following situation: a patient has been living in the same area for almost three years. She has never had any allergies. This autumn, she suddenly has developed allergic symptoms, and her physician suspects she has allergies. Based on what students have learned, have them explain why she has developed allergies now and not when she first moved to the area three years ago. *Class Activity* **Have students write down the steps in performing a tuberculin tine test. What exactly is injected under the skin? When can the result be obtained? Explain the possible test results in terms of immune response. What is the significance of a positive result? A negative result? Does this test tell you if the patient has tuberculosis?**
Discuss and contrast the development and functions of B and T cells.	■ Immune system cells (p. 348) ☐ Phagocytes (p. 349) ☐ Lymphocytes (p. 349) – Development of B cells (p. 349) – Function of B cells (p. 352) – Development of T cells (p. 353) – Functions of T cells (p. 353)	Slides 28-36 Immune System Cells questions 36-57 (pp. 153-155) *e* Multiple Choice questions 26-32, 39; True or False questions 40-50, 61-65; Matching questions 13, 16, 18; Short Answer questions 11-13 **Book Resources** Figure 13-11 Phagocytosis (p. 350) Figure 13-12 B-cell development (p. 351) Figure 13-13 T-cell development (p. 353) Figure 13-14 T cells (p. 353) Figure 13-15 T-cell function (p. 354) Quick Check questions 1-4 (p. 354) Review questions 13, 14 (p. 358) ▶ Discuss the two primary cells of the immune system. Which are most numerous? Explain how macrophages act to combat foreign bodies. (pp. 346-349) ▶ Discuss Clinical Application: Interferon (p. 349). What is interferon and what is its function? In which cells of the body is it produced? Why is the synthesis of human interferon for clinical use so important?

OBJECTIVES	CONTENT	TEACHING RESOURCES
		Class Activity Break into teams to discuss Clinical Application: AIDS (p. 320). Explain the growing problem of AIDS and identify patients at risk. Have teams list strategies for controlling the spread of AIDS. Discuss current drug regimens and the rationale behind their use. Why do some infected people not show any signs of the disease for years? Why is development of a vaccine for AIDS so difficult?
		Class Activity Ask students to work together in small groups. Both B cells and T cells are important lymphocytes that develop from stem cells. Stem cell research is a controversial topic today. List the pros and cons of allowing stem cell research. What role does stem cell research play in the search for cures for diseases? Stage a small debate between student teams to argue the pros and cons of stem cell research, with students taking sides according to their assessment of the issue.
Compare and contrast humoral and cell-mediated immunity.	■ Immune system cells (p. 348) □ Phagocytes (p. 349) □ Lymphocytes (p. 349) – Development of B cells (p. 349) – Function of B cells (p. 352) – Development of T cells (p. 353) – Functions of T cells (p. 353)	⊠ Slide 37 ▶ Discuss the two major types of lymphocytes (pp. 349-353). How does the function of B cells contribute to humoral immunity? How do T cells produce cell-mediated immunity? *Class Activity Divide the class into small groups. Chart the life cycle of B cells (Figure 13-12, p. 351). Make a chart that briefly outlines Figure 13-13 (p. 353) on the development of T cells.* *Class Activity Working in small groups, have students choose one immunization and describe artificial active immunity in terms of the following: What agents (live or dead pathogens or their components, toxins, etc.) are commonly used to produce artificially acquired active immunity? Make a diagram of how the process of artificially acquired active immunity works (i.e., What happens first after immunization? What blood components or cell types are involved? How long will immunity last?) Have each group choose a different immunization. After each group has completed this analysis, have them report their findings to the rest of the class. Stress what component is used to make the vaccine, and compare and contrast the periods of immunity achieved by various immunizations. Which immunizations are more likely to evoke an allergic response and why?*

ELSEVIER

Structure & Function of the Body, 13th ed.

Thibodeau/Patton

OBJECTIVES	CONTENT	TEACHING RESOURCES
Performance Evaluation		*e* Chapter 13 Computerized Test Bank questions
		Student Assignment (pp. 178-181)
		e Student Post-Test questions
		Book Resources
		Review questions (p. 358)
		Chapter Test (pp. 358-359)

13.2 Homework/Assignments:

As a homework assignment, the students can research the development of the smallpox vaccine by Edward Jenner. A short paper can be written to explain the concept behind vaccination. This is also a topic of current relevance to homeland security.

In preparation for the debate class activity for the second objective in Lesson 13.2, students can be assigned to research the issue of using stem cells for research purposes. They should be able to support their positions factually for the debate.

13.2 Teacher's Notes:

ELSEVIER
Copyright © 2008, 2005 by Mosby, Inc., an affiliate of Elsevier Inc.

Structure & Function of the Body, 13th ed.
Thibodeau/Patton

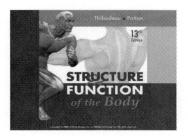

Slide 1

Chapter 13
The Lymphatic System
and Immunity

Slide 2

Learning Objectives

- Describe the generalized functions of the lymphatic system and list the primary lymphatic structures
- Discuss and compare nonspecific and specific immunity, inherited and acquired immunity, and active and passive immunity
- Discuss the major types of immune system molecules and indicate how antibodies and complements function
- Discuss and contrast the development and functions of B and T cells
- Compare and contrast humoral and cell-mediated immunity

Slide 3

Chapter 13
Lesson 13.1

Slide 4

The Lymphatic System

• Lymph
  ▪ Fluid in the tissue spaces that carries protein molecules and other substances back to the blood

• Many substances that cannot enter the capillary walls of blood vessels, such as protein molecules and excess fluid, are returned to the bloodstream as lymph.

• Lymph is a specialized fluid that, like blood, flows through its own elaborate set of lymphatic vessels.

Slide 5

The Lymphatic System (cont'd.)

• Functions of the lymphatic system
  ▪ Allows exchange of substances, such as excess fluid and protein molecules, that cannot occur in the capillary beds
  ▪ Filters out harmful substances from the lymph before returning it to the blood
  ▪ Acts as sewer system of the body

• Primary function of the lymphatic system is to return tissue fluid, proteins, fats, and other substances to the circulatory system.

• What is the role of lymph nodes in the spread of cancer? (Nodes attempt to filter out cancer cells. However, if cancer cells have entered the nodes, this means that the cancer has left the site of origin and has entered the vascular system.)

• What is lymph? (Lymph is specialized fluid formed in tissue spaces.)

• How does lymph form? (Formed from filtration of blood plasma, becomes tissue fluid, then enters the lymphatic system.)

• What role do tonsils play in preventing the spread of infection to the lower respiratory tract? (Tonsils can trap microbes and keep them from entering the lower respiratory tract.)

Slide 6

The Lymphatic System (cont'd.)

• Lymphatic vessels
  ▪ One-way only movement of lymph through lymphatic vessel capillaries
  ▪ **Lymphatic vessel capillaries:** Tiny blind-ended tubes distributed in tissue spaces
    □ Microscopic in size
    □ Sheet consisting of one cell layer of simple squamous epithelium
    □ Poor "fit" between adjacent cells results in porous walls
    □ Called *lacteals* in the intestinal wall (for fat transportation)

• Lymphatic vessels may have the appearance of a string of beads due to the presence of numerous valves that assure one-way flow of lymph through the vessel.

• Ask students to compare and contrast the structure of the lymphatic vessels with those of the circulatory system.

• What is interstitial fluid? (tissue fluid formed from blood plasma)

Slide 7

The Lymphatic System (cont'd.)

Role of Lymphatic System in Fluid Homeostasis

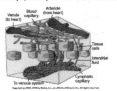

• Point out the relatively larger size of the lymphatic capillary in comparison to the blood capillary.

• What happens to fluid from blood plasma that is not resorbed by blood vessels? (It drains into the lymphatic vessels.)

• Lymphatic drainage prevents accumulation of excess fluid in the tissues. If lymph drainage is impaired, it results in a condition called *lymphedema.*

ELSEVIER

Slide 8

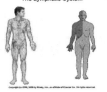

The Lymphatic System (cont'd.)

- Lymphatic vessels
  - Right lymphatic duct
    - Drains lymph from the right upper extremity and right side of the head, neck, and upper torso
  - Thoracic duct
    - Largest lymphatic vessel
    - **Cisterna chyli:** an enlarged pouch along the course of the lymphatic vessels in the abdomen
    - Drains lymph from about three quarters of the body

8

- Lymph flows from the small lymphatic venules to progressively larger lymphatic veins and finally to one of two ducts, depending on the position in the body.
- These are the only two ducts that drain lymph from the body.

Slide 9

The Lymphatic System (cont'd.)

The Lymphatic System

9

- Which lymphatic duct drains most of the body? (thoracic duct)
- What is the function of the cisterna chyli? (a pouchlike structure that serves as a storage for lymph moving to enter the venous system.)
- What are lacteals? Lymphatic capillaries in the walls of the small intestines.

Slide 10

The Lymphatic System (cont'd.)

- Lymph nodes
  - Filter lymph
  - Located in clusters along the pathways of lymphatic vessels
  - Functions include defense and WBC formation
  - Flow of lymph
    - To node via several afferent lymph vessels
    - From node by a single efferent lymph vessel

10

- Why are lymph nodes often removed during surgery for breast cancer? (To examine them for the spread of the cancer.)
- What are the consequences of removal of regional lymph nodes in breast cancer therapy? (possibility of lymphedema)
- Afferent = "to carry forward"
- Efferent = "to carry away"

Slide 11

The Lymphatic System (cont'd.)

Lymph Node Structure and Function

11

- Note the afferent lymph vessels and single efferent lymph vessel.
- What is the inset diagram showing? (how the lymph nodes prevent local infection from spreading)
- Remember the action of the tonsils.

ELSEVIER

Structure & Function of the Body, 13th ed.

Thibodeau/Patton

Slide 12

The Lymphatic System (cont'd.)

- **Thymus:** Lymphoid tissue organ located in mediastinum
  - Total weight of 35 to 40 g (a little more than an ounce)
  - Plays a vital and central role in immunity
  - Produces T lymphocytes, or T cells
  - Secretes hormones called *thymosins*
  - In adults, lymphoid tissue is largely replaced by fat and connective tissue in the process called *involution*

12

- Thymosins stimulate the development of what? (T lymphocytes, T cells)
- What function do T cells perform? (critical to functioning of the immune system)
- What would you expect the course of therapy to be if a baby were born without a thymus gland? (The baby would be treated as an immunosuppressed patient at risk for infections.)

Slide 13

The Lymphatic System (cont'd.)

- Tonsils
  - Composed of three masses of lymphoid tissue around the openings of the mouth and throat
    - Palatine tonsils ("the tonsils")
    - Pharyngeal tonsils (adenoids)
    - Lingual tonsils
  - Subject to chronic infection
  - Enlargement of pharyngeal tonsils may impair breathing

13

- Where is each type of tonsil located? (palatine—throat; pharyngeal—nasal cavity; linguinal—near base of tongue)
- Why would you try to avoid removal of the tonsils if at all possible? (They trap harmful microorganisms.)
- What may be some reasons to remove them? (chronic infection or difficulty breathing)

Slide 14

The Lymphatic System (cont'd.)

- Spleen
  - Largest lymphoid organ in body
  - Located in upper left quadrant of abdomen
  - Often injured by trauma to abdomen
  - Surgical removal called *splenectomy*
  - Functions include phagocytosis of bacteria and old RBCs; acts as a blood reservoir

14

- How much blood can the spleen contain? (about 500 mL of blood)
- What does the spleen salvage from RBC hemoglobin and store for future use? (iron)
- What are the consequences of splenectomy? (impaired immune system)

Slide 15

The Immune System

- Functions of the immune system
  - Protects the body from pathologic bacteria, foreign tissue cells, and cancerous cells
  - Made up of specialized cells and molecules

15

- How does the the immune system differ from most other systems of the body? (It is made up of cells and molecules rather than organs.)

Thibodeau/Patton

Slide 16

The Immune System (cont'd.)

- Nonspecific immunity
  - **Skin:** Mechanical barrier to bacteria and other harmful agents
  - **Tears and mucus:** Wash eyes and trap and kill bacteria
  - Inflammation
    - □ Attracts immune cells to site of injury, increases local blood flow, increases vascular permeability
    - □ Promotes movement of WBCs to site of injury or infection

16

- What is an example of a nonspecific form of immunity? (phagocytosis of bacteria by WBCs)
- What can you do to prevent the spread of infection that involves the body's first line of defense? (careful and frequent handwashing)

Slide 17

The Immune System (cont'd.)

- Inflammatory Response
  - Inflammation is a generalized response to an invader, such as bacteria that are causing tissue damage
  - This triggers release of factors from immune cells
  - The presence of immune factors attracts WBCs
  - Factors also cause increased blood flow (site becomes warm and reddened) and increased vascular permeability (site swells with associated discomfort)
  - These immune factor-mediated changes help phagocytic WBCs reach the site and enter the affected tissue

17

- Describe what happens when a cut gets infected. (Inflammatory response is activated and WBC appear.)
- What causes the swelling? (increased blood flow and increased vascular permeability)
- What causes the redness? (increased blood flow)
- What causes the discomfort? (swelling and tissue damage)

Slide 18

The Immune System (cont'd.)

Inflammatory Response

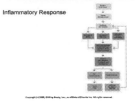

18

- What function do the mediators perform? (attract WBCs to the area)
- What causes inflammation? (tissue damage) And what are some characteristic signs? (redness, pain, heat, and swelling)

Slide 19

The Immune System (cont'd.)

- Specific Immunity
  - Ability of body to recognize, respond to, and remember harmful substances or bacteria

19

- Specific immunity involves memory—the second time a person is exposed to the offending organism, no symptoms occur, because the organism is quickly recognized and destroyed.

ELSEVIER

Slide 20

The Immune System (cont'd.)

• Inherited or inborn immunity
    ▪ Inherited immunity to certain diseases
      from birth

20

• What are examples of inherited immunity? (humans are immune to many animal diseases, such as the distemper virus)

Slide 21

The Immune System (cont'd.)

• Acquired immunity
    ▪ Natural immunity occurs when exposure to
      causative agent is not deliberate
        ▫ **Active:** Active disease produces immunity
        ▫ **Passive:** Immunity passes from mother to
          fetus through placenta or from mother to
          child through mother's milk

21

• Ask the students for examples of active immunity. (after contracting childhood diseases such as measles)

• How long is passive immunity effective after birth? (approximately 3-6 months)

• Which immunity lasts longer—active immunity or passive immunity? (active)

Slide 22

The Immune System (cont'd.)

• Acquired immunity
    ▪ Artificial immunity occurs when exposure to
      causative agent is deliberate
        ▫ **Active:** Vaccination results in immunity
        ▫ **Passive:** Protective material developed in
          another individual's immune system and
          given to previously nonimmune individual

22

• What is an example of active acquired artificial immunity? (immunization)

• What is an example of passive acquired artificial immunity? (injection of gamma globulin)

• What are the pros and cons of passive artificial immunity, and in what situations is it likely to be used? (Passive artificial immunity is helpful as direct antibodies are provided and they act immediately; however the immunity is short term. These direct antibodies can be given in cases of hepatitis exposure.)

Slide 23

Chapter 13
Lesson 13.2

23

Structure & Function of the Body, 13th ed.

Thibodeau/Patton

Slide 24

- Antibodies are specific to their antigens.

Slide 25

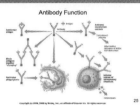
- Antibodies can bind to antigens and disable them via several methods:

  - Invader is inactivated by becoming part of the antigen-antibody complex.

  - Invading cells may clump together as a result of combination with antibody, making them easier for arriving macrophages or other phagocytic cells to destroy.

  - Antibodies may promote phagocytosis by helping phagocytic cells attach to the invader.

  - Complement cascade: inflammation occurs, WBCs are attracted, and cell destruction results.

Slide 26

- Complement fixation: Shape of antibody may be slightly altered when it binds to an antigen or foreign cell.

  - This exposes two hidden regions on the antibody called *complement-binding sites*.

  - A doughnut-shaped assemblage is formed by the combination of antibody, antigen, plasma membrane, and complement molecules. This initiates a series of events that kill the invading cell.

  - Annihilation of the invader is accomplished by drilling holes in the plasma membrane, allowing sodium to diffuse into the cell. Water follows by osmosis, and the cell literally bursts.

Thibodeau/Patton

Slide 27

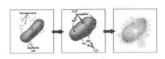

- Complement fixation:
- Complement molecules are activated by antibodies and form doughnut-shaped complexes in the plasma membrane of a bacterium.
- Holes are drilled in the complement complex that allow sodium in, and then, by osmosis, water.
- The swollen complex bursts under increased water pressure.

Slide 28

Immune System Cells

- **Phagocytes:** Ingest and destroy foreign cells or other harmful substances via phagocytosis
  - Types
    - Neutrophils
    - Monocytes
    - Macrophages
      - Kupffer's cells
      - Dust cells

- Where do phagocytes and lymphocytes originate? (from bone marrow cells)
- When do phagocytes wander out of the blood and into the tissue? (in response to infection)
- What do monocytes develop into once they enter tissues? (macrophages)

Slide 29

Immune System Cells (cont'd.)

- Lymphocytes
  - Most numerous of immune system cells
  - Development of B cells
    - Primitive stem cells migrate from bone marrow and go through two stages of development

- How many lymphocytes are in the body? (several million)
- Where are dense populations of lymphocytes found? (in the lymph nodes, spleen, thymus, and liver, but also found in all body fluids)
- What are lymphocytes responsible for? (antibody production)

Slide 30

Immune System Cells (cont'd.)

- Development of B Cells
  - Stage 1
    - Stem cells develop into immature B cells
      - Immature B cells are small lymphocytes; each synthesizes highly specific antibody molecules in their plasma membranes
    - Migrate via the bloodstream chiefly to lymph nodes
    - Become seed cells in the lymph nodes
    - Undergo mitosis to make clones of themselves containing their specific antibody

- What is an important source of stem cells? (Bone marrow)
- What is the role of bone marrow transplants in cancer treatments? (Bone marrow transplants are being used for patients with leukemia and other aplastic conditions. The hope is that the new bone marrow will grow and replace the existing defective marrow.)

Thibodeau/Patton

Slide 31

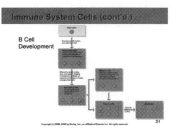

Immune System Cells (cont'd.)

B Cell
Development

- What is a clone? (an identical duplication of a cell)

Slide 32

Immune System Cells (cont'd.)

- Development of B Cells
  - Stage 2
    - Immature B cell develops into activated B cell if it comes in contact with its specific antigen
    - B cell is activated by antigens binding to its surface antibodies
    - Activated B cell divides repeatedly, forming two clones of cells:
      - Plasma cells
      - Memory cells

- What is the function of plasma cells? (to produce antibodies)
- What is the function of memory cells? (to "remember" [recognize] an antigen)

Slide 33

Immune System Cells (cont'd.)

- Function of B Cells
  - Humoral immunity
    - Activated B cells develop into plasma cells
    - Plasma cells secrete antibodies into the blood
    - Circulating antibodies produce humoral immunity

- What is the significance of the development of monoclonal antibody techniques? (The ability to develop monoclonal antibodies has been compared in importance to genetic engineering. As a result of these techniques, extremely pure antibodies against specific disease-causing agents have been developed.)

Slide 34

Immune System Cells (cont'd.)

- Development of T Cells
  - Stage 1
    - Stem cells from bone marrow migrate to thymus gland
    - Stem cells develop into T cells several months before and after birth
    - T cells have protein molecules on their cytoplasmic membrane shaped to bind to only one kind of antigen
    - T cells migrate from thymus chiefly to lymph nodes, liver, and spleen
  - Stage 2
    - Occurs only if a specific antigen binds to T cells' surface proteins
    - T cells develop into sensitized T cells

Thibodeau/Patton

Slide 35

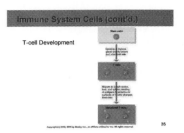

- When does a T cell become sensitized? (when it meets its specific antigen)

Slide 36

Immune System Cells (cont'd.)

- Functions of T Cells
  - Provide cell-mediated immunity
  - Kill invading cells directly by releasing a substance that poisons cells
  - Release chemicals that attract and activate macrophages to kill cells by phagocytosis

- What happens when T-cell function is impaired? (Immunity is compromised.)

- Describe the effect of AIDS on T cells. (AIDS invades T cells and renders them useless.)

- What is interferon? What is its clinical significance? (Interferon is a substance that provides immunity from viral infections. Synthetic interferon is used to decease the severity of many virus-related diseases including chickenpox, measles, and hepatitis C.)

Slide 37

Humoral vs. Cell-mediated Immunity

- Humoral immunity
  - Immunity conferred by the action of antibodies
  - Activated B cells → plasma cells and memory cells
- Cell-mediated immunity
  - Immunity conferred by the action of cells
  - Sensitized T cells
  - Kill invading cells directly by releasing lymphotoxin or releasing lymphokines that attract and activate macrophages to kill cells by phagocytosis

- What is antibody-mediated immunity? (resistance to disease organisms as a result of circulating antibodies)

- What is cell-mediated immunity? (resistance to disease organisms as a result of actions of cells)

ELSEVIER

Structure & Function of the Body, 13th ed.

Thibodeau/Patton

TEACHING FOCUS

In this chapter, students will have the opportunity to learn the generalized functions of the respiratory system and will be introduced to the major respiratory organs and their functions. The process of respiration is explained in terms of the exchange of gases that occurs during internal and external respiration. The volumes of air exchanged during pulmonary ventilation and the regulators of respiration are discussed.

MATERIALS AND RESOURCES

- ☐ Anatomical charts, diagrams, or other teaching materials (model of the human body) (Lesson 14.1)
- ☐ Blue and red cards (Lesson 14.2)
- ☐ Chest x-ray (Lesson 14.1)
- ☐ Microscopes and tissue slides or PowerPoint presentation with tissue sections (Lesson 14.1)

- ☐ Slides of healthy and diseased respiratory mucosa, or PowerPoint presentation of same (Lesson 14.1)
- ☐ Spirometers (Lesson 14.2)
- ☐ Spirometer tracings demonstrating various disease states (Lesson 14.2)
- ☐ Computer (all Lessons)

LESSON CHECKLIST

Preparations for this lesson include:

- lecture
- demonstration
- guest speaker: a nurse or other healthcare professional, speaker from a smoke-enders group.
- student performance evaluation of all entry-level skills required for student comprehension of
  - ○ the generalized functions of the respiratory system
  - ○ the major organs of the respiratory system
  - ○ the mechanisms responsible for the exchange of gases during internal and external respiration
  - ○ the volumes of air exchanged during pulmonary ventilation
  - ○ mechanisms that regulate respiration

KEY TERMS

adenoids (p. 366)
air distributor (p. 359)
alveolar ducts (p. 370)
alveolar sacs (p. 370)
alveoli (p. 370)
aortic body (p. 382)
apnea (p. 384)
bronchi (p. 370)
bronchioles (p. 370)
carbaminohemoglobin (p. 379)
carotid body (p. 382)
chemoreceptors (p. 382)
conchae (p. 365)
diaphragm (p. 376)
dyspnea (p. 384)
epiglottis (p. 368)
eupnea (p. 384)
eustachian (auditory) tube (p. 366)
expiration (pp. 374, 376)
expiratory center (p. 379)

expiratory muscles (p. 376)
expiratory reserve volume (ERV) (p. 380)
external nares (p. 365)
external respiration (p. 374)
gas exchanger (p. 361)
glottis (p. 368)
Heimlich maneuver (p. 384)
homeostatic mechanism (p. 361)
hyperventilation (p. 384)
hypoventilation (p. 384)
inspiration (pp. 374, 376)
inspiratory center (p. 382)
inspiratory muscles (p. 376)
inspiratory reserve volume (IRV) (p. 380)
internal respiration (p. 374)
larynx (p. 368)
laryngopharynx (p. 364)
lower respiratory tract (p. 364)
lungs (p. 371)
nasal cavities (p. 365)

ELSEVIER

Structure & Function of the Body, 13th ed.
Thibodeau/Patton

nasopharynx (p. 365)
oropharynx (p. 365)
oxyhemoglobin (p. 379)
palatine tonsils (p. 366)
paranasal sinus (p. 365)
pharyngeal tonsils (p. 366)
pharynx (p. 362)
pleura (p. 371)
pleurisy (p. 371)
pneumothorax (p. 373)
primary bronchi (p. 372)
pulmonary ventilation (p. 374)
residual volume (RV) (p. 380)
respiration (p. 374)
respiratory arrest (p. 384)

respiratory control centers (p. 382)
respiratory membrane (pp. 364, 370)
respiratory mucosa (p. 364)
secondary bronchi (p. 370)
sinusitis (p. 365)
spirometer (p. 380)
surfactant (p. 370)
tidal volume (TV) (p. 380)
tonsillectomy (p. 366)
tonsillitis (p. 368)
trachea (p. 368)
upper respiratory tract (p. 364)
vital capacity (VC) (p. 380)
vocal cords (p. 368)

ADDITIONAL RESOURCES

AnimationDirect (Book Companion CD)
Instructor's Electronic Resource (IER) (CD)
PowerPoint slides (CD, Evolve)
Test Bank (Evolve)

Legend

ESLR
EVOLVE Student
Learning Resource

EILR TB
EVOLVE Instructor
Learning Resource
Test Bank

AnimationDirect
on Book Companion
CD

PPT
PowerPoint
Slides

SG
Study
Guide

IRM
Instructor's
Resource Manual

Class Activities are indicated in ***bold italic***.

LESSON 14.1

PRETEST
Study Guide Multiple Choice questions 1-10 (pp. 171-172)

BACKGROUND ASSESSMENT
Question: Will antibiotics help a common cold or a respiratory flu? Name some possible complications of the common cold or flu and the symptoms associated with each. Can these complications be treated successfully with antibiotics?

Answer: Antibiotic therapy is not appropriate for treatment of the common cold or flu. Colds and flu are caused by a wide variety of viruses; antibiotics are used to treat infections caused by bacteria. Taking antibiotics inappropriately can lead to more virulent and resistant bacteria. Symptoms of a cold are runny or stuffy nose, sore throat, and possibly a low-grade fever. Symptoms of respiratory flu are similar, but often are accompanied by sudden onset of muscle aches and fever. Often the complications of a cold or flu result in a secondary infection in the ear, sinuses, or lungs. This is because the ear, nose, throat, and lungs are interconnected, and when mucous membranes are compromised by viral infection, bacterial infections can then develop more easily and spread from one structure to another. Symptoms of a middle ear infection (otitis media) are earache, reddened and inflamed eardrum with fluid present, and frequently hearing loss or fever. Symptoms of a sinus infection include reddened, inflamed nasal mucosa, yellow or green discharge from the nose, headache, pain around the teeth, fatigue, and often fever. Infection in the lungs includes bronchitis and pneumonia. Productive cough and fever are common symptoms. Antibiotics are used to combat secondary bacterial infections in the ear, sinuses, and lungs.

Question: Why is oxygen so important to the body? How does the body get its supply of oxygen and make it available to all the tissues of the body?

Answer: A person can survive only a few minutes without oxygen. Oxygen fuels all the body's cellular processes. Proper cell function requires an exchange of gases: oxygen, which fuels the metabolic processes, is exchanged with carbon dioxide, a waste product of metabolism. With each inhalation of air, gas exchange occurs in the smallest structures of the lungs, the alveoli. Alveoli are extremely thin walled and densely covered by blood capillaries. Air from the alveoli can easily enter the capillaries. There, it combines with hemoglobin, becoming oxyhemoglobin, and is transported through the bloodstream. When the oxyhemoglobin reaches a tissue in need of oxygen, the oxygen dissociates from the hemoglobin and is available directly to that tissue. Waste products such as carbon dioxide enter the bloodstream at this point. Some carbon dioxide joins to hemoglobin, becoming carbaminohemoglobin, and is transported back to the lungs, where the carbon dioxide dissociates, enters the alveoli, and is then expelled from the lungs with the next breath.

CRITICAL THINKING QUESTION
What happens when a person takes in a breath of air? Start with the moment before inspiration actually occurs, and describe the path the air takes and the structures through which it flows.

Guidelines: The respiratory control centers located in the medulla and pons are influenced by the input of a number of receptors located in various parts of the body. The main receptors are located in the carotid and aortic bodies and in the lungs (pulmonary stretch receptors). Information from these receptors stimulates the brain to send a nerve impulse that initiates respiration. Air is inspired through the nose and warmed and humidified as it passes over the conchae, where harmful agents or particular matter becomes stuck in the mucous membrane lining. Air then flows through the pharynx and into the trachea. From there, it flows into the bronchi, bronchioles, and finally the alveoli, which are densely covered with blood capillaries. It is here that gas exchange occurs: oxygen can be transferred into the bloodstream through the capillaries. "Spent" blood transfers its major waste product—carbon dioxide—back to the alveoli, where the process of expiration begins. Air from the alveoli, now containing carbon dioxide, is expelled from the lungs.

ELSEVIER

Structure & Function of the Body, 13th ed.

Thibodeau/Patton

OBJECTIVES	CONTENT	TEACHING RESOURCES
Discuss the generalized functions of the respiratory system.	■ Structural plan (p. 362) ■ Respiratory tracts (p. 364) ■ Respiratory mucosa (p. 364)	Slides 5-10 Structural Plan, Respiratory Tracts, and Respiratory Mucosa questions 1-25 (p. 164) Applying What You Know question 79 (p. 168) Multiple Choice questions 1-4 (p. 171) Multiple Choice questions 1-6, 36-39; True or False questions 1-11, 62-67; Short Answer questions 2, 3, 17 Learning Objectives with Rationale 1 (p. 183); Review question 1 (p. 189); Critical Thinking questions 15, 16 (p. 191); Practical/Creative Learning Activities 5 (p. 192) Respiratory Mucosa **Book Resources** Figure 14-1 Structural plan of the respiratory organs showing the pharynx, trachea, bronchi, and lungs (p. 363) Figure 14-8 Gas-exchange structure of the lung (p. 371) Figure 14-2 Respiratory mucosa lining the trachea (p. 364) Clinical Application: Oxygen Therapy (p. 36) Quick Check questions 1-3 (p. 365) Outline Summary (p. 384) Review question 1 (p. 388) Critical Thinking question 16 (p. 388) ▸ Discuss how the process of respiration is an important homeostatic mechanism for the body. ▸ Discuss the three other functions that the respiratory system performs in addition to air distribution and gas exchange (filtration, warming, humidifying the air). What structures and tissues are involved in these functions? Why is it important that the air entering the body be warmed, filtered, and humidified? ***Class Activity Divide the class into small groups of three or four students. Ask each group to examine slides of healthy and***

OBJECTIVES	CONTENT	TEACHING RESOURCES
		diseased respiratory mucosa under the microscope (cystic fibrosis, emphysema, lung cancer, etc.). Ask each group to identify cilia, epithelium, submucosa, and so on. Ask each group to discuss the differences between the healthy and diseased tissue they observed at the cellular level. Ask one student from each group to present the group's findings to the class. Ask the representatives from each group to discuss how the various disease states differ from one another.
List the major organs of the respiratory system, and describe the function of each.	■ Nose (p. 365) ■ Pharynx (p. 365) ■ Larynx (p. 368) ■ Trachea (p. 368) ■ Bronchi, bronchioles, and alveoli (p. 370) ■ Lungs and pleura (p. 371)	Slides 11-28 Nose, Pharynx, Larynx questions 26-41 (p. 165) Trachea, Bronchi, Bronchioles, Alveoli, Lungs, and Pleura questions 42-50 (p. 165) Applying What You Know question 80 (p. 178) Sagittal View of Face and Neck and Respiratory Organs diagrams (pp. 173-174) Multiple Choice questions 7-19, 40-42; True or False questions 12-37, 64-79; Matching questions 1-10; Short Answer questions 1, 4-8 Learning Objectives with Rationale 2 (p. 183); Review questions 2-6 (pp. 189-190); Practical/Creative Learning Activities 6 (p. 192) Respiratory Membrane **Book Resources** Figure 14-3 The paranasal sinuses (p. 366) Figure 14-4 Sagittal section of the head and neck (p. 367) Figure 14-5 The larynx (p. 368) Figure 14-6 Cross section of the trachea (p. 369) Figure 14-7 Alveoli (p. 370) Quick Check questions 1-4 (p. 370) Figure 14-8 Gas exchange structure of lung (p. 371) Figure 14-9 Lungs (p. 372)

Structure & Function of the Body, 13th ed.

Thibodeau/Patton

OBJECTIVES	CONTENT	TEACHING RESOURCES
		Figure 14-10 Lungs and pleura (p. 373)
		Review questions 2-6 (p. 388)
		Clear View of the Human Body
		▸ Discuss the pros and cons of tonsillectomy. What is the general recommendation today?
		▸ Discuss the possible problems a premature infant might have with regard to the lungs. Enumerate possible therapies.
		▸ Discuss pneumothorax and when you might expect to encounter this condition. What symptoms can you expect? What are common techniques for treating pneumothorax?
		▸ Discuss possible effects that air pollution might have on the respiratory system.
		▸ Discuss allergies with regard to the fact that a child has been referred to an allergist, because she has allergylike symptoms and frequent sinus infections. How can the allergist help? How would you explain it if no allergies could be detected with allergy testing?
		Class Activity Invite a nurse or other healthcare professional to demonstrate correct execution of the various techniques of the Heimlich maneuver, including its correct use in children.
		Class Activity Divide the class into small groups. Ask each group to label as many structures of the respiratory system as possible on p. 182 of the SG without consulting the textbook. After everyone has filled out the form, ask a representative from each group to present an assigned section of the form to the class. After each representative has presented, ask the class to check the accuracy of their charts against textbook diagrams.

Structure & Function of the Body, 13th ed.

Thibodeau/Patton

14.1 Homework/Assignments:

Research one of the other inventions or techniques developed by the highly innovative Henry Heimlich (see Science Applications, p. 384). Write a short paper describing the technique or invention, and state whether or not it is still in use today.

14.1 Teacher's Notes:

LESSON 14.2

CRITICAL THINKING QUESTION

What is carbon monoxide poisoning? What are the symptoms? Based on what you have learned about the process of respiration, what is happening at the cellular level?

Guidelines: Carbon monoxide is a poisonous, colorless, odorless gas. It is the greatest source of poisoning in the United States, with half of all poisonings due to motor vehicle exhaust. The main symptoms of early-stage toxicity are headache, nausea, and fatigue. These symptoms are a direct response of the heart and lungs to a lack of oxygen (hypoxia). Carbon monoxide combines with hemoglobin in the blood with an affinity up to 250 times higher than that of oxygen. When carbon monoxide is inhaled, it preempts the binding of oxygen to hemoglobin (oxyhemoglobin) for transport to the tissues, where it is needed for vital cellular processes. Cells cannot get enough oxygen to continue proper functioning. The cells of the brain and heart are most susceptible, resulting in neurological symptoms and cardiac failure.

OBJECTIVES	CONTENT	TEACHING RESOURCES
Compare, contrast, and explain the mechanism responsible for the exchange of gases that occurs during internal and external respiration.	■ Respiration (p. 374) ☐ Mechanics of breathing (p. 374) – Inspiration (p. 376) – Expiration (p. 376)	Slides 30-34 Respiration questions 51-53 (p. 166) Multiple Choice questions 20-25; True or False questions 38-46, 80, 81; Matching questions 11-20; Short Answer questions 8-15 Learning Objectives with Rationale 2 (p. 183); Review questions 7-9 (p. 190); Classroom Application 1, 2 (p. 191); Lab Activities 1, 3, 4 (p. 192); Practical/Creative Learning Activities 1, 4 (p. 192) **Book Resources** Clinical Application: Infant Respiratory Distress Syndrome (p. 374) Research, Issues and Trends: Lung Volume Reduction Surgery (LVRS) (p. 375) Figure 14-11 Mechanics of breathing (p. 376) Quick Check questions 1-3 (p. 380) Clinical Application: Sudden Infant Death Syndrome (SIDS) (p. 382) Review questions 7-9 (p. 388) ▶ Discuss the mechanics involved in inspiration and expiration. ▶ Discuss the role hemoglobin plays in the process of respiration. ▶ Discuss why LVRS is an effective procedure in the treatment of late-stage emphysema.

ELSEVIER

Structure & Function of the Body, 13th ed.

Thibodeau/Patton

OBJECTIVES	CONTENT	TEACHING RESOURCES
		▸ Discuss the acute symptoms of carbon monoxide poisoning and the difficulties in distinguishing it from other disorders. Discuss possible neurological sequelae that are likely to occur as a result of poisoning. List likely sources of poisoning. *Class Activity Divide the class into two teams. Ask each team to create definitions of terms used in this chapter (such as "The voice box located just below the pharynx"). Have students answer in the form of a question, (such as "What is the larynx?"). Ask each team a question created by the opposing team. Use as many respiratory system terms as possible, such as pulmonary ventilation, external respiration, SIDS, alveoli, Heimlich maneuver, respiratory mucosa, and so on. See which team gets the most correct answers.* *Class Activity Have students discuss how diet and exercise can improve respiratory function. Students can obtain and share information from organizations such as "better breathers" clubs.*
Compare, contrast, and explain the mechanisms responsible for the exchange of gases that occurs during internal and external respiration.	☐ Exchange of gases in lungs (p. 377) ☐ Exchange of gases in tissues (p. 377)	Slides 35-38 Respiration question 54 (p. 166) Multiple Choice questions 26, 27; True or False questions 47-50, 82, 83 Review questions 10, 11 (p. 6) Gas Exchange **Book Resources** Figure 14-12 Exchange of gases in lung and tissue capillaries (p. 378) Quick Check questions 1-3 (p. 380) Review questions 10, 11 (p. 388) Critical Thinking question 16 (p. 388) ▸ Discuss the principle of diffusion in the exchange of gases in the lungs and tissues. ▸ Discuss the difference between internal and external respiration. Compare and contrast the direction of movement of oxygen and carbon dioxide in internal and external respiration. What is cellular respiration?

Thibodeau/Patton

OBJECTIVES	CONTENT	TEACHING RESOURCES
		*Class Activity **Divide the class into two or three large teams. Ask each team to demonstrate for the class the exchange of gases in lung and tissue capillaries. Students can act out the process as described in Figure 14-12 on page 378. Remind each team to assign parts for the heart, lung alveoli, tissue cells, and hemoglobin. The systemic veins and arteries can be simulated by lining up desks or chairs and having the students representing hemoglobin travel the route between the lungs, tissues, and heart. Students could hold a blue card to represent carbon dioxide at appropriate points in the pathway of respiration and red cards to represent oxygen-rich blood. Students representing tissue or lung cells could pass red or blue cards as appropriate to the students who represent hemoglobin traveling through the bloodstream. Vote on which team presented the most memorable demonstration. Consider awarding small "prizes" to all participants, such as red and blue pencils.*** *Class Activity **Have students create a brochure on the effects of smoking and list community resources that offer smoking-cessation programs. Have students distribute them to schools, supermarkets, and other locations.*** *Class Activity **Have students seek donations of CO detectors from local hardware stores to distribute to members of the community.***

14.2 Homework/Assignments:

Research carbon monoxide poisoning in medical dictionaries or through Web research. Based on what you have learned about the process of respiration, what is happening at the cellular level? What are likely sources of carbon monoxide? What are common symptoms of carbon monoxide poisoning? What are possible sequelae to poisoning? What precautions can be taken to reduce exposure to carbon monoxide? The following interactive Web site helps point out likely sources of environmental poisoning: http://toxtown.nlm.nih.gov/town/main.html

---

14.2 Teacher's Notes:

LESSON 14.3

CRITICAL THINKING QUESTION

A patient has recently been diagnosed with asthma. The patient is unsure if the medication regimen prescribed is actually helping. The physician orders pulmonary function testing. What information might testing provide that will aid in the patient's treatment regimen?

Guidelines: Asthma is characterized by reversible airway obstruction and hyper-responsiveness of the airways. The airways constrict, and mucous production is increased. When airways constrict during an acute attack, air is often trapped in the smaller airways, leaving the lung overinflated. Overinflation makes normal respiration difficult, because differences in air pressure no longer have a significant effect on forcing air into or out of the lungs. The various types of asthma produce characteristic spirometric or functional testing results. Pulmonary function testing also allows the physician to evaluate lung volumes and function during an attack. Medications, such as bronchodilators, can also be administered at the time of testing, and the effect on lung volume and function can be determined to ascertain whether a medication is effective.

OBJECTIVES	CONTENT	TEACHING RESOURCES
List and discuss the volumes of air exchanged during pulmonary ventilation.	☐ Volumes of air exchanged in pulmonary ventilation (p. 380)	Slides 39, 40 Respiration questions 64-66 (p. 167) Check Your Knowledge questions 8, 16, 19 (pp. 171-172) *e* Multiple Choice questions 28-30; True or False questions 51-54 Learning Objectives with Rationale 4 (p. 184); Lab Activities 2, 5 (p. 192); Practical/Creative Learning Activities 2 (p. 192) **Book Resources** Figure 14-13 Pulmonary ventilation volumes (p. 381) Health and Well-Being: Maximum Oxygen Consumption (p. 380) Review question 12 (p. 388) ▶ Discuss what the VO_{2max} of an athlete might be in comparison to an untrained individual. What might the spirogram of an athlete look like? *Class Activity **Divide the class into small groups. Using a spirometer, ask each group to determine the tidal volume, expiratory reserve volume, inspiratory reserve volume, and vital capacity of each student in the group. Ask a representative from each group to present information to the class about the group's pulmonary capacity.***

OBJECTIVES	CONTENT	TEACHING RESOURCES
Identify and discuss the mechanisms that regulate respiration.	■ Regulation of respiration (p. 380) □ Cerebral cortex (p. 382) □ Receptors influencing respiration (p. 382) – Chemoreceptors (p. 382) – Pulmonary stretch receptors (p. 383) ■ Types of breathing (p. 384)	Slides 41-44 Regulation of Respiration, Receptors Influencing Respiration, and Types of Breathing questions 67-73 (p. 167) Check Your Knowledge questions 9-20 (p. 173) Multiple Choice questions 31-35; True or False questions 55-61; Short Answer question 16 Learning Objectives with Rationale 5 (pp. 184-185); Critical Thinking Questions 18 (p. 191); Lab Activities 1, 6, 7 (p. 192); Practical/Creative Learning Activities 4, 6 (p. 192) **Book Resources** Figure 14-14 Regulation of respiration (p. 383) Science Applications: Respiratory medicine (p. 384) Quick Check questions 1-3 (p. 384) Review questions 13, 14 (p. 388) ▶ Discuss why the body increases the rate of respiration during periods of increased physical activity. What other body systems also adjust to accommodate increased physical activity? ▶ Discuss possible causes of apnea. ▶ Discuss possible causes of sleep apnea and why it is a condition that should not be ignored. Current research suggests that persons with sleep apnea are more prone to cardiac problems. Why might this be? ▶ Discuss circumstances under which CPR is an appropriate measure. Are there conditions where CPR might not be indicated and even detrimental if performed? ▶ Discuss what hyperventilation is and what the possible causes may be. What are currently recognized measures for dealing with hyperventilation? Compare and contrast hyperventilation with dyspnea. ▶ Discuss what happens when a 2-year-old threatens to hold his breath in order to get his way. Is he in danger? Why or why not? What is the worst thing that might happen if he does hold his breath? What regulators are involved, and where are they located?

Structure & Function of the Body, 13th ed.
Thibodeau/Patton

OBJECTIVES	CONTENT	TEACHING RESOURCES
		▸ Discuss what happens when a woman in labor uses breathing techniques to control the labor pains. Which control centers are involved in her respiration control? Is a woman in labor more likely to hyperventilate or hypoventilate? Why? What measures are implemented to correct these conditions? ***Class Activity** **Work in small groups. Ask each group to compare and contrast IRDS and SIDS in terms of causes, at-risk populations, treatment modalities, ages of occurrence, and so on. Ask each group to prepare a 30-second PSA (public service announcement) to teach parents about IRDS and SIDS and how to protect their children against both.***
Performance Evaluation		🅔 Chapter 14 Computerized Test Bank questions 📓 Student Assignment (pp. 193-197) 🅔 Student Post-Test questions **Book Resources** Review questions (p. 388) Chapter Test (pp. 388-389)

14.3 Homework/Assignments:

14.3 Teacher's Notes:

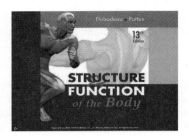

Slide 1

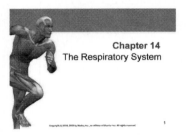

Chapter 14
The Respiratory System

Slide 2

Learning Objectives

- Discuss the generalized functions of the respiratory system
- List the major organs of the respiratory system and describe the function of each
- Compare, contrast, and explain the mechanism responsible for the exchange of gases that occurs during internal and external respiration

2

Slide 3

Learning Objectives (cont'd.)

- List and discuss the volumes of air exchanged during pulmonary ventilation
- Identify and discuss the mechanisms that regulate respiration

3

Thibodeau/Patton

Slide 4

Chapter 14
Lesson 14.1

Slide 5

Respiratory System Function

- Air distributor
- Gas exchanger
- Homeostatic mechanism
- Filters, warms, and humidifies air for breathing
- Speech and sound production
- Olfaction

- How long can a person live without food? Water? Oxygen? (A person can live a few weeks without food, a few days without water, but only a few minutes without oxygen.)

- What gases are exchanged during respiration? (oxygen and carbon dioxide)

- Why is a constant environment important for the cells of the body to function effectively? (Maintaining homeostasis is necessary for optimum functioning.)

- Explain that structures play a role in speech and sound.

- Production and why. (The larynx contains vocal cords which vibrate when one speaks. The sinuses and sinus cavities are air cavities and serve as resonant chambers for the production of sound.)

- Which respiratory structure plays a role in olfaction and how? (The nose contains olfactory [smell] nerve endings that communicate with the brain.)

Slide 6

Structural Plan

- Inverted tree (trachea to alveoli)
- Structure of the alveoli
  - Single-cell outer layer less than 1 micron thick (respiratory membrane)
  - Numerous—provide an extremely large surface area for gas exchange to occur
- Function of the alveoli
  - Distribute air in close proximity to blood capillaries in order for gas exchange to occur (diffusion)

- Explain the close relationship between structure and function in the alveoli. (Alveoli are made up of a single layer of cells and so are the walls of the capillaries that surround them. These characteristics facilitate the diffusion of gases. In addition, there are millions of alveoli.)

- What is the role of the respiratory membrane? (The respiratory membrane is an extremely thin barrier between the blood in the capillaries and the air in the alveoli. This structure allows for diffusion.)

- How does the proximity of alveoli to blood capillaries facilitate exchange? (Gases are easily exchanged due to the close contact of the alveoli and capillaries. The gases have a very short distance to travel.)

- How does the structure of the capillaries facilitate diffusion? (Since the capillary walls are made up of a single layer of cells, the gases readily diffuse.)

- Review the concept of diffusion from Chapter 3.

ELSEVIER

Copyright © 2008, 2005 by Mosby, Inc., an affiliate of Elsevier Inc.

Structure & Function of the Body, 13th ed.
Thibodeau/Patton

Slide 7

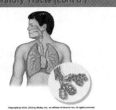

Respiratory Tracts

- Upper respiratory tract
  - Nose
  - Pharynx
  - Larynx
- Lower respiratory tract
  - Trachea
  - Bronchial tree
  - Lungs

- Compare and contrast a "head cold" with a "chest cold" in terms of symptoms and organs involved.
- Compare and contrast a "head cold" with allergies.

Slide 8

Respiratory Tracts (cont'd.)

- Point out the boundaries of the upper and lower respiratory tracts and the structures belonging to them.
- Note the alveoli resembling a bunch of grapes and the alveolar sacs. Stress the microscopic size of these structures.

Slide 9

Respiratory Mucosa

- Specialized membrane that lines the air distribution tubes in the respiratory tree
- Covered with mucous—"mucous blanket"
  - Air purification and filtration function
  - More than 125 ml of mucus produced each day
- Cilia
  - Move in one direction toward the pharynx

- Differentiate between "respiratory membrane" and "respiratory mucosa." (The respiratory membrane separates the air in the alveoli from the blood in the surrounding capillaries. The respiratory mucosa is covered with mucus and lines the tubes of the respiratory tree.)
- What function does the respiratory mucosa perform? (air purification)
- What function do the cilia perform? (Cilia move mucus towards the pharynx in an effort to help expel it.)
- What happens in the respiratory tract when cigarette smoke is inhaled? (Smoke paralyzes the cilia and mucus accumulates.)

Slide 10

Respiratory Mucosa (cont'd.)

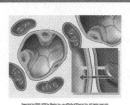

- Identify the gas-exchange structures.
- In particular, look at the inset and explain the flow of gases into and out of the capillaries and alveoli.
- Locate the respiratory membrane (on both the capillary and the alveolus) and explain its function.

ELSEVIER

Structure & Function of the Body, 13th ed.
Thibodeau/Patton

Slide 11

Nose

- Structure
  - Nasal septum separates interior of nose into two cavities
  - Mucous membrane lines nose
  - Frontal, maxillary, sphenoidal, and ethmoidal sinuses drain into nose
- Function
  - Warms and moistens inhaled air
    - Conchae
  - Contains sense organs of smell

11

- What other function do the sinus cavities have? (They lighten the weight of the skull; they play a role in the production of sounds.)
- Explain the path of tears. (Tears flow from the lacrimal sacs into the lacrimal ducts and into the nasal cavities.)
- Which is more effective at humidifying air: breathing through the nose or breathing through the mouth? Why? (Breathing through the nose is more effective, because the nose has conchae, which increases the surface area over which the air flows.)
- Why and how is supplemental oxygen humidified before administration? (Supplemental oxygen is humidified through the use of a "bubbler," because oxygen can be very drying to the mucous membranes.)

Slide 12

Nose (cont'd.)

12

- Identify the structures of the nose and the sinuses.
- What purposes do the sinuses serve? (Help lessen the weight of the skull bones.)
- Note the location of the ethmoidal and sphenoidal sinuses on the inset.

Slide 13

Pharynx (throat)

- Structure
  - 12.5 cm (5 inches) long
  - Three segments
    - Nasopharynx
    - Oropharynx
    - Laryngopharynx
  - Lined by mucous membrane
  - Two sinuses, mouth, esophagus, larynx, and auditory (eustachian) tubes all have openings into pharynx

13

- Pharynx is like the hallway of a house. It allows passage of substances to which two different body systems? (respiratory and digestive)
- What function does the eustachian tube perform? (permits equalization of air pressure between the middle and exterior ear)
- Explain how a sinus infection can develop.
- Explain how a middle ear infection (otitis media) can develop. Why do children sometimes "outgrow" their tendency to have frequent ear infections? (Children will often outgrow the condition, because the eustachian tube becomes more vertical as the child grows, which lessens the ability of microbes to travel and produce infection.)

Thibodeau/Patton

Slide 14

Pharynx (throat)(cont'd.)

- Tonsils
  - Pharyngeal tonsils (adenoids) are located in the nasopharynx
  - Palatine tonsils are located in the oropharynx

14

- What kind of tissue are tonsils composed of? (lymphatic)
- What is a complication of swelling of the adenoids? (Difficulty with air passing from nose to throat.)
- What are the pros and cons of tonsillectomy? (Removing the tonsils is indicated if they are a frequent source of infection. Routine removal of the tonsils is not necessary, because the tonsils serve to protect the lower respiratory tract from microbes.)

Slide 15

Pharynx (throat)(cont'd.)

0

- Point out the structures from the previous topics: sinuses, conchae, etc.
- Highlight the segments of the pharynx.

Slide 16

Pharynx (throat)(cont'd.)

- Functions
  - Digestive and respiratory systems
    - Passageway for food and liquids to the esophagus
    - Passageway for air to the respiratory tree

16

- At what point do the pathways to the digestive system and respiratory system diverge? (epiglottis)

Slide 17

Larynx

17

- Note the close proximity of trachea and esophagus. Discuss the mechanisms in place to allow smooth functioning of each system.
- What causes laryngitis? (inflammation of the larynx) What structures might be involved? (larynx and vocal cords) What role does proximity of those structures to one another play? (Inflammation can be easily spread.)

Structure & Function of the Body, 13th ed.

Thibodeau/Patton

Slide 18

Larynx (cont'd.)

- Structure
  - Several pieces of cartilage form framework
    - Thyroid cartilage (Adam's apple) is largest
    - Epiglottis partially covers opening into larynx
  - Mucous lining
  - Vocal cords stretch across interior of larynx
- Functions
  - Air distribution; passageway for air to move to and from lungs
  - Voice production

18

- Why is the epiglottis so important? (It prevents food from entering the respiratory tract.)
- What mechanisms are in place to assure that food does not get into the respiratory system? (Action of the epiglottis. The epiglottis closes off the larynx during swallowing, preventing food from entering the trachea.)
- Under what circumstances might these mechanisms be disrupted? (patients who have had strokes, patients who are anesthetized, patients who are heavily sedated)
- How do the vocal cords produce sound? (through vibration)

Slide 19

Trachea

- Structure
  - Tube about 11 cm (4.5 inches) long extends from larynx to the bronchi
  - C-shaped rings of cartilage hold trachea open
  - Mucous lining
  - Ciliated epithelium

19

- Discuss the structural characteristics that make the trachea practically incollapsible.
- What role does the ciliated epithelium play? (The ciliated epithelium produces mucus, which can trap microbes.)

Slide 20

Trachea (cont'd.)

20

- Point out the layers of the trachea in the center inset.
- What role does the hyaline cartilage play? (keeps trachea from collapsing.)
- What is the significance of the C-shaped sections of cartilage ring being open to the posterior side and not to the anterior side of the body? (The anterior portion of the trachea is more exposed, thus its need for protection. The C-shaped rings are considered almost noncollapsible.)

Slide 21

Trachea (cont'd.)

- Function
  - Passageway for air to move to and from lungs
- Obstruction
  - Complete occlusion of the airway causes death in minutes
  - 4000+ deaths annually in the United States due to tracheal obstruction
  - Heimlich maneuver

21

- Under what circumstances might the trachea become blocked? (aspiration, suffocation)
- Discuss measures and techniques for dealing with tracheal obstruction.
- Demonstrate correct execution of the Heimlich maneuver.

ELSEVIER

Structure & Function of the Body, 13th ed.

Thibodeau/Patton

Slide 22

Bronchi, Bronchioles, and Alveoli

- Structure
  - Right and left bronchi (primary bronchi)
    - Trachea branches into right and left bronchi
  - Bronchioles
    - Each bronchus branches into increasingly smaller tubes leading to bronchioles
  - Alveolar sacs
    - Bronchioles end in clusters of microscopic alveolar sacs
  - Alveoli
    - Located in the walls of the alveolar sacs
    - Millions of alveoli per lung

22

- What structural feature keeps the bronchi open? (rings of cartilage)
- Alveolar sacs resemble a bunch of grapes, with each of the alveoli resembling a single grape.

Slide 23

Bronchi, Bronchioles, and Alveoli (cont'd.)

23

- Review the structure from the bronchiole to the alveolar duct, alveolar sac, and finally, the alveoli, with their close contact to the blood capillaries.
- Why are the alveoli so densely covered with blood capillaries? (to facilitate diffusion of gases)

Slide 24

Bronchi, Bronchioles, and Alveoli (cont'd.)

- Function
  - Bronchi and bronchioles
    - Air distribution to alveoli
  - Alveoli
    - Exchange of gases between air and blood
    - Thin walled
    - Direct contact with blood capillary
    - Surfactant

24

- Gas exchange is facilitated by the close contact of blood capillaries to the thin-walled alveoli.
- Surfactant reduces surface tension in the alveoli and keeps it from collapsing as air moves in and out. The presence of surfactant is critical to breathing. This is of great concern in premature babies, because surfactant does not develop in a fetus until late in the pregnancy (approximately 37 weeks).

Slide 25

Lungs and Pleura

- Structure of lungs
  - Right lung: Three lobes
  - Left lung: Two lobes
  - Apex: Narrow upper part of each lung, under collarbone
  - Base
    - Broad lower part of each lung
    - Rests on diaphragm

25

- Lungs fill the chest cavity from the collarbone to the diaphragm, except for the middle space occupied by the heart and large blood vessels.

ELSEVIER

Thibodeau/Patton

Slide 26

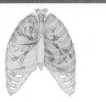

Lungs and Pleura (cont'd.)

- Use the diagram to review anatomy and locate structures that are not mentioned in the text.

Slide 27

 Lungs and Pleura (cont'd.)

- Structure of the pleura
  - Moist, smooth, slippery membrane that lines chest cavity and covers outer surface of lungs
  - **Parietal:** Lines walls of thoracic cavity
  - **Visceral:** Covers lungs
  - **Intrapleural space:** Lies between parietal and visceral
- Function
  - Pulmonary ventilation (breathing)
  - Reduces friction between the lungs and chest wall during breathing

- Explain the function of the fluid in the intrapleural space.
- What is pneumothorax? (collapse of the lung due to air in the intrapleural space)
- What is pleurisy? (Inflammation of the pleura [lining of the lung] which causes pain.) What are possible causes and treatments? (Can be caused by infection or inflammation. Treatments include antibiotics and pain medications.)

Slide 28

Lungs and Pleura (cont'd.)

- Use this diagram of a transverse section to gain a better perspective of the viseral and parietal pleura and pleural spaces.
- What is the function of the pleura? (reduces friction between the lungs and chest wall during breathing)

Slide 29

Chapter 14
Lesson 14.2

Slide 30

Respiration

- Mechanics of breathing (pulmonary ventilation)
  - **Inspiration:** movement of air into lungs
  - **Expiration:** movement of air out of lungs
- Changes in size and shape of thorax cause changes in air pressure within the thoracic cavity and the lungs
- Air pressure differences actually cause air to move into and out of the lungs

30

- A classic jar/balloon model can to be used to demonstrate the principle, or use the figure on the next slide.

Slide 31

Respiration (cont'd)

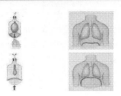

31

- Have students explain the sequence of events depicted here for inspiration and expiration.

Slide 32

Respiration (cont'd.)

- Inspiration
  - Inspiratory muscles:
    - **Diaphragm:** Flattens during inspiration; increases top-to-bottom length of thorax
    - **External intercostals:** Contraction elevates ribs and increases size of thorax from front to back and from side to side
  - Increase in size of chest cavity reduces pressure within, and air enters the lungs

32

- What is the most important muscle of inspiration? (diaphragm)
- Nerve impulses passing through the phrenic nerve stimulate contraction of the diaphragm.
- What factors might have an influence on phrenic nerve stimulation of the diaphragm? (drugs, anesthesia, paralysis)

Slide 33

Respiration (cont'd.)

- Expiration
  - Passive process—air moves out of lungs
  - During expiration, thorax returns to its resting size and shape
  - Elastic recoil of lung tissues aids in expiration

33

- Quiet expiration is a passive process that begins when the inspiratory muscles relax.

ELSEVIER

Structure & Function of the Body, 13th ed.

Thibodeau/Patton

Slide 34

Respiration (cont'd.)

- Forceful expiration involves decreasing the size of the thoracic cavity by these expiratory muscles
  - **Internal intercostals:** Contraction depresses rib cage, decreasing front-to-back size of the thorax
  - **Abdominal muscles:** Contraction elevates the diaphragm, decreasing size of thoracic cavity from top to bottom
- Reduction in the size of the thoracic cavity increases its pressure, and air leaves the lungs

34

- Forceful expiration is common during heavy work, singing, and some speech patterns.

Slide 35

Exchange of Gases in Lungs

- Route of blood flow
  - Right ventricle → pulmonary artery → lungs → lung capillaries
- Mechanism
  - Close proximity of capillaries in the lungs allows exchange of gases between blood and alveoli by diffusion
  - **Diffusion:** Passive movement down a concentration gradient
    - Oxygen → bloodstream
    - Carbon dioxide → alveoli

35

- Reiterate the path of blood flow and the state of the blood (rich in carbon dioxide from cellular metabolism) as it makes contact with the alveoli.

- Review structural features of the alveoli that make transfer of gases possible.

- Review principle of diffusion.

Slide 36

Exchange of Gases in Lungs (cont'd.)

- **Oxygen** moves from alveoli (high oxygen concentration) into lung capillary blood (low oxygen concentration)
- **Carbon dioxide** moves out of lung capillary blood (high concentration) into alveolar air (low concentration) and out of body in expired air

36

- Oxygen moves by diffusion from an area of high concentration (alveoli in the lungs) to an area of low concentration (blood capillaries). These blood capillaries are returning "spent" blood to the lungs for replenishment with oxygen.

- Likewise carbon dioxide moves by diffusion from an area of high concentration (blood) to an area of low concentration (alveoli) from where it can be expelled from the lungs.

- What is oxyhemoglobin and what is its purpose? (It is a molecule formed from oxygen and hemoglobin. Oxygen can then be delivered via the vascular system to the body's tissues and cells.)

- What is carbaminohemoglobin and what is its purpose? (It is a molecule formed from combining carbon dioxide and hemoglobin. In this form, CO_2 can be delivered to the lungs for elimination.)

ELSEVIER

Structure & Function of the Body, 13th ed.
Thibodeau/Patton

Slide 37

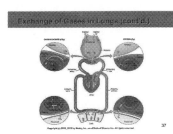

- Have students explain the sequence of events in this diagram showing exchange of gases.
- Have students recall the differences between the right and left sides of the heart.

Slide 38

Exchanges of Gases in Tissues

- Internal respiration
  - Oxygen moves out of tissue capillary blood into tissue cells
  - Oxyhemoglobin breaks down into oxygen and hemoglobin
  - Carbon dioxide moves from tissue cells into tissue capillary blood
  - Hemoglobin combines with carbon dioxide, forming carbaminohemoglobin

- Agent of transport for these gases is hemoglobin.
- What is the combination of oxygen with hemoglobin for transport throughout the blood system? (oxyhemoglobin)
- When carbon dioxide binds to hemoglobin for transport away from the tissues to the lungs for disposal, what is it called? (carbaminohemoglobin)
- Discuss the importance and other functions of hemoglobin.

Slide 39

Volumes of Air Exchanges in Pulmonary Ventilation

- **TV:** Tidal volume—approx. 500 ml with normal inspiration
- **ERV:** Expiratory reserve volume
- **IRV:** Inspiratory reserve volume
- **VC:** Vital capacity—VC = TV + IRV + ERV
  - Largest amount of expiratory air possible
- **RV:** Residual volume

- How did tidal volume get its name? (cyclic nature, like the tides in the ocean)
- What is the normal vital capacity for a young man? (4800 ml)
- What is the normal rate of respiration? (12 to 18 breaths per minute)
- Define each of the terms on the slide.

Slide 40

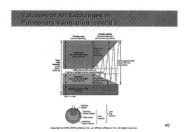

- Figure A represents a spirometer tracing.
- Figure B represents pulmonary volumes as relative proportions of an inflated balloon.
- Review the normal-range capacities for each pulmonary ventilation volume parameter.

Structure & Function of the Body, 13th ed.

Thibodeau/Patton

Slide 41

> **Regulation of Respiration**
>
> - Permits the body to adjust to varying demands for oxygen supply and carbon dioxide removal
> - Respiratory control centers simulate muscles of respiratory system with nervous impulses
>   - Medulla
>   - Inspiratory center
>   - Expiratory center
>   - Pons
>   - Exerts a modifying effect
>
> Copyright (c) 2008, 2005 by Mosby, Inc., an affiliate of Elsevier Inc. All rights reserved.   41

- Note that the circulatory system also responds. The heart beats faster and harder, pumping more blood through the body per minute.
- How does the body maintain homeostasis.
- What are the two most important central regulatory centers in the medulla called? (inspiratory and expiratory respiratory control centers)

Slide 42

> **Regulation of Respiration (cont'd.)**
>
> - Cerebral cortex
>   - Individual can change respiration characteristics voluntarily (singing, swimming, blowing balloon, etc.)
> - Receptors
>   - Chemoreceptors
>   - Located in carotid and aortic bodies
>   - Pulmonary stretch receptors
>   - Located throughout the pulmonary airways including the alveoli
>
> Copyright (c) 2008, 2005 by Mosby, Inc., an affiliate of Elsevier Inc. All rights reserved.   42

- These receptors sense various factors: carbon dioxide, oxygen, blood acid levels, amount of stretch in lung tissues, etc.
- Emotional and sensory input can alter normal breathing patterns.
- Ask students to name some activities that individuals engage in where the cerebral cortex momentarily controls respiration. (swimming, speaking, eating, stress, etc.)
- What receptors respond to changes in carbon dioxide, oxygen, and blood acid levels? (chemoreceptors)
- What is the purpose of the pulmonary receptors? (to protect the respiratory system from excess stretching caused by harmful overinflation)

Slide 43

> **Regulation of Respiration (cont'd.)**
>
>
>
> Copyright (c) 2008, 2005 by Mosby, Inc., an affiliate of Elsevier Inc. All rights reserved.   43

- Note the areas of the brain where the respiratory control centers are located and what they control.
- Where does the input come from? (Receptors from various parts of the body sense the need of a change in rate and depth of respirations and deliver the input to the medulla and pons.)
- Explain how the cerebral cortex can override respiration control by the brainstem. To what extent is this effective? (The cerebral cortex can voluntarily change the breathing rate and/or pattern by modifying the rate at which neurons fire in the respiratory centers of the medulla. However, cerebral control is limited. Carbon dioxide levels are much more powerful in controlling respirations.)
- Note locations of the various receptors. Why are there receptors located near the heart? (Adequate oxygenation is essential for proper cardiac function. Chemoreceptors lie near the heart. These receptors can sense increased CO_2 levels and will send nerve impulses to the respiratory center of the brain to modify respiratory rates so that more oxygen is made available.)

Slide 44

> **Types of Breathing**
>
> - **Eupnea:** normal breathing
> - **Hyperventilation:** rapid and deep respirations
> - **Hypoventilation:** slow and shallow respirations
> - **Dyspnea:** labored or difficult respirations
> - **Apnea:** stopped respirations
> - **Respiratory arrest:** failure to resume breathing after a period of apnea
>
> Copyright (c) 2008, 2005 by Mosby, Inc., an affiliate of Elsevier Inc. All rights reserved.   44

- Discuss possible remedies for these altered types of breathing in terms of what causes the altered respiration.

- What is sleep apnea? (Sleep apnea is a condition that results in brief but often frequent stops in breathing during sleep.) Discuss new research that indicates individuals with sleep apnea may be more prone to cardiac disorders.

- What is CPR, when is it indicated, and why is it effective? (Cardiopulmonary resuscitation is indicated when a person has suffered a cardiac and respiratory arrest. It can be effective in reviving patients. The heart is compressed, creating a pumping action. Air (oxygen) is delivered to the patient via artificial respiration. This can be a life-saving measure and should be learned by all people.)

Thibodeau/Patton

15 Lesson Plan
The Digestive System

TEACHING FOCUS

In this chapter, students will have the opportunity to learn the component parts of the gastrointestinal tract, their structures, and functions. Accessory organs to the digestive organs will be discussed in terms of their significance to the digestive process. Students will also have the opportunity to learn about the microscopic layers of the GI tract, the mechanical and chemical nature of digestion, and the process of carbohydrate, protein, and fat metabolism.

MATERIALS AND RESOURCES

☐ Anatomical charts, diagrams, or other teaching materials (diagram of the human body) (all Lessons)

☐ Microscopes and tissue slides or slide presentation with tissue sections (Lesson 15.1)

☐ Mirrors and penlights (Lesson 15.1)

☐ Computer (all Lessons)

LESSON CHECKLIST

Preparations for this lesson include:

- lecture
- guest speaker: laparoscopic GI surgeon, support group member
- student performance evaluation of all entry-level skills required for student comprehension and knowledge of the digestive system including:
  - o anatomical structures and their role in the digestive process
  - o mechanical and chemical digestion
  - o the function of digestive enzymes
  - o nutrient absorption and waste processes

KEY TERMS

absorption (pp. 392, 413)
alimentary canal (p. 391)
anal canal (p. 410)
anal sphincter (inner and outer) (p. 410)
anus (p. 407)
appendicitis (p. 410)
bicuspid (p. 396)
bile (p. 404)
bolus (p. 396)
cardiac (gastroesophageal) sphincter (p. 399)
cavity (p. 395)
cecum (p. 407)
chemical digestion (p. 408)
cholecystectomy (p. 405)
cholecystokinin (CCK) (p. 406)
chyme (p. 399)
colon (ascending, descending, transverse) (p. 408)
constipation (p. 407)
cuspid (p. 395)
deglutition (p. 412)
diarrhea (p. 407)

digestion (pp. 392, 404)
digestive system (p. 391)
duodenal papillae (minor and major) (p. 404)
duodenum (p. 403)
emulsify (p. 406)
esophagus (p. 399)
feces (p. 392)
frenulum (p. 394)
fundus (p. 400)
gastric glands (p. 400)
gastrointestinal (GI) tract (p. 391)
gastroesophageal reflux disease (GERD) (pp. 399, 401)
greater curvature (p. 400)
greater omentum (p. 410)
hepatic (right) colic flexure (p. 407)
hiatal hernia (p. 399)
ileocecal valve (p. 406)
ileum (p. 403)
intestinal glands (p. 403)
jaundice (p. 406)
jejunum (p. 403)

lacteal (p. 403)
large intestine (p. 406)
lesser curvature (p. 400)
lumen (p. 392)
mastication (p. 412)
mechanical digestion (p. 391)
mesentery (p. 392)
metabolism (p. 392)
microvilli (p. 403)
mucosa (p. 391)
muscularis (p. 392)
oral cavity (p. 393)
palate (hard and soft) (p. 393)
parotid gland (p. 397)
periodontal membrane (p. 395)
peristalsis (pp. 392, 395)
peritoneum (p. 410)
pharynx (p. 398)

plica (p. 403)
pyloric sphincter (p. 400)
pylorus (p. 400)
rectum (p. 410)
rugae (p. 400)
serosa (p. 392)
sigmoid colon (p. 410)
small intestine (p. 403)
splenic (left) colic flexure (p. 407)
stomach (p. 399)
submandibular gland (p. 397)
submucosa (p. 392)
tricuspid (p. 396)
ulcer (p. 403)
uvula (p. 394)
vermiform appendix (p. 410)
villus (p. 403)

ADDITIONAL RESOURCES

AnimationDirect (Book Companion CD)
Instructor's Electronic Resource (IER) (CD)
PowerPoint slides (CD, Evolve)
Test Bank (Evolve)

Legend

ESLR EVOLVE Student Learning Resource	**EILR TB** EVOLVE Instructor Learning Resource Test Bank	AnimationDirect on Book Companion CD	**PPT** PowerPoint Slides	**SG** Study Guide	**IRM** Instructor's Resource Manual

Class Activities are indicated in *bold italic*.

LESSON 15.1

PRETEST
Study Guide Multiple Choice questions 1-10 (pp. 188-189)

BACKGROUND ASSESSMENT
Question: Why is orthodontics an important dental specialty? Are the results achieved purely cosmetic? What are complications that can be expected from malocclusion?

Answer: Orthodontics can indeed play a cosmetic role in alleviating some structural problems of the teeth; however, it also provides important techniques for dealing with malocclusion and other structural irregularities. If left untreated, certain types of malocclusion can cause chronic headaches and pain in the temporomandibular joint. If the upper and lower teeth do not meet, mastication might be impeded. Food could spend a shorter time in the mouth and be swallowed in larger bits than normal. Digestion that normally occurs in the mouth might be shortened. This can affect the further process of digestion in the stomach, where digestive enzymes will have larger particles to deal with, and indigestion could result. Patients with malocclusion might also avoid certain foods, because they are too difficult to bite or chew, thus interfering with a balanced diet.

Question: A 19-year-old female patient visits the college infirmary with complaints of constant heartburn often accompanied by chest pain. The patient is very thin and is dressed warmly although it is a warm day. Would you suspect gastroesophageal reflux disease (GERD)? What other signs might be important in the assessment of this patient?

Answer: Although it is entirely possible that this patient might have GERD, the medical assistant should stay alert to other signs. A young student in the first year of college is facing many new situations and might be unsure of herself during this first year away from home. Insecurity might encourage eating disorders, which are very common among women in this age group. Patients with eating disorders such as anorexia nervosa might restrict eating and become very thin. Because there is little food to fuel metabolism, they might constantly feel chilly. Individuals with bulimia nervosa binge and purge. Consequences of purging include the presence of irritating stomach acid in the esophagus, much the same as in GERD. Another consequence of frequent purging is the destruction of tooth enamel due to prolonged contact with stomach acid during frequent episodes of vomiting. Such observations of the patient's emotional state might aid the physician in diagnosis, and if there is suspicion of an eating disorder, the patient can be directed to appropriate therapy. Eating disorders that are left untreated can be fatal. One tenth of all anorexia cases end in death. Survivors might have permanent damage to the heart and digestive system. Approximately 1% of females aged 15 to 30 have an eating disorder such as anorexia nervosa. This is an important consideration when dealing with this age group.

CRITICAL THINKING QUESTION
An 8-year-old child has extensive tooth decay in the second molar but no pain. Repairing the damage is expensive and will involve placement of a crown or cap, because there will be little supportive structure left after the decay has been removed. The parents question the value of this expensive treatment, because the tooth is due to fall out anyway between ages 10 and 14.

Guidelines: Tooth decay is caused by bacteria. It will probably be a number of years before the tooth falls out naturally and the decay will continue to progress if left unchecked. This can result in an infection in the pulp of the tooth, which can cause toothache involving the nerve. Entry of the infection into the bloodstream is also possible, with an attendant risk of systemic infection. It is also possible for the decay to progress to the roots and infect the adult tooth below it before it erupts. This could cause decay and damage to the permanent tooth. If the baby tooth is lost prematurely due to tooth decay, and the permanent tooth is not ready to erupt, a spacer will need to be placed to make sure that the other teeth do not encroach on the empty space left by the lost tooth and prevent the adult tooth from growing in.

OBJECTIVES	CONTENT	TEACHING RESOURCES
List and describe the four layers of the wall of the alimentary canal. Compare the lining layer in the esophagus, stomach, small intestine, and large intestine.	■ Wall of the digestive tract (p. 392) ■ Mouth (p. 393) ■ Teeth (p. 395) □ Typical tooth (p. 395) ■ Salivary glands (p. 397) ■ Pharynx (p. 398) ■ Esophagus (p. 399) ■ Stomach (p. 399) ■ Small intestine (p. 403) ■ Liver and gallbladder (p. 404) ■ Pancreas (p. 406) ■ Large intestine (p. 406)	⌧▤ Slides 6-9 ▥ Wall of the Digestive System questions 1-13 (p. 178) ✦ Multiple Choice questions 5-8, 42; True or False questions 7-9, 64; Short Answer question 3 ⊙ Mouth and Initiation of Mechanical Digestion ⊙ Pharynx ⊙ Esophagus ⊙ Stomach ⊙ Small Intestine ⊙ Large Intestine **Book Resources** Review question 1 (p. 419) Figure 15-1 Location of digestive organs (p. 393) ▸ Discuss the structure and length of the alimentary canal. What are the three kinds of processing that foods undergo in the alimentary canal? ▸ Discuss Figure 15-2 and describe the structure of the four layers of the alimentary canal wall as well as the function of each layer (p. 394). *Class Activity Have students work in groups of two or three and list the characteristics of the inner lining of the esophagus, stomach, small intestine, and large intestine, as well as the function of each structure. Have students explain how these characteristics contribute to their function in the body and describe what separates each of these structures from the others. Have each group present its list and descriptions to the entire class.* *Class Activity Have students work in small groups and examine slides of esophageal mucosa and stomach mucosa. Students should consider how these layers are different in the two structures. Based on the function of each structure, each group should explain why that particular type of mucosa is suited to that structure.*

OBJECTIVES	CONTENT	TEACHING RESOURCES

List in sequence each of the component parts or segments of the alimentary canal from the mouth to the anus and identify the accessory organs of digestion.	■ Mouth (p. 393)
	
	■ Teeth (p. 395)
	
	  ☐ Typical tooth (p. 395)
	
	■ Salivary glands (p. 397)
	
	■ Pharynx (p. 398)
	
	■ Esophagus (p. 399)
	
	■ Stomach (p. 399)
	
	■ Small intestine (p. 403)
	
	■ Liver and gallbladder (p. 404)
	
	■ Pancreas (p. 406)
	
	■ Large intestine (p. 406)
	
	■ Appendix (p. 410)
	
	■ Peritoneum (p. 410)
	
	  ☐ Extensions (p. 410)
		⊠ Slides 7-33
		
		Wall of the Digestive System questions 14-250 (p. 178)
		
		Mouth, Teeth, Salivary Glands questions 26-40 (pp. 179-180)
		
		Pharynx, Esophagus, Stomach questions 41-50 (p. 181)
		
		Applying What You Know questions 92, 93 (p. 185)
		
		e Multiple Choice questions 9-27, 41, 43-45; True or False questions 10-47, 65-74; Matching questions 1, 3-15; Short Answer questions 4-15
		
		Review questions 2, 6, 8, 10-12 (pp. 205-206); Critical Thinking question 18 (p. 207); Classroom Applications 1, 2 (p. 207); Lab Activities 1-5 (pp. 207-208); Practical/Creative Learning activities 1-3 (p. 208)
		
		Mouth and Initiation of Mechanical Digestion
		
		Pharynx
		
		Esophagus
		
		Stomach
		
		Small Intestine
		
		Large Intestine
		
		Book Resources
		
		Table 15-1 Organs of the digestive system (p. 392)
		
		Figure 15-3 Peristalsis (p. 395)
		
		Figure 15-4 The mouth cavity (p. 396)
		
		Quick Check questions 1-4 (p. 394)
		
		Figure 15-5 Longitudinal section of a tooth (p. 397)
		
		Figure 15-6 The deciduous (baby) teeth and adult teeth (p. 398)
		
		Figure 15-7 Location of the salivary glands (p. 399)

OBJECTIVES	CONTENT	TEACHING RESOURCES
		Figure 15-8 Stomach (p. 401)
		Figure 15-9 Small intestine (p. 402)
		Figure 15-10 The gallbladder and bile ducts (p. 404)
		Figure 15-11 Horizontal (transverse) section of the abdomen (p. 407)
		Figure 15-12 The large intestine (p. 408)
		Figure 15-13 Barium enhanced x-ray examination of the GI tract (p. 409)
		Figure 15-14 The peritoneum (p. 408)
		Figure 15-15 Digestion and absorption of nutrients, minerals, and water (p. 412)
		Review Questions 2-6, 8, 10-12 (pp. 418-419)
		Critical Thinking question 18 (p. 419)
		Clear View of the Human Body
		▶ Discuss Clinical Application Malocclusion (p. 400), including how dental malocclusion can affect mastication of food, and potential preventive and corrective approaches to malocclusion.
		▶ Discuss what the effect might be of blocked salivary ducts. Under what circumstances might this condition occur? (e.g., mumps, bacterial infection: sialadenitis, Sjögren's syndrome).
		▶ Discuss Figure 15-10 (p. 404), including the interrelationship of structure and function with regard to the small intestine.
		▶ Discuss Clinical Application: Gallstones and Weight Loss (p. 405). Explain the relationship of dieting and weight loss to gallstone formation. Discuss laparoscopic techniques for gallstone removal.
		▶ Discuss Figure 15-12 (p. 408), including identification of the divisions of the large intestine. Compare and contrast the structures and functions of the small and large intestines (diameter, length, mucosa, absorption, etc.).
		▶ Discuss why the pancreas is such an important organ, and name the functions it performs. Name and discuss several disorders that can result if the pancreas is unable to function normally.

OBJECTIVES	CONTENT	TEACHING RESOURCES
		Class Activity Have students work together in groups of two or three and list as many organs of the digestive system as possible; have one person write them down. This person acts as resource person to prompt the other members for any organs that have been left out, based on the information in Figure 15-1 (p. 393). Then groups try to locate the organs on the diagram of the human body on p. 198 of the Student Guide. The resource person checks the accuracy by consulting Figure 15-1 in the text and confirms or corrects the group's responses.
		Class Activity Working in groups of two, have students label the diagrams on pp. 199-204 of the Student Guide. After they have completed as much as they can, they may consult the labeled diagrams in the text to confirm their responses.
		Class Activity Have students work in groups of two or three and list the organs of the digestive system that are exocrine organs. Have them list what is secreted by each organ and the function it performs.
		Class Activity Using mirrors and penlights, have each student locate their own three pairs of salivary glands.
		Class Activity Working in small groups, have students consider what to say to encourage a patient diagnosed with moderately severe GERD to continue to take the medication prescribed on a regular basis. What long-term complications are possible if the condition is left untreated?
		Class Activity Invite a laparoscopic GI surgeon to speak to the class about laparoscopic surgery. Compare and contrast it to laparotomy. How does a surgeon train to perform laparoscopy?

15.1 Homework/Assignments:

Research eating disorders. Choose one eating disorder (anorexia nervosa, bulimia nervosa, or subthreshold eating disorders). Research signs and symptoms, treatment, prevention, and outcomes. Students who have chosen the same disorder should report their findings to the class as a group. Compare and contrast the disorders based on each group's findings.

15.1 Teacher's Notes:

LESSON 15.2

CRITICAL THINKING QUESTION

Low carbohydrate diets have been very popular recently. Many people today are going on variations of the high-protein, low-carbohydrate diet. Describe what happens in the body when only proteins and fat are ingested and carbohydrates are excluded. Are diets that are high in proteins and fat healthy weight-loss alternatives?

Guidelines: Restrictive diets such as this limit the amount of nutrients that can be ingested from the restricted foods, in this case, fruits, vegetables, and carbohydrates. Deficiencies in vitamins and minerals can result. Without carbohydrates as a source of energy, the body turns to burning its own fat. This can produce excess ketones in the bloodstream, a process called ketosis. This mimics a state similar to that of diabetic ketosis where, due to the presence of excess ketones in the bloodstream, the blood becomes more acidic than normal. Ketoacidosis can cause nausea and vomiting, and in extreme cases, death. Because the byproducts of this kind of metabolism are eliminated through the kidneys, this condition produces extra stress on the kidneys. Patients with heart problems should avoid stressing their bodies with a diet of this sort. Also, diets that include daily consumption of red meat have been related to colon cancer. Studies have shown that balanced, calorie-restricted diets produce weight loss comparable to high-protein diets, in spite of sensational media reports to the contrary. Patients should be encouraged to follow healthy weight-loss plans. Any patient who is on a restrictive weight-loss diet should be carefully monitored.

OBJECTIVES	CONTENT	TEACHING RESOURCES
Define *peristalsis, bolus, chyme, jaundice, ulcer,* and *diarrhea.*	These definitions appear throughout the chapter. Also see Key Terms list above for citations for each term.	Slide 33 Pharynx, Esophagus, Stomach questions 51-60 (p. 181) Small Intestine, Liver and Gallbladder, Pancreas questions 61-70 (pp. 182-183) Large Intestine, Appendix, Peritoneum questions 71-80 (p. 183) Digestive System crossword puzzle (p. 195) **Book Resources** Figure 15-3 Peristalsis (p. 395) Review question 7 (p. 419) ▶ Discuss Clinical Application: Treatment of Ulcers (p. 403). What are stomach ulcers and what causes them? What is the current standard of treatment for the majority of ulcers? ▶ Discuss the BRAT diet and when it is used. What is the principle on which it is based? ***Class Activity Work together in small groups and evaluate the following situation: A young child has been diagnosed with otitis media and the physician has prescribed antibiotics. Two days later, the mother calls to report that the child has diarrhea. What is going on, and how would you advise the mother? Report your findings/suspicions to the other groups.***

OBJECTIVES	CONTENT	TEACHING RESOURCES
		Class Activity **Provide each group with the drug insert for several different antibiotics that are commonly prescribed for pediatric otitis media. Have each group report on the common side effects listed in the inserts, and make recommendations based on the information provided.**
		Class Activity **One of the major complications of diarrhea is dehydration, especially in infants. Students can break into small groups and discuss why this is a problem and identify the symptoms of dehydration. Groups should list methods for rehydration and indicate under what circumstances they would be used, then report to the entire class.**
Define and contrast mechanical and chemical digestion.	■ Digestion (p. 412) ☐ Enzymes and chemical digestion (p. 412) ☐ Carbohydrate digestion (p. 413) ☐ Protein digestion (p. 413) ☐ Fat digestion (p. 413) ■ Absorption (p. 413)	⊠▪ Slide 36 📖 Chemical Digestion question 86 (p. 184) 📖 Applying What You Know question 94 (p. 185) ❷ Multiple Choice questions 28, 47; True or False question 48 **Book Resources** Table 15-2 Chemical Digestion (p. 414) Quick Check questions 1-3 (p. 415) Review question 13 (p. 419) ▸ Discuss the sequence of events that occurs when fat enters the digestive system. ▸ Discuss why the large intestine is less suited for absorption than the small intestine. What substances are absorbed by the large intestine? What causes constipation? *Class Activity* **Have students list the organs and structures involved in mechanical digestion and those involved in chemical digestion. What are the associated chemicals involved in these processes?** *Class Activity* **Work in small groups. Discuss which comes first, mechanical digestion or chemical digestion. Groups should list the sequential processes involved in both types of digestion, then report to the group.**

Structure & Function of the Body, 13th ed.

Thibodeau/Patton

OBJECTIVES	CONTENT	TEACHING RESOURCES
Discuss the basics of protein, fat, and carbohydrate digestion, and give the end products of each process.	■ Digestion (p. 412) □ Carbohydrate digestion (p. 413) □ Protein digestion (p. 413) □ Fat digestion (p. 413) ■ Absorption (p. 413)	⊠▤ Slides 37-40 ▨ Digestion, Absorption, Metabolism questions 81-85 (pp. 183-184) ▨ Check Your Knowledge questions 11-20 (p. 189) 𝒆 Multiple Choice questions 29-40; True or False questions 49-60; Matching questions 2, 16-25; Short Answer questions 16-21 ▨ Lab Activity 6 (p. 208); Practical/Creative Learning Activity 4 (p. 208) **Book Resources** Review Questions 14-17 (p. 419) ▸ Discuss Figure 15-15, including the digestion and absorption of nutrients, minerals, and water. Differentiate which items are transferred by osmosis, diffusion, and active transport. Observe the "breakdown" that must occur for some complex molecules to be absorbed. ▸ Discuss Table 15-2 and identify which enzymes are found in more than one location. Why? Which nutrient is only digested in the small intestine? What enzyme is involved in the digestion of fat? Where does fat digestion occur? ▸ Discuss food absorption. Describe the structural adaptations of the alimentary canal that allow absorption of nutrients. *Class Activity **Compare and contrast where carbohydrate, protein, and fat digestion begin. Students should list the enzymes involved in each process.*** *Class Activity **Have students form small groups and prepare a table listing the digestive enzymes and juices found in the following components of the digestive system: mouth, stomach, pancreas, small intestine. List the substance that each enzyme digests and the resulting product.***

OBJECTIVES	CONTENT	TEACHING RESOURCES
Performance Evaluation		*e* Chapter 15 Computerized Test Bank questions Student Assignment (pp. 209-223) *e* Student Post-Test questions

---

15.2 Homework/Assignments:

Research the symptoms of appendicitis, its diagnosis, and treatment. Write a short paper that describes the results of your research. Structure your results in such a way that it can become an easy reference work in clinical practice.

Work together in small groups. List as many conditions as you can that can cause jaundice. Choose one condition, and research it on the Internet. Report back to the other groups about this condition (other symptoms, diagnosis, common treatments) and explain what causes the jaundice.

15.2 Teacher's Notes:

ELSEVIER

Structure & Function of the Body, 13th ed.

Thibodeau/Patton

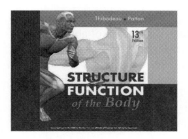

Slide 1

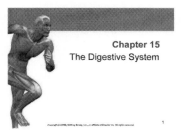

Chapter 15
The Digestive System

Slide 2

Chapter 15
Lesson 15.1

Slide 3

Learning Objectives

- List in sequence each of the component parts or segments of the alimentary canal from the mouth to the anus and identify the accessory organs of digestion
- List and describe the four layers of the wall of the alimentary canal. Compare the lining layer in the esophagus, stomach, small intestine, and large intestine
- Discuss the basics of protein, fat, and carbohydrate digestion and give the end products of each process

- How long is the gastrointestinal tract? (9 m, about 29 feet, long)
- Foods are digested in and absorbed from the gastrointestinal tract.
- Metabolism: products of digestion are metabolized in the cells of the body

Slide 4

Learning Objectives (cont'd.)

- Define and contrast mechanical and chemical digestion
- Define *peristalsis, bolus, chyme, jaundice, ulcer,* and *diarrhea*

4

- What is the name of the inside, or hollow space, within the tube of the digestive tract? (lumen)
- Mucosa: Varies according to structure
- Muscularis: Responsible for peristalsis
- Serosa: Serous membrane that covers the outside of abdominal organs; it attaches the digestive tract to the wall of the abdominopelvic cavity by forming folds called *mesenteries.*

Slide 5

Digestive System

- Structure
  - Alimentary canal or gastrointestinal (GI) tract
- Functions
  - Digestion
  - Absorption

5

- Note the locations of the major digestive organs. Point out the accessory organs of each major organ.

Slide 6

Wall of the Digestive Tract

- Four layers of tissue (inside to outside)
  - Mucosa
  - Submucosa
  - Muscularis
  - Serosa

6

Slide 7

Organs and Structures of the GI Tract

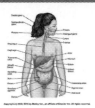

7

- Note the four layers of the wall of the digestive tract. Although this is a section of the small intestine, the layers are typical throughout the intestinal tract.
- Point out the location of blood vessels, lymph nodules, and nerves.
- Explain why the nerves are located closest to the muscular layer and the blood vessels are closest to the mucosal layer.

ELSEVIER
Copyright © 2008, 2005 by Mosby, Inc., an affiliate of Elsevier Inc.

Structure & Function of the Body, 13th ed.
Thibodeau/Patton

Slide 8

- What is the function of the uvula? (It prevents food from entering the nasal cavities.)
- What is the lingual frenulum? (a membrane which attaches the tongue to the floor of the mouth)
- What happens when the frenulum is too short? Discuss therapies for this condition. (Free movements of the tongue are impaired, and one has difficulty in enunciating words.)

Slide 9

Wall of the Digestive Tract

Section of the Small Intestine

- What might be the effect of deformities in the hard palate? (The hard palate has an important role in making speech sounds. Deformities may affect speech and speech development. The high arched palate may hamper visualization of the larynx and impede placement of airway.)

Slide 10

Mouth

- Roof
  - Hard palate
  - Soft palate
  - Uvula
- Floor
  - Tongue and its muscles
  - Papillae
    - Taste buds
  - Lingual frenulum

- Compare and contrast the epiglottis and the uvula.
- Note the entry of salivary ducts into the mouth.

ELSEVIER

Structure & Function of the Body, 13th ed.

Thibodeau/Patton

Slide 11

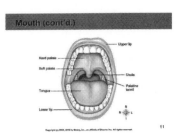

- What is the major function of the bicuspids and tricuspids? (extensive breakdown of food in the mouth, chewing)
- How are they structurally suited for performing this function? (These teeth have large flat surfaces with two [bi] or three [tri] crushing "cusps" on their surface.)
- Crown: Visible part of tooth.
- What covers the outside of the tooth? (enamel)
- What is the neck of the tooth? (the portion in direct contact with the gums)
- Root: Holds the tooth in the socket which is lined with a fibrous periodontal membrane; connected to the pulp which is the central-most part of the tooth
- What important structures are found in the pulp? (nerves; blood and lymphatic vessels)
- Why does a dentist anesthetize when drilling? (to decrease the sensation of pain as nerve endings are present in the tooth)

Slide 12

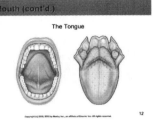

- Point out the parts of the tooth.
- Note that the tooth socket is actually set in the bone of the jaw, rooted in place by the periodontal membrane.
- What causes tooth decay? (bacteria)
- What is a root canal procedure? Under what circumstances would a dentist perform a root canal? (Exploration of the inner portion of the tooth, or root, due to infection.)

Slide 13

Teeth

- Four major types
  - Incisors
  - Cuspids
  - Premolars
  - Molars
- Sections of a typical tooth
  - Crown
  - Neck
  - Root

- Discuss the importance of the baby teeth in maintaining the health of the permanent teeth.
- When are baby teeth formed as opposed to when they erupt? (Initial dental development beings in utero at about 5-6 weeks, with tooth bud formation beginning around week 17.)
- What is gum disease, and why is it significant? (Gum disease is called periodontitis and is a generalized and serious type of inflammation and infection. The infection invades the deeper portions of the tooth and can result in tooth loss.)
- Why do heart patients and diabetics take prophylactic antibiotics prior to a dental visit? (to prevent infection; heart patients are at risk for endocarditis and diabetics are at risk for various localized and systemic infections)
- What does the current literature suggest? (The current literature supports the use of antibiotics in these patients. However there is ongoing debate regarding use of antibiotics for patients who have joint replacements.)

ELSEVIER

Structure & Function of the Body, 13th ed.

Thibodeau/Patton

Slide 14

Teeth (cont'd.)

- ● Point out the locations and the names of the teeth.
- ● Correlate baby teeth with corresponding adult teeth (note premolars and wisdom teeth in adult set).
- ● What are some common problems associated with the wisdom teeth? (failure of wisdom teeth to erupt; decay)

Slide 15

Teeth (cont'd.)

- Deciduous teeth (baby teeth)
  - 20 teeth
  - 6 months: average age for first eruption
  - Complete set at about 2 years of age
- Permanent teeth (adult teeth)
  - 32 teeth
  - 6 years: Average age for first eruption
  - Complete set between 17-24 years of age

- ● What do the salivary glands secrete? (saliva)
- ● What important digestive enzyme is in saliva? (salivary amylase, which begins the chemical digestion of carbohydrates)
- ● Where does the process of digestion begin? (in the mouth)

Slide 16

Teeth (cont'd.)

- ● Identify where each of these glands opens into the mouth.
- ● What are mumps? Which salivary gland is involved? (Mumps is an infection of the parotid gland.)
- ● What happens when the salivary glands fail to function? (When the salivary glands fail to function, digestion could be compromised, because saliva contains amylase, a substance that assists with the digestion of carbohydrates [CHO]. One would also have a dry mouth and difficulty with chewing.)

Slide 17

Salivary Glands

- Parotid glands
- Submandibular glands
- Sublingual glands

- ● What two systems are served by the pharynx? (It serves both the respiratory system and the digestive system.)

ELSEVIER

Slide 18

Salivary Glands (cont'd.)

Location of the Salivary Glands

Slide 19

Pharynx

- Dual function
- Tubelike structure made of muscle and lined with mucous membrane
  - Air must pass through pharynx on its way to the lungs
  - Food must pass through pharynx on its way to the stomach

- Discuss the location of the stomach relative to other structures of the gastrointestinal tract and other structures of the body.
- Discuss gastric juice composition and function.
- Explain how the three muscle layers running lengthwise, crosswise, and obliquely contribute to the process of digestion.
- What are rugae? (Folds in the lining of the stomach.)

Slide 20

Esophagus

- Muscular, mucus-lined tube that connects the pharynx with the stomach
- Peristaltic action conducts food to the stomach
- Mucous secretion facilitates passage of food

- Subdivisions of the stomach: fundus, body, pylorus
- Describe the areas of the stomach called the *lesser curvature* and *greater curvature*.
- Describe the location and function of the gastroesophageal (cardiac) sphincter and pyloric sphincter
- Discuss hiatal hernia.
- Discuss gastroesophageal reflux disease (GERD) and treatment options.
- Why do lay people refer to *GERD* as *heartburn?* (The sensation of heartburn occurs in the chest in the espophagus, near the location of the heart.)

Slide 21

Stomach

- Size
  - About size of a large sausage when empty
  - Expands after large meal
- **Pylorus:** Lower part of stomach
  - Pyloric sphincter muscle
- Wall
  - Smooth muscle fibers
  - Contractions produce churning movements
- Lining
  - Mucous membrane
  - Microscopic glands

- Discuss the function of the villi and microvilli and how they are a prime example of the intimate relationship between structure and function.

ELSEVIER

Structure & Function of the Body, 13th ed.
Thibodeau/Patton

Slide 22

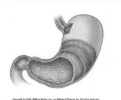

Stomach (cont'd.)

- Observe the structural details of the mucosal wall. Why is the small intestine so well suited for the absorption of nutrients? (Due to the numerous villi, which increase its surface area.)
- What is the function of the lacteal and where is it located? (Lacteals are responsible for the absorption of fats and are located in the villi of the small intestine.)
- What is a plica? (plicae [plural] are the circular folds present in the small intestine.)

Slide 23

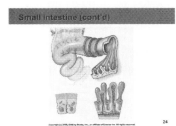

Small Intestine

- Size
  - 7 m (20 feet) long and 2 cm in diameter
- Divisions
  - Duodenum
  - Jejunum
  - Ileum
- Smooth muscle fibers stimulate peristalsis
- Mucous membrane lining—microscopic glands
- Villi and microvilli

- Point out the location of the liver and note its size relative to the other organs.
- What are the two main components of bile? (cholesterol and bile salts)
- What effect might dieting have on the production of bile? (There can be imbalances in bile chemistry and delayed emptying of the gallbladder, which can lead to gallstone formation.)
- What is jaundice? (yellowish discoloration of the skin) Explain under what circumstances it might occur. (Jaundice can occur in hepatitis or other liver disorders, as well as disorders which obstruct the flow of bile, such as gallstones in the hepatic duct or the common bile duct.)

Slide 24

Small Intestine (cont'd)

- What hormone comes into play when fat is detected in the chyme? (cholecystokinin)
- Discuss under what conditions gallstones might form. (rapid weight loss, inadequate emptying of the gallbladder, poor gallbladder contraction)
- What are the symptoms of a "gallstone attack"? (Abdominal pain that can radiate to the right shoulder; nausea and vomiting)
- What would happen if the common hepatic duct was obstructed? (jaundice)

Slide 25

Liver and Gallbladder

- Liver
  - Largest gland in the body
    - Fills upper right section of abdominal cavity and extends into left side
  - Secretes bile
  - Ducts
    - **Hepatic duct:** Drains bile from liver
    - **Cystic duct:** Bile enters and leaves gallbladder
    - **Common bile duct:** Drains bile from hepatic or cystic ducts into duodenum

25

- What would happen if the common bile duct was obstructed by a gallstone? What signs and symptoms would appear? (An obstructed CBD would result in a backup of bile into the gallbladder and liver. Fats would not be properly emulsified. Patients with an obstructed CBD would experience pain, digestive problems, and possibly jaundice.)

- What would happen if the cystic duct was blocked? (Bile can no longer enter the gallbladder but will flow directly into the small intestine. There is no jaundice.)

- What extreme diets are more commonly associated with the formation of gallstones? (very low calorie or ultra low fat diets)

- Point out the location of the pancreas and pancreatic duct in preparation for the next slide.

Slide 26

Liver and Gallbladder (cont'd.)

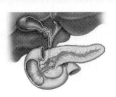

26

- Pancreatic duct joins common bile duct and empties into the duodenum.

- Why is pancreatic juice the most important digestive juice? (The juices are capable of digesting all three major kinds of food, proteins, fats and carbohydrates.) What would happen if someone had pancreatitis? (Pancreatitis causes abdominal pain and can impair digestion and also raise blood sugars.)

- The pancreas is both an endocrine and an exocrine gland.

Slide 27

Liver and Gallbladder (cont'd.)

- Gallbladder
  - Located under surface of the liver
  - Concentrates and stores bile produced in the liver

27

- How long does it normally take for food to pass through the entire alimentary canal? (3-5 days)

- What consistency is the chyme by the time it reaches the large intestine? Is it still referred to as chyme at this point? (In the large intestine the former chyme is now the consistency of fecal matter, and is referred to as such.)

- From what food materials can the large intestine extract some nutrient value? (cellulose and other fibrous materials)

- What is in the large intestine that enables this digestion? (bacteria)

- What other functions do the intestinal bacteria perform? (synthesis of vitamin K and some B-complex vitamins)

Slide 28

Pancreas

- Located behind stomach
  - Main duct empties into duodenum
- Functions
  - Pancreatic juice is the most important digestive juice
  - Pancreatic islets (islets of Langerhans)
    - Cells not connected with pancreatic ducts
    - Secrete hormones, glucagon, and insulin into the blood

28

- Locate and name the sphincters or valves that control intake and output from the large intestine. (ileocecal sphincter at the junction of the ileum and cecum and the anal sphincters at the terminal portion of the large intestine) How many surround the anal opening? (2, inner and outer)

- Locate the ascending colon. Explain how fecal matter is pushed upwards (against gravity) in the ascending colon.

- Where is the appendix located? (right lower quadrant of the abdomen) What are current theories about what function (if any) the appendix performs (or performed)? (May play a role in immunologic defense mechanisms.)

- What is appendicitis? (inflammation of the appendix) What are symptoms of appendicitis? (RLQ pain, nausea, vomiting, diarrhea, elevated WBC count) With what other conditions can it be confused? (mesentery adenitis, ectopic pregnancy, bowel obstruction) What diagnostic procedures aid in the diagnosis? (CT scans, CBC)

Slide 29

Large Intestine

- Size
  - 1.5 m (5 ft) long, 6.3 cm (2.5 inch) diameter
- Segments
  - Cecum, ascending colon, transverse colon, descending colon, sigmoid colon, rectum, anal canal
- Composition
  - Smooth muscle fibers promote churning, peristalsis, and defecation
  - Lining—mucous membrane

9

- Parietal layer lines the abdominal cavity.

- Visceral layer forms the outer covering of each abdominal organ.

- Peritoneal space is the space between the two layers.

- What is contained in the peritoneal space and what function does it serve? (Peritoneal fluid is present to keep the peritoneal layers moist and able to freely slide against each other during breathing and digestive movements.)

Slide 30

Large Intestine (cont'd.)

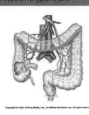

30

- Point out the color-coded spaces, organs, and layers in relationship to other organs.

- What structures or organs lie retroperitoneally? (pancreas, duodenum, rectum, bladder, kidneys) What does this mean? (outside of the peritoneum)

- Explain peritonitis.

ELSEVIER

...

Slide 31

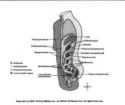

Peritoneum

- Serous membrane lining abdominal cavity and covering abdominal organs
  - Parietal layer
  - Visceral layer
  - Peritoneal space

Slide 32

Peritoneum (cont'd.)

Slide 33

Peritoneum (cont'd.)

- Extensions
  - Mesentery
    - Shaped like a pleated fan
    - Extension of parietal peritoneum
    - Attaches most of small intestine to posterior abdominal wall
  - Greater omentum (lace apron)
    - Pouchlike extension of the visceral peritoneum
    - Hangs down from lower edge of stomach and transverse colon over intestines
    - May obscure inflamed appendix

- Additional time can be spent discussing clinical aspects of conditions such as jaundice, ulcers, and diarrhea.

Slide 34

**Chapter 15
Lesson 15.2**

- How do mechanical and chemical digestion differ?
- Mechanical digestion: chewing, swallowing, and peristalsis break food into tiny particles, mix them well with digestive juices, and move them along the digestive tract.
- Chemical digestion: digestive enzymes break up large food molecules into smaller molecules that can be absorbed into the blood and lymph.

Structure & Function of the Body, 13th ed.
Thibodeau/Patton

Slide 35

Review of important terms

- Peristalsis
- Bolus
- Chyme
- Jaundice
- Ulcer
- Diarrhea

35

- Note and discuss the processes involved in transporting substances from the cells of walls of the GI tract into the blood and lymph systems (active transport, osmosis, diffusion, secretion).

Slide 36

Digestion

- **Definition:** Process by which foods are altered so that they can be absorbed and used by cells
  - Mechanical digestion
  - Chemical digestion

36

- What is the difference between simple sugars and complex sugars? (Simple sugars are monosaccharides [one sugar molecules]. Complex sugars are composed of two or more sugar molecules.)
- Why do complex sugars have to be broken down in order to be absorbed? (Only simple sugars are able to pass from the small intestine into the bloodstream.)
- What are the major end products of carbohydrate digestion? (monosaccharides)
- Discuss the cause and treatment of lactose intolerance.
- Only monosaccharides are capable of being absorbed (e.g., glucose).

Slide 37

Digestion (cont'd.)

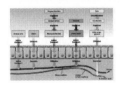

37

Slide 38

Digestion (cont'd.)

- **Carbohydrate digestion:** Occurs mainly in small intestine
  - Pancreatic amylase breaks polysaccharides down to disaccharides
  - Intestinal juice enzymes
    - **Maltase:** Changes maltose to glucose
    - **Sucrase:** Changes sucrose to glucose
    - **Lactase:** Changes lactose to glucose

38

- Is bile a component of chemical digestion or mechanical digestion? Why? (mechanical, as it only breaks fat into smaller components)
- Why aren't fatty acids secreted into the blood capillaries instead of the lacteals? (Because fatty acids enter the lymphatic system.)

Structure & Function of the Body, 13th ed.
Thibodeau/Patton

Slide 39

Digestion (cont'd.)

- Protein digestion: Starts in stomach; completes in small intestine
  - Pepsin: Gastric juice, partially digests proteins
  - Trypsin: Pancreatic enzyme, continues digestion of proteins
  - Peptidases: Intestinal enzymes, complete digestion of partially digested proteins to amino acids

- What is the difference between digestion and absorption of foods? (Digestion involves the breakdown of foods into components that can enter the bloodstream through absorption. Digestion must precede absorption.)

- What is the significance of salt being absorbed into the bloodstream? (Salt contains important chemicals, sodium and chloride, which are necessary for proper fluid and electrolyte balance.)

- What is the principle on which fluid replacement drinks, such as Gatorade and other sport drinks, are based? (contain important chemicals, called *electrolytes,* which are often lost during exercise and need to be replaced)

- Summarize the end products of digestion; reinforce absorption process.

- Discuss the digestion and absorption of nutrients, minerals, and water as seen on page 412, Figure 15-16.

Slide 40

Digestion (cont'd.)

- Fat digestion
  - Bile
    - Contains no enzymes but emulsifies fats (breaks fat droplets into very small droplets)
  - Pancreatic lipase
    - Changes emulsified fats to fatty acids and glycerol in small intestine
  - End products
    - Fatty acids
    - Glycerol

- Is bile a component of chemical digestion or mechanical digestion? Why? (mechanical, as it only breaks fat into smaller components)

- Why aren't fatty acids secreted into the blood capillaries instead of the lacteals? (Because fatty acids enter the lymphatic system.)

Slide 41

Absorption

- Movement of digested food molecules from the mucous membrane of the intestine into blood or lymph
- Where does absorption occur?
  - Small intestine: Foods and most water
  - Large intestine: Some water and vitamins synthesized in the large intestine

- What is the difference between digestion and absorption of foods? (Digestion involves the breakdown of foods into components that can enter the bloodstream through absorption. Digestion must precede absorption)

- What is the significance of salt being absorbed into the bloodstream? (Salt contains important chemicals, sodium and chloride, which are necessary for proper fluid and electrolyte balance.)

- What is the principle on which fluid replacement drinks, such as Gatorade and other sport drinks, are based? (contain important chemicals, called *electrolytes*, which are often lost during exercise and need to be replaced)

- Summarize the end products of digestion; reinforce absorption process.

- Discuss the digestion and absorption of nutrients, minerals, and water as seen on page 412, Figure 15-16.

Structure & Function of the Body, 13th ed.

Thibodeau/Patton

Lesson Plan
16 | Nutrition and Metabolism

TEACHING FOCUS

In this chapter, students will have the opportunity to focus on the basic principles of nutrition and metabolism, including the basics of the metabolic cycles involved in the processing of nutrients. Principles of nutrition are covered in terms of the functions performed by the various nutrients. Basal metabolic rate and the physiological regulators of body temperature are also presented.

MATERIALS AND RESOURCES

☐ Anatomical charts, diagrams, or other teaching materials (diagram of the human body) (all Lessons)

☐ Computer (all Lessons)
☐ Ear thermometers (Lesson 16.2)
☐ Oral thermometers (Lesson 16.2)

LESSON CHECKLIST

Preparations for this lesson include:

- lecture
- demonstration
- guest speaker: exercise physiologist, dietician, nutritionist
- student performance evaluation of all entry-level skills required for student comprehension and application of nutrition and metabolism principles including:
  - the anatomy and physiology of the metabolic process
  - the function of nutrients and associated terminology
  - the metabolic cycles and related terminology
  - the relationship between nutrition and metabolism

ELSEVIER

KEY TERMS

aerobic (p. 424)
anabolism (p. 423)
anaerobic (p. 424)
assimilation (p. 423)
basal metabolic rate (BMR) (p. 428)
calorie (p. 431)
catabolism (p. 423)
citric acid cycle (p. 424)
electron transfer system (p. 424)
essential amino acids (p. 428)
glycogenesis (p. 425)

glycolysis (p. 424)
insulin (p. 426)
kilocalorie (p. 431)
metabolism (p. 423)
mineral (p. 428)
nonessential amino acids (p. 428)
nutrition (p. 423)
thermoregulation (p. 431)
total metabolic rate (TMR) (p. 430)
vitamin (p. 428)

ADDITIONAL RESOURCES

AnimationDirect (Book Companion CD)
Instructor's Electronic Resource (IER) (CD)
PowerPoint slides (CD, Evolve)
Test Bank (Evolve)

Legend

ESLR	**EILR TB**	AnimationDirect	**PPT**	**SG**	**IRM**
EVOLVE Student Learning Resource	EVOLVE Instructor Learning Resource Test Bank	on Book Companion CD	PowerPoint Slides	Study Guide	Instructor's Resource Manual

Class Activities are indicated in ***bold italic.***

Structure & Function of the Body, 13th ed.
Thibodeau/Patton

LESSON 16.1

PRETEST

1. In the process of glucose catabolism _____ changes glucose into pyruvic acid.
2. The liver secretes a substance called _____, which helps the digestive process by breaking down lipids.
3. If cells have insufficient amounts of glucose to catabolize for energy, they shift to the catabolism of _____.
4. _____ amino acids can be made by the body.
5. The _____ is the number of calories of heat that must be produced per hour by catabolism to keep the body functioning at normal, comfortable levels.
6. Which of the following is NOT a step in the process of glucose catabolism?
   a. citric acid cycle
   b. avitaminosis
   c. glycolysis
   d. electron transfer system
7. Which of the following is not primarily catabolized for energy?
   a. carbohydrates
   b. fats
   c. proteins
   d. none of the above
8. Which of the following processes do not require oxygen?
   a. anaerobic
   b. aerobic
   c. both of the above
   d. none of the above
9. A deficiency in which of the following vitamins may result in scurvy?
   a. vitamin A
   b. vitamin B
   c. vitamin C
   d. vitamin D
10. At the skin, heat can be lost from the blood through which of the following mechanisms?
    a. radiation
    b. conduction
    c. convection
    d. all of the above

Answers: 1. glycolysis; 2. bile; 3. fats; 4. Non-essential; 5. basal metabolic rate (BMR); 6. b; 7. c; 8. a; 9. c; 10. d

BACKGROUND ASSESSMENT

Question: Two individuals are on the same weight-loss diet. One weighs 180 lbs. and the other 160 lbs. The total intake per day is 2,000 kcal for each person. The 180-lb. person is losing weight much faster than the lighter individual in spite of consuming identical amounts of the same foods. How can you explain this?

Answer: The number of calories needed per hour to support the bodily functions (BMR) of the heavier individual is likely to be higher than that of the lighter individual, because there are 20 more pounds of organs and tissue to support. The 180-lb. person needs more calories just to keep the body functioning. In other words, his/her basal metabolic rate is higher. On the same calorie-restricted diet, the heavier person will lose more quickly, all other factors being equal. Furthermore, the total metabolic rate of the heavier person might be higher, the heavier individual might be more active than the lighter individual, or there could be differences in the environmental temperatures.

Question: At the beginning of an episode of the flu, a patient reports that he felt chilly although he covered himself with more blankets. Then he reported having a fever. Hours later, he was feeling hot and started sweating. What's happening?

Answer: The hypothalamus regulates body temperature, keeping it within the normal range at the body's set point. When a person is in a cold or warm environment, or an infection is being fought off, the hypothalamus might reset the set point to initiate homeostatic mechanisms that will cause body temperature to change as needed. When a fever occurs in response to a pathogen, the set point is raised. Because the body temperature at this point is still lower than the set point, a person will feel cold and vasoconstriction and other mechanisms will kick in to raise the body temperature to the new set point, where it is maintained. When the pyrogenic influence is removed, the set point is lowered back to normal. At this moment, the body temperature is now higher than the set point, so the individual will feel hot, and the body will strive to lower the temperature by measures such as sweating and vasodilation of the blood vessels in the skin.

CRITICAL THINKING QUESTION

A friend is considering becoming a vegetarian. How would you advise him from a health standpoint? What things are important to consider? What deficiencies could result from eating a vegetarian diet that does not take these things into consideration?

Guidelines: Vegetarian diets can be very healthy if certain requirements are maintained. Meat supplies large amounts of protein in the human diet. Plant sources also supply protein but in lesser amounts. To attain recommended dietary allowances of protein, one might have to consume more plant sources of protein, gram for gram, than if one were eating meat. However, the recommended daily amount of protein for an adult male is only 60-80 grams. This is relatively easy to achieve even when following a vegetarian diet. In general, both plant and animal protein sources contain all essential amino acids, although some sources are richer in some amino acids than others. Eggs, cow's milk, soybeans, quinoa (a grain), and spinach (as well as meat and fish) are considered high-quality protein that contain all the essential amino acids. If the diet includes a wide variety of healthy foods, vitamin and mineral deficiencies are unlikely. Refer your friend to USDA recommendations and to the American Dietetic Association's Web site for vegetarian diet guidelines.

OBJECTIVES	CONTENT	TEACHING RESOURCES
Define and contrast catabolism and anabolism.	■ Role of the liver (p. 424)	Slides 4, 5
		The Role of the Liver questions 1-5 (p. 198)
		Check Your Knowledge questions 1, 10 (pp. 203-204)
		Multiple Choice questions 1-8, 31, 32 (pp. 1-2, 6)
		True or False questions 1-7, 54-56 (pp. 7-8, 13)
		Short Answer questions 1-3 (p. 15)
		Classroom Application questions 1, 2 (p. 219)
		Book Resources
		Review questions 1, 2 (p. 435)
		Critical Thinking questions 16, 17 (p. 435)
		▶ Discuss nutrition versus metabolism.

OBJECTIVES	CONTENT	TEACHING RESOURCES
		▸ Discuss and define catabolism and anabolism. Note anabolic bodybuilding. Is this a healthy way to build muscle? Why or why not? *Class Activity Divide the class into small groups and have them list at least six functions of the liver. Each group should have a representative describe the functions their group listed, focusing on the substances that the liver synthesizes in as much detail as possible.* *Class Activity Have groups discuss the consequences of liver failure*
Describe the metabolic roles of carbohydrates, fats, proteins, vitamins, and minerals.	■ Nutrient metabolism (p. 424) ☐ Carbohydrate metabolism (p. 424) ☐ Fat metabolism (p. 427) ☐ Protein metabolism (p. 427) ■ Vitamins and minerals (p. 428)	▣ Slides 6-13 📖 Nutrient Metabolism questions 6-20 (p. 198) 📖 Applying What You Know questions 36, 37 (p. 200) 📖 Nutrition/Metabolism crossword puzzle (p. 202) 📖 Check Your Knowledge questions 2-8, 11-14 (pp. 203-204) 📧 Multiple Choice questions 9-23, 33-35; True or False questions 8-42, 57-61; Matching questions 11-18; Short Answer questions 4-11, 15 📖 Classroom Application question 4 (p. 220); Practical/Creative Learning Activities questions 1-3 (p. 220) 💿 Glycolysis 💿 Citric Acid Cycle **Book Resources** Figure 16-2 The structure of ATP (p. 426) Figure 16-3 Catabolism of nutrients (p. 427) Table 16-1 Amino Acids (p. 428) Quick Check questions 1-4 (p. 428) Review questions 3-13 (p. 435) Critical Thinking questions 18 (p. 435) ▸ Discuss how the process described in Figure 16-1 Catabolism of glucose (p. 428) releases energy, and note the anaerobic and aerobic

Thibodeau/Patton

OBJECTIVES	CONTENT	TEACHING RESOURCES
		phases.
		▶ Discuss the role and function of vitamins and minerals in metabolism. Refer to Table 16-2 Major Vitamins (p. 429) and Table 16-3 Major Minerals (p. 430).
		Class Activity Divide the class into small groups. Have each group make a table to compare and contrast glycolysis, the citric acid cycle, and the electron transfer system. Each table should list where each reaction occurs and whether or not it requires oxygen. Furthermore, the tables should list what bonds are broken and what molecules result from each of these chemical reactions.
		Class Activity Have the class work in small groups to design a well-balanced weight-maintenance diet for one day for one of the following: an adult male weighing 170 lbs., an adult male vegan weighing 170 lbs., an adult female weighing 130 lbs., or a child weighing 35 lbs. Consult the American Dietetic Association Web site for information on nutrition at http://www.eatright.org/Public. *Compare and contrast the nutritional needs of the various subjects.*
		Class Activity On a separate sheet of paper, have the class list all the major vitamins and minerals from Tables 16-2 and 16-3 (pp. 429-430). Without consulting these tables, ask the students to list as many food sources for each vitamin and mineral as possible in five minutes. After the time is up, ask students to consult the text or other nutrition sources for accuracy. Discuss foods that were surprising sources for certain vitamins and minerals.
		Class Activity Have students keep a record of their food consumption for 48 hours. Divide students into small groups and have them determine the approximate amount of calorie consumption.
		Class Activity Have students review the nutritional information listed on the labels of the snacks they bring to class.

16.1 Homework/Assignments:

Ask students to research current theories about BMI with regard to the point at which an individual is considered to be overweight or obese.

16.1 Teacher's Notes:

LESSON 16.2

CRITICAL THINKING QUESTION

What is body temperature and how does the body regulate it? What gland oversees thermoregulation in the body? What mechanisms allow heat to be lost from blood?

Guidelines: Body temperature is a measure of the body's ability to generate and get rid of heat. The body is very good at keeping its temperature within a narrow range despite large variations in temperature outside the body. The hypothalamus operates negative-feedback mechanisms that maintain body temperature within its normal range. When the body must conserve heat, blood flow in the warm organs of the body's core increases; when heat must be lost to maintain homeostasis, flow of warm blood to the skin increases. The skin is often involved in negative-feedback loops that maintain body temperature. When the body is overheated, the blood vessels in the skin expand (dilate) to carry excess heat to the skin's surface. At the skin surface, heat can be lost from blood through radiation, conduction, convection, or evaporation.

OBJECTIVES	CONTENT	TEACHING RESOURCES
Define basal metabolic rate and list some factors that affect it.	■ Metabolic rates (p. 428)	⊠ Slides 15-17 Metabolic Rates, Body Temperature questions 21-23 (p. 199) Applying What You Know question 35 (p. 200) Check Your Knowledge questions 15-16 (p. 212) *e* Multiple Choice questions 24-27, 36; True or False questions 43-48; Matching questions 1-10; Short Answer questions 12, 13 Practical/Creative Learning Activities question 5 (p. 220) **Book Resources** Review question 14 (p. 435) Critical Thinking question 19 (p. 435) Appendix A: Body Mass Index (BMI) (p. 546) ▸ Discuss the basal metabolic rate and some of the factors that affect it. Refer to Figure 16-4 Factors that determine the basal and total metabolic rate (p. 431). ▸ Discuss the epidemic of obesity. What are some reasons that obesity is more prevalent than it has been? Identify risks and medical conditions associated with being overweight. ***Class Activity On a blank sheet of paper (no names), have students write down their height and weight. Using Appendix A, students should compute their BMI and record if they are underweight, overweight,***

OBJECTIVES	CONTENT	TEACHING RESOURCES
		obese, or a healthy weight. Collect the sheets from the class, and calculate the percentage of students in each category. Discuss nutrition and metabolic factors that could lead to concentrations in certain categories. **Class Activity** *Based on what they have learned in this chapter, ask students to identify changes they can make to their diets and eating habits that will help them achieve a healthier diet or weight. Discuss different approaches.* **Class Activity** *Invite an exercise physiologist to discuss the impact of exercise on metabolic rates, weight gain, and weight loss.*
Discuss the physiological mechanisms that regulate body temperature.	■ Body temperature (p. 431)	☒ Slides 18-20 Metabolic Rates, Body Temperature questions 24-29 (pp. 199-200) Check Your Knowledge question 17 (p. 204) *❷* Multiple Choice questions 28-30; True or False questions 49-53; Short Answer question 14 Classroom Application question 3 (p. 219); Lab Activities questions 2-4 (p. 220); Practical/Creative Learning Activities question 4 (p. 220) **Book Resources** Quick Check question 4 (p. 432) Review Question 15 (p. 435) ▶ Discuss Figure 16-5 The skin as a thermoregulatory organ (p. 432). Describe changes in the flow of blood to accommodate changes in the body's environment. Discuss the purposes of sweating and shivering. ▶ Discuss antipyretics and their uses, indications, and restrictions. **Class Activity** *Provide the class with oral and ear thermometers calibrated to read in degrees Fahrenheit. Working in pairs, have students take and note each other's oral and aural temperatures. If the readings differ for the same person, students should indicate possible reasons for the difference. Provide students with correct conversion formulas, and have them practice converting temperatures from Fahrenheit to*

OBJECTIVES	CONTENT	TEACHING RESOURCES
		Celsius. Ask students if their temperatures fall within the normal ranges. *Class Activity Working in groups of four or five, have students ascertain what might be the cause of the following malady in an infant: A mother notices abnormal crying from her 2-month-old infant. It is a hot day, and she has been carrying the baby around outdoors in a sling next to her body. The baby seems feverish and irritable and also has sudden diarrhea. Answers may vary slightly, but students should at least mention that the regulatory mechanism of the hypothalamus is not yet fully functional in infants. Therefore, this infant's body may be having trouble regulating its temperature. Because of the hot day, this may have resulted in overheating and dehydration.* *Class Activity Have students compare and contrast the signs and symptoms of heat exhaustion and heatstroke. Have them discuss when these conditions are likely to occur and the recommended therapy for each condition.*
Performance Evaluation		Chapter 16 Computerized Test Bank questions Student Assignment (pp. 221-223) Student Post-Test questions **Book Resources** Chapter Test (pp. 435-436)

16.2 Homework/Assignments:

16.2 Teacher's Notes:

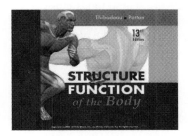

Slide 1

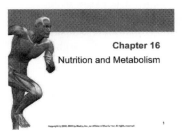

Chapter 16
Nutrition and Metabolism

Slide 2

Learning Objectives

- Define and contrast catabolism and anabolism
- Describe the metabolic roles of carbohydrates, fats, proteins, vitamins, and minerals
- Define *basal metabolic rate* and list some factors that affect it
- Discuss the physiological mechanisms that regulate body temperature

---

Slide 3

Chapter 16
Lesson 16.1

Structure & Function of the Body, 13th ed.

Thibodeau/Patton

Slide 4

Definitions

- **Metabolism**: process of using food molecules
  - **Catabolism**: destructive phase of metabolism
    - Breaks food molecules down into simple molecules
    - Releases stored energy
  - **Anabolism**: constructive phase of metabolism
    - Opposite of catabolism
    - Cells take simple molecules from the blood to make complex molecules for growth and repair

4

- The two aspects of metabolism are catabolism and anabolism. Catabolism + anabolism = metabolism

- How do nutrition and assimilation relate to metabolism? (Metabolism is the use of food by the body. These foods must be provided through nutritional intake and subsequently assimilated into the cells so that the metabolic processes can take place.)

Slide 5

Role of the Liver

- Processes blood immediately after it leaves the gastrointestinal tract
- Major role in the metabolism of all three major food types
- Helps maintain normal blood glucose level
- Synthesis of plasma proteins such as prothrombin, fibrinogen, and albumin
- Removes toxins from the blood
- Storage (glycogen, iron, vitamins A and D)

5

- What is the significance of the hepatic portal vein? (It delivers nutrient-rich blood directly from the GI tract into the liver.)

- Why is it desirable for the liver to have the first access to blood that comes directly from the gastrointestinal tract? (This arrangement allows blood that has just absorbed nutrients and other substances to be processed by the liver before being distributed throughout the body.)

- What is the role of the liver in carbohydrate, fat, and protein metabolism? (The liver stores excess CHO as glycogen and can release this stored glycogen when needed by the body. Therefore the liver helps maintain proper blood glucose levels. The liver also carries on the first step in the metabolism of fats and synthesizes proteins.)

- What are the functions of prothrombin, fibrinogen, and albumin? (Prothrombin and fibrinogen are essential for blood clotting and albumin helps maintain blood volume.)

- What role does the liver play in drug metabolism? (The liver detoxifies drugs.)

- What kinds of problems might a patient have if his/her liver began to fail? (jaundice, bleeding, hypertension, malnutrition)

Slide 6

Nutrient Metabolism

- Carbohydrates
  - Primarily catabolized for energy
  - Excess amounts are anabolized by glycogenesis into glycogen and stored in liver
- Glucose catabolism
  - Glycolysis
  - Citric acid cycle
  - Electron transfer system

6

- Carbohydrates are the body's preferred source of energy.

- Glucose catabolism occurs in a series of three chemical reactions: *glycolysis, citric acid cycle,* and *electron transfer.*

- What occurs in each chemical reaction of glucose catabolism? (The release of energy.)

ELSEVIER

Slide 7

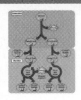

Nutrient Metabolism (cont'd.)

- Discuss the process of catabolism of glucose in terms of the splitting of glucose molecules and energy release.

- What are anaerobic and aerobic processes? How do they apply to glycolysis? (An anaerobic process is one that does not use oxygen, and aerobic process does. Glycolysis is an anaerobic process.)

- Where does the oxygen come from in the citric acid cycle? (available oxygen in the body; from the respiratory and circulatory system; for use by the mitochondria)

- In what part of the cell does glycolysis occur? (cytoplasm) In what part of the cell does the citric acid cycle occur? (mitochondria)

Slide 8

Nutrient Metabolism (cont'd.)

- Carbohydrate metabolism
  - Blood glucose
    - **Normal range: 70--100 mg per 100 ml of blood**
  - Role of insulin
    - Accelerates the movement of glucose out of the blood into cells
    - Decreases blood glucose
    - Insulin is the only hormone that decreases blood glucose

- How are blood glucose levels measured? (Through a blood test, either by a finger stick or a venipuncture. Results are labeled as milligrams per deciliters.)

- Define hyperglycemia and hypoglycemia.

- Discuss medical conditions where elevated blood glucose levels are found.

- Hormones that can increase levels of blood glucose include growth hormones, hydrocortisone, epinephrine, and glucagon.

Slide 9

Nutrient Metabolism (cont'd.)

- Adenosine triphosphate (ATP)
  - Molecule in which energy obtained from breakdown of foods is stored
  - Direct source of energy for cellular work
- Fats catabolized to yield energy and anabolized to form adipose tissue
- Proteins primarily anabolized and secondarily catabolized

- ATP is the powerhouse molecule.

- If ATP's components are no longer needed for energy requirements, they can be resynthesized later into ATP by adding energy from carbohydrate catabolism.

- If insufficient carbohydrate is available, fats will be broken down to yield energy.

- In what situations are proteins catabolized? (when CHO and or fats are not available for catabolism into energy)

Slide 10

Nutrient Metabolism (cont'd.)

- Image A. Point out the structure of ATP and the location of the high-energy bonds.

- Image B. Follow the ATP energy cycle.

- What types of cellular processes are fueled by energy from ATP? (Cells use energy from ATP to synthesize macromolecules, such as proteins, nucleic acids, and polysaccharides. ATP also supplies the energy needed to move individual cells from one location to another, to contract muscle cells, and to transport molecules into or out of the cell, usually against a concentration gradient.)

ELSEVIER

Structure & Function of the Body, 13th ed.
Thibodeau/Patton

Slide 11

- What is the difference between essential and nonessential amino acids? (Essential amino acids are those that must be in the diet. Nonessential amino acids can be made by the body.)
- Are any of these amino acids familiar to you? Explain.
- Amino acids are the building blocks of proteins.

Slide 12

- What functions do vitamins perform? (Vitamins are organic molecules needed in small amounts for metabolism. Vitamins support the actions of enzymes.)
- What are the dangers of avitaminosis and hypervitaminosis? (Avitaminosis could would interfere with needed metabolic processes. Hypervitaminosis could cause toxicity and damage cells.)
- With which vitamins might these conditions occur? (These conditions are most likely to occur with the water-soluble vitamins.)
- Discuss which vitamins the body can store for future use and why. (The body stores the fat-soluble vitamin A, D, E, and K, because enzymes need these vitamins in order to carry out bodily functions.)
- Why is folic acid recommended for pregnant women and women prior to becoming pregnant? (helps decrease incidence of neural-tube disorders in infants)
- Does vitamin C really prevent colds, or does it diminish the adverse effects of colds? (Although much literature supports this notion, there is also literature that negates it. Ask students to share their experiences.)

ELSEVIER

Structure & Function of the Body, 13th ed.
Thibodeau/Patton

Slide 13

- What functions do minerals perform? (Minerals help enzymes work.)
- Which mineral deficiencies occur most often? (Deficiencies in iron, calcium, and potassium are common.)
- Which minerals have deleterious effects if an overdose is consumed? (All minerals if consumed in too large quantities can have deleterious effects. Excess iron in men has been shown to increase risk of cardiovascular disease.)
- Discuss the "goiter belt." (The 'goiter belt' was a term used to describe areas of the country, such as the Midwest, that did not have access to salt water fish. These fish contain iodine, which is necessary for proper thyroid function. Goiter is a symptom of improper thyroid functioning.)
- What mineral might be effective for leg cramps during physical exertion? (calcium)

Slide 14

Chapter 16
Lesson 16.2

Slide 15

Metabolic Rates

- Basal metabolic rate (BMR)
  - Rate of metabolism when a person is awake, not moving, and not digesting food in a comfortably warm environment
  - Number of calories that must be produced by catabolism just to allow the body to perform its basic functions, stay alive, awake, and comfortably warm

- To provide energy for muscular work and digestion and absorption of food, an additional amount of food must be catabolized.
- Higher activity = higher metabolic rate

ELSEVIER

Slide 16

Metabolic Rates (cont'd.)

- Total metabolic rate (TMR)
  - The total amount of energy, expressed in calories, used by the body per day

16

- What is a calorie? A kilocalorie? How many excess calories would you have to consume in order to gain a pound of weight? (A calorie is the amount of energy needed to raise the temperature of 1g of
  water 1° C. A kilocalorie is 1,000 calories.)
- What mechanism generally protects the body from rapid weight loss or gain? (TMR)
- If a person's TMR is 3,100 kcal, how many calories would he have to consume daily in order to maintain his weight at its current level? (3,100)
- What happens when your food intake supplies more calories than your TMR? (Weight gain occurs.)
- Discuss issues of fad diets.

Slide 17

Metabolic Rates (cont'd.)

17

- What factors affect a person's basal metabolic rate? (body temperature, energy expenditure, body size)
- Can an individual's basal metabolic rate be altered? How? (yes, through diet and exercise. Discuss further with students)
- Can an individual's total metabolic rate be altered? How? (yes, through exercise, increased muscle mass, correction of metabolic imbalances, such as thyroid disease)

Slide 18

Body Temperature

- Hypothalamus
  - Regulates the homeostasis of body temperature through a variety of processes

18

- The hypothalamus operates a variety of negative-feedback mechanisms that keep the body temperature in normal range.
- Why are the elderly and infants more susceptible to temperature-related illnesses? (As part of the aging process, the thermoregulatory ability of the body decreases. Infants have an immature thermoregulation system.)

ELSEVIER

Slide 19

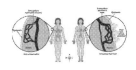

- Skin
  - Negative feedback loops regulate temperature
  - Four processes
    - Radiation
    - Conduction
    - Convection
    - Evaporation

- The blood vessels close to the surface of the skin allow the blood to cool down by radiation or warm up. They dilate or constrict. Vasodilation and vasoconstriction.

- Why does your body sweat when you perform heavy physical activity? (Physical activity generates heat and sweating is a mechanism to dissipate that heat.)

- Why is heatstroke more likely when the weather is hot and humid, as opposed to hot and dry? (When humidity is high, the "heat index" increases, and the body responds by increasing its sweat production.)

- How does the body protect itself against hypothermia? (shivering) What are signs of hypothermia? (The skin may become pale, numb, and waxy. Muscles become tense, shivering, fatigued, and weak.) What is happening in the body? (Hypothermia causes several reactions within the body as it tries to protect itself and retain its heat. The most important of these is *vasoconstriction,* which halts blood flow to the extremities in order to conserve heat in the critical core area of the body.)

- What is frostbite? (It is a condition in which damage occurs in the skin and other tissues due to extreme cold.) What are the signs? (Discoloration of the skin, numbness, and tingling.)

Slide 20

- Discuss the body's survival mechanism for preserving normal body temperature of vital organs.

- Discuss vasoconstriction vs. vasodilation.

- Why do chills often accompany a fever? (The temperature of the body is controlled by a section of the brain that acts like a "thermostat." When fever occurs the body's thermostat is "reset" higher. When the body temperature is set higher than usual, the body senses it is cold and sends out a signal to the muscles. The muscles begin to shake. This involuntary shaking, or chills, results.)

17 Lesson Plan
The Urinary System

TEACHING FOCUS

In this chapter, students will have the opportunity to learn the major organs and functions of the urinary system. Students will also have the opportunity to learn about the microscopic structures in the nephron and their role in the production of urine, as well as the vital renal functions—filtration, tubular reabsorption, and tubular secretion—and their role in maintaining homeostasis. Finally, students will have the opportunity to learn the various common disorders of the urinary tract, their diagnosis, and treatment.

MATERIALS AND RESOURCES

☐ Catch cups (Lesson 17.2)
☐ Colored pencils (Lesson 17.2)
☐ Dipsticks for routine urinalysis (Lesson 17.2)
☐ Drug inserts from drugs requiring high fluid intake (expectorants, antibiotics, etc.) (Lesson 17.2)

☐ Kidney stones (Lesson 17.1)
☐ Pig kidney for dissection (Lesson 17.1)
☐ Prepared slides of the walls of the ureter and bladder and components of the nephron (Lesson 17.1)
☐ Computer (all Lessons)

LESSON CHECKLIST

Preparations for this lesson include:

- lecture, guest lecturer from dialysis unit
- demonstration
- student performance evaluation of all entry-level skills required for student comprehension of the anatomy and physiology of the urinary system including:
  o common disorders of the urinary tract and their treatment
  o function and location of major urinary system organs
  o key terminology associated with the urinary system
  o role of the kidney in homeostasis

ELSEVIER

Structure & Function of the Body, 13th ed.
Thibodeau/Patton

KEY TERMS

afferent arteriole (p. 442)
anuria (p. 448)
atrial natriuretic hormone (ANH) (p. 448)
Bowman's capsule (p. 442)
CAPD (continuous ambulatory peritoneal dialysis) (p. 450)
calyx (p. 442)
collecting tubule (p. 442)
cystitis (p. 451)
distal convoluted tubule (p. 442)
efferent arteriole (p. 442)
emptying reflex (p. 451)
external urethral sphincter (p. 451)
filtration (pp. 446, 447)
glomerulus (p. 442)
glomerular filtrate (p. 446)
glycosuria (p. 446)
hemodialysis (p. 450)
incontinence (p. 451)
internal urethral sphincter (p. 451)
lithotripsy (p. 452)
lithotriptor (p. 452)
loop of Henle (p. 442)
micturition (p. 451)
nephron (p. 442)

oliguria (p. 448)
overactive bladder (p. 452)
papilla (p. 442)
polyuria (p. 448)
proximal convoluted tubule (p. 442)
reabsorption (pp. 446, 447)
renal calculi (p. 452)
renal colic (p. 449)
renal corpuscle (p. 442)
renal cortex (p. 442)
renal medulla (p. 442)
renal papilla (p. 442)
renal pelvis (pp. 442, 448)
renal pyramid (p. 442)
renal tubule (p. 442)
secretion (p. 447)
sphincter (p. 451)
trigone (pp. 448, 449)
uremia (p. 440)
urethra (p. 450)
urinary meatus (p. 450)
urinary retention (p. 451)
urinary suppression (p. 451)
urination (p. 451)
voiding (p. 451)

ADDITIONAL RESOURCES

AnimationDirect (Book Companion CD)
Instructor's Electronic Resource (IER) (CD)
PowerPoint slides (CD, Evolve)
Test Bank (Evolve)

Legend

ESLR
EVOLVE Student
Learning Resource

EILR TB
EVOLVE Instructor
Learning Resource
Test Bank

AnimationDirect
on Book Companion
CD

PPT
PowerPoint
Slides

SG
Study
Guide

IRM
Instructor's
Resource Manual

Class Activities are indicated in ***bold italic.***

Structure & Function of the Body, 13th ed.

Thibodeau/Patton

LESSON 17.1

PRETEST
Study Guide Multiple Choice questions 1-10 (pp. 213-214)

BACKGROUND ASSESSMENT

Question: In the clinical laboratory or a physician's practice, urine samples are often analyzed to diagnose urinary tract infections. The most common way of obtaining the sample is the "clean catch" method. How would you make sure that patients obtain their samples in the correct way, so that cross-contamination of the sample does not occur?

Answer: Respect the patient's privacy by giving the patient instructions in a location where other patients cannot overhear. Explain to the patient that the inside of the sample cup is sterile, and the rim or inside of the cup should not be touched. Explain proper cleansing and voiding techniques. Point out where extra wipes are kept, and where the sample is to be placed when finished. Ask the patient if he or she has any questions, and explain again if the patient is confused. Parents of young children should assist their children. It is important to have the instructions posted on the wall of the restroom used for providing the samples, so that patients can consult them in the middle of the process if necessary. Most important, however, are clear, verbal instructions in case the patient cannot or does not read the posted instructions.

Question: A middle-aged male friend has to make frequent (and long) restroom stops. This has been going on for quite some time now, and, except for this, he claims to be healthy. His friends have started to make good-natured jokes about the pit-stops. Is this something to be taken lightly? What would you advise your friend to do?

Answer: Although this condition does not seem to be painful for your friend or infection-related (urinary tract infection), it nonetheless requires medical attention. Older men often develop symptoms like this (weak stream of urine, hesitancy when starting to urinate, and the need for frequent voiding). Most often symptoms like this are due to obstruction of the urethra by an enlarged prostate gland. The cause of the enlarged prostate gland should be investigated by the family physician, because malignancy will need to be ruled out. The physician can also recommend treatment to improve his quality of life, if the cause of the enlarged prostate is benign. It is also important to take action before urinary retention becomes a problem with its resulting tendency toward infection of the urinary tract.

CRITICAL THINKING QUESTION

A patient has been having pain in the back and groin, renal colic, reduced urine output, and painful voiding. The physician orders a urinalysis. Crystalline substances are observed in the urine on microscopic analysis as well as some blood cells. Based on the results of an ultrasound examination, the physician recommends lithotripsy. What do you suspect might be wrong with the patient? What further diagnostic techniques do you think might be ordered?

Guidelines: The symptoms that the patient is experiencing could point to a number of disorders, including infection, structural abnormality, and obstruction. Blood in the urine could be due to infection or mechanical irritation of the mucous membranes of the tract caused by stones rubbing against the walls. The presence of crystalline substances in the urine is indicative of stones in the urinary tract. Apparently, the ultrasound has revealed stones in the urinary tract, because the physician has recommended lithotripsy. Lithotripsy is an ultrasound treatment that can break renal calculi into small pieces that can be passed more easily through the ureters and urethra. It is an effective, noninvasive procedure. Culturing the urine could confirm an infection, which often results from renal calculi. Twenty-four hour urine and blood analyses for high levels of substances that are known to produce stones, such as calcium and uric acid, will help confirm the diagnosis and shed some light on the cause. Analysis of the composition of the stones that are passed will aid the physician in advising the patient on how to prevent further formation of stones.

OBJECTIVES	CONTENT	TEACHING RESOURCES

Identify the major organs of the urinary system and give the generalized function of each.	■ Kidneys (p. 441)
	  □ Location (p. 441)
	  □ Internal structure (p. 441)
		🖾 Slides 5-10
		
		📖 Kidneys questions 1, 2 (p. 206)
		
		📖 Check Your Knowledge questions 1, 9 (pp. 213-214)
		
		💻 Multiple Choice questions 1-7, 37; True or False questions 1-15, 67-69; Short Answer question 1
		
		📓 Lab Activities question 4 (p. 232)
		
		💿 Urinary System
		
		💿 Kidney
		
		Book Resources
		
		Review questions 1, 2 (p. 456)
		
		Clear View of the Human Body
		
		  ▶ Discuss the position of the kidneys relative to other abdominal organs. In Figure 17-1 B, note the location relative to the spinous processes and twelfth rib. Note the role the large diameter of the renal arteries plays in renal function
		
		  ▶ Discuss the internal structure of the kidney. Use Figure 17-2 to point out the location of the renal cortex, renal medulla, renal pyramids, renal papillae, renal pelvis, and calyx.
		
		Class Activity Working with a partner, have students follow the instructions described in Location (p. 440) for locating their own kidneys, and use the spinous processes and the ribs to pinpoint the location. Ask the following questions: Why is this an advantageous position? What structures protect the kidneys? How does this location facilitate interventions on the kidney?
		
		Class Activity After the material has been presented in class, have students work in pairs to label the Urinary System and Kidney diagrams (pp. 223-224 of the Student Guide) without consulting the textbook. After they have labeled as many structures as possible, consult textbook Figures 17-1 and 17-2 (pp. 440-441) to correct their answers.
		
		Class Activity Divide the class in half and hold a mock debate. One side should argue for trade in human organs; one side should argue against. Issues covered should include the features of

OBJECTIVES	CONTENT	TEACHING RESOURCES
		the kidney that make it especially vulnerable to the body parts trade, the ability of individuals to sell their own organs, and harvesting organs from condemned prisoners.
Name the parts of a nephron and describe the role each component plays in the formation of urine.	☐ Microscopic structure (p. 442)	Slides 11-15 Kidneys question 3 (p. 206) Check Your Knowledge questions 2-4, 10 (pp. 213-214) Multiple Choice questions 8-13; True or False questions 16-27, 70; Matching questions 1-10; Short Answer question 2 Lab Activities question 1 (p. 232) Nephron **Book Resources** Figure 17-3 Location and components of the nephron (p. 443) Figure 17-4 The nephron unit (p. 445) Critical Thinking question 14 (p. 456) *Class Activity Compare and contrast two medical alternatives in cases of kidney failure:* **dialysis** *and* **transplantation.** *What is dialysis? What function of the kidney does it perform? Is transplantation technically easy or difficult to perform from an anatomical standpoint? What are several major drawbacks of transplantation operations? (shortage of donors, rejection reactions, etc.)* *Class Activity Arrange to have students visit a dialysis unit.*
Explain how the kidneys act as vital organs in maintaining homeostasis.	☐ Function (p. 442)	Slide 16 Kidneys question 4 (p. 206) Multiple Choice questions 14, 15, 38, 39; True or False questions 29-31, 71, 72 Classroom Application question 1 (p. 231); Lab Activities question 2 (p. 232); Practical/Creative Learning Activities question 2 (p. 232) Kidney

OBJECTIVES	CONTENT	TEACHING RESOURCES
		Book Resources Quick Check questions 1-3 (p. 448) Review questions 5, 6 (p. 456) ▸ Discuss what is happening in terms of the body's regulatory mechanisms and hormones when, on a hot day, a person working outside all day has a low volume of urine, and it is dark in color. What should the person do? *Class Activity Have the students collect a clean-catch sample of their own urine. Perform a routine urinalysis (protein, glucose, ketones, blood, nitrites, leukocyte esterase, acidity, specific gravity) using dipsticks. If blood is detected, use a microscope to identify the cells.* *Class Activity Make a list of compounds normally found in urine (mineral ions, creatinine, etc.). Make a list of compounds that may be found if certain disorders are present (bile, albumin, glucose, etc.). Indicate what disorder is associated with each compound. What odor might be present if the patient has uncontrolled diabetes? What common household item does this smell like? What characteristic odor is detected on the breath of diabetics in ketosis?*

17.1 Homework/Assignments:

17.1 Teacher's Notes:

Thibodeau/Patton

LESSON 17.2

CRITICAL THINKING QUESTION

What is urinary incontinence and how is it classified? What treatment options are available for urinary incontinence?

Guidelines: Urinary incontinence is a condition in which the patient voids urine involuntarily if the bladder is overfull or in patients who have experienced a stroke or spinal cord injury. Approximately 13 million Americans have urinary incontinence, and it occurs twice as often in women as in men. Urinary incontinence is classified as acute (short-term) or chronic (long-term). Acute incontinence is temporary loss of urine control that ends when the problem causing it—such as urinary tract infection, a medication side effect, constipation, or bladder stones—is successfully treated. Chronic incontinence, such as stress incontinences or urge incontinence, is a long-term loss of urine control. Generally, treatment for incontinence proceeds in stages based on the cause of the incontinence and also personal preferences. Treatments include behavioral strategies, exercise, use of absorbent materials, medications, antispasmodics and anticholinergics for urge incontinence, antibiotics for incontinence caused by infection, and surgery (if all other methods fail).

OBJECTIVES	CONTENT	TEACHING RESOURCES
Explain the importance of filtration, tubular reabsorption, and tubular secretion in urine formation.	■ Formation of urine (p. 446)	Slides 18-21 Multiple Choice questions 5-8 (pp. 206-207) Applying What You Know question 62 (p. 210) Check Your Knowledge questions 4, 10 (pp. 213-214) Multiple Choice questions 16-19, 40, 41; True or False questions 28, 32-48, 73-75, 77; Short Answer questions 3-7 Practical/Creative Learning Activities 1, 3 (p. 232) **Book Resources** Table 17-1 Characteristics of urine (p. 444) Figure 17-5 Formation of urine (p. 446) Table 17-2 Functions of parts of nephron in urine formation (p. 447) Review questions 3, 4 (p. 456) ▸ Discuss Health and Well-Being: Proteinuria After Exercise (p. 448). ▸ Discuss Clinical Application: Artificial Kidney (p. 450). ▸ Discuss differences and similarities between lithotripsy and traditional techniques for removing renal stones.

OBJECTIVES	CONTENT	TEACHING RESOURCES
		▸ Discuss the relationship between the kidney and blood pressure. Note how a severe hemorrhage can result in kidney failure. *Class Activity Divide the class into four groups, and have each group evaluate one of the following scenarios: 1. A pregnant woman has proteinuria. What serious condition could this indicate? 2. Routine urinalysis shows glucosuria. What does this indicate? 3. Urinalysis shows ketones in the urine. What is this called? Would you expect to see ketones in the urine of a healthy individual? What are some possible causes of ketonuria? 4. A urine sample shows abnormally high specific gravity. Why would you be concerned? Have each group report its findings to the class.* *Class Activity Divide the class into small groups, and have each group review drug inserts that recommend high fluid intake while taking the medication. Each group should indicate why they think this is important for the particular drugs involved.*
Discuss the mechanisms that control urine volume.	☐ Control of urine volume (p. 447)	Slides 22, 23 Kidneys questions 9-12 (p. 207) Applying What You Know question 61 (p. 210) Check Your Knowledge questions 7, 8 (p. 213) Multiple Choice questions 20-23, 42; True or False question 76 Classroom Application questions 2-5 (p. 231) **Book Resources** Quick Check questions 1-3 (p. 448) Critical Thinking questions 13, 15 (p. 456) *Class Activity Divide the class into four groups and have each group evaluate one of the following patient situations: 1. A pregnant woman presents with frequent urination. 2. A patient complains of frequent, painful urination. In spite of frequency and urgency, the volume of urine produced is small. 3. A bicyclist exhibits proteinuria and low urine volumes shortly after a long bicycle competition. Would you suspect kidney disease? 4. A physician suspects hydronephrosis. What is this,*

OBJECTIVES	CONTENT	TEACHING RESOURCES
		and what signs and symptoms might the patient be exhibiting? Groups should list possible treatments if required. If the condition is not serious, they should indicate why it is not and what is causing the condition. *Class Activity Working together in small groups, students should explain why increased urine output is one sign of diabetes. Ask groups to diagram the organs and homeostatic mechanisms that come into play. Ask them why increased thirst is also a sign of diabetes.*
Identify the major organs of the urinary system and give the generalized function of each.	■ Ureters (p. 448) ■ Urinary bladder (p. 449) ■ Urethra (p. 450) ■ Micturition (p. 451)	Slides 24-33 Kidneys questions 13-24 (p. 208) Ureters, Urinary Bladder, Urethra questions 25-43 (pp. 208-209) Micturition questions 44-55 (p. 209) Applying What You Know question 63 (p. 210) Multiple Choice questions 24-35; True or False questions 49-66, 78; Matching questions 11-20; Short Answer questions 8-15 Lab Activities questions 3, 5 (p. 232) Urinary System **Book Resources** Figure 17-6 Ureter cross section (p. 449) Figure 17-7 The urinary bladder (p. 449) Quick Check questions 1-4 (p. 452) Review questions 7-12 (p. 456) Clear View of the Human Body ▶ Discuss Clinical Application: The Aging Kidney (p. 451). What is important to remember about medication dosages in older individuals? ▶ Discuss Clinical Application: Removal of Kidney Stones Using Ultrasound (p. 452). ▶ Discuss Science Applications: Fighting Infection (p. 453). Note why it is important to keep all types of catheters sterile.

Structure & Function of the Body, 13th ed.

Thibodeau/Patton

OBJECTIVES	CONTENT	TEACHING RESOURCES
		▸ Discuss the problem of antibiotic resistance. Why are antibiotic-resistant strains becoming more prevalent? What efforts are being made to combat this problem?
		▸ Discuss why urinary retention often results in urinary tract infection. Note why urinary tract infections are more common in women.
		▸ Discuss kidney stone causes, symptoms, diagnostic procedures, therapies, and prevention.
		Class Activity Working in small groups, have the class assess each of the following situations and present their findings to the rest of the class: 1. A man in his fifties dribbles urine when voiding, and it takes a long time to void the bladder. What is a possible cause? 2. A postmenopausal woman is experiencing involuntary voiding of small amounts of urine when she coughs or laughs. What is this called, and what could the cause be? 3. A patient paralyzed from the waist down suffers from frequent urinary tract infections. What is a possible cause of this? 4. Why is urine used to clean wounds in developing countries?
		Class Activity Ask students to compose patient instructions for obtaining urine samples. The instructions are to be laminated and posted in the restroom where patients give urine samples. Instructions should be concise, with steps that are easy to follow. Before beginning, ask students to consider the following questions: What is important that you wish to emphasize? Will you make separate instructions for men and women?
		Class Activity Discuss the importance of skin care in patients with incontinence.
Performance Evaluation		🄴 Chapter 17 Computerized Test Bank questions
		Student Assignment (pp. 223-237)
		🄴 Student Post-Test questions
		Book Resource
		Chapter Test (pp. 456-457)

17.2 Homework/Assignments:

One often hears that cranberry juice will cure or prevent a urinary tract infection. Is this medically supportable? Research this issue and write a short statement about the validity of this therapy. Support your conclusions with references.

17.2 Teacher's Notes:

Thibodeau/Patton

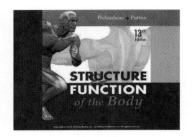

Slide 1

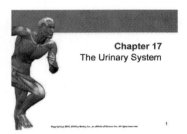

Chapter 17
The Urinary System

Slide 2

Learning Objectives

- Identify the major organs of the urinary system and give the generalized function of each
- Name the parts of a nephron and describe the role each component plays in the formation of urine
- Explain the importance of filtration, tubular reabsorption, and tubular secretion in urine formation

Slide 3

Learning Objectives (cont'd.)

- Discuss the mechanisms that control urine volume
- Explain how the kidneys act as vital organs in maintaining homeostasis

Slide 4

Chapter 17
Lesson 17.1

Slide 5

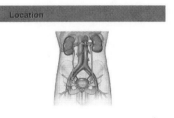

Kidneys

- Location
  - Under eleventh rib, just above waistline
  - Retroperitoneal
  - Right kidney usually a little lower than left

- Discuss the exact location with the help of the next slide and noting the spinous processes. Recall the term *retroperitoneal*.
- The location of the kidneys is commonly mistaken to be lower than they actually are.

Slide 6

Location

- Note the location with respect to other organs and structures.
- Note the relatively large diameter of the renal artery. How does this facilitate the supply of blood to the kidney? How is this important for the function the kidney serves? (The large diameter of the renal artery promotes more blood flow to the kidneys. This is necessary to support glomerular filtration.)

Slide 7

Location (cont'd.)

- Note the location with respect to the ribs and lumbar vertebra.

Slide 8

Location (cont'd.)

- What makes the kidneys, renal pelvis, ureters, and bladder visible on x-ray? (these soft tissues absorb some of the electromagnetic waves, thus making these urinary structures visible.)

Slide 9

Internal Structure

- **Cortex:** Outer layer of kidney
- **Medulla:** Inner portion of kidney
- **Pyramids:** Triangular divisions of medulla
- **Papilla:** Narrow, innermost end of pyramid
- **Pelvis:** Expansion of upper end of ureter
- **Calyces:** Divisions of renal pelvis

- The renal pyramids contain millions of the microscopic functional units of the kidney called *nephrons*.

- Renal pelvis: where the ureter attaches to the kidney

- Calyces: divisions of the renal pelvis that connect the pyramids of the medulla with the renal pelvis

Slide 10

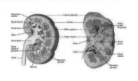

Internal Structure (cont'd.)

- Point out structures of the kidney.

- Compare structures of diagram A with photograph B.

Slide 11

Microscopic Structure

- **Nephrons:** Microscopic units of the kidney consisting of renal corpuscles and renal tubules
- **Renal corpuscle:** Bowman's capsule with its glomerulus

- How many nephrons are in a typical kidney? (more than a million)

- What is Bowman's capsule? (the cup-shaped portion of the nephron)

- What is the glomerulus? (a network of capillaries in the Bowman's capsule)

ELSEVIER

Thibodeau/Patton

Slide 12

Microscopic Structure (cont'd.)

- Follow the path of urine from the collecting tubules to the ureter.

Slide 13

Microscopic Structure (cont'd.)

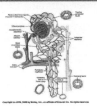

- Note that the afferent arteriole is larger in diameter than the efferent arteriole.
- What is the significance of this? (This structural feature helps keep high blood pressure within the glomerulus to facilitate filtration of the blood.)
- How is this important to the function of the glomerulus? (The filtration function of the glomerulus is contingent upon the pressure of blood.)
- What would happen if there was insufficient blood pressure to perfuse the kidneys? (Waste products could accumulate in the body as glomerular filtration decreased.)

Slide 14

Microscopic Structure (cont'd.)

- Note the high density of blood capillaries in the glomerulus.
- Trace the path of blood and filtrate along the entire pathway.
- Note differences in cross sections of tubular cells. How does this relate to varying functions of these cells? (The structural differences allow for the functions of filtration, reabsorption, and secretion to take place. The proper amount of solutes and water flow into and out of the nephron partly due to the cellular structure of the tubular system. See Table 17-2, p. 447.)

Slide 15

Microscopic Structure (cont'd.)

- Renal tubule
  - **Proximal convoluted tubule:** Extension of ascending limb of the loop of Henle that is convoluted
  - **Loop of Henle:** Straight, descending limb with a hairpin turn and a straight ascending limb
  - **Distal convoluted tubule:** The part of the renal tubule distal to the loop of Henle
  - **Collecting tubule:** Straight extension of the renal tubule

- Compare and contrast the proximal and collecting tubule.
- Note: Renal corpuscle and both the proximal and distal convoluted tubules are located in the renal cortex.
- The loop of Henle and collecting tubules are located in the medulla.

Slide 16

Function

- Functions of the kidney
  - Filter blood
  - Excrete toxins and nitrogenous wastes
  - Regulate levels of many chemicals in blood
  - Maintain water balance
  - Help regulate blood pressure via secretion of renin and angiotensin
  - Maintain homeostasis
  - Secretes erythropoietin for RBC production

16

- Fluid, electrolytes, and wastes are filtered from the blood into the nephron.
- Wastes are further secreted into the tubules while useful substances are reabsorbed into the blood.
- Kidneys regulate chloride, sodium, potassium, and bicarbonate levels.
- What kidney hormone is secreted when blood pressure is low? (renin)
- Because of all these important regulatory functions, the kidney is often considered the most important homeostatic organ.

Slide 17

Chapter 17
Lesson 17.2

17

Slide 18

Formation of Urine

- Occurs by a series of three processes that take place in successive parts of nephron
  - **Filtration**
  - Secretion
  - Reabsorption

18

- Goes on continually in renal corpuscles
- Glomerular blood pressure causes water and dissolved substances to filter out of glomeruli into Bowman's capsule.
- Normal glomerular filtration rate is 125 ml per minute.
- 180 L of glomerular filtrate is produced per day. If so much filtrate is produced, why don't we excrete this much urine? (Most of the filtrate returns to the body during the process of reabsorption.)

Slide 19

Formation of Urine (cont'd.)

- Occurs by a series of three processes that take place in successive parts of nephron
  - Filtration
  - **Secretion**
  - Reabsorption

19

- Secretion is the movement of substances into urine in the distal and collecting tubules from blood in peritubular capillaries.
- Hydrogen ions, potassium ions, and certain drugs are secreted by active transport.
- Ammonia is secreted by diffusion.

ELSEVIER

Structure & Function of the Body, 13th ed.

Thibodeau/Patton

Slide 20

Formation of Urine (cont'd.)

- Occurs by a series of three processes that take place in successive parts of nephron
  - Filtration
  - Secretion
  - **Reabsorption**

20

- Reabsorption is the movement of substances out of renal tubules into blood in peritubular capillaries.
- Water, nutrients, and ions are reabsorbed by means of osmosis from proximal tubules.

Slide 21

Formation of Urine (cont'd.)

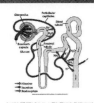

21

- Trace the path of urine formation.
- Where does filtration occur? (glomerulus and bowman's capsule, see green arrow in figure on the left;)
- Where does reabsorption occur? (proximal convoluted tubule, loop of Henle, distal convoluted tubules, and the collecting tubules, see light blue arrows)
- Where does secretion occur? (distal and collecting tubules, see purple arrows)

Slide 22

Control of Urine Volume

- **ADH:** Water-retaining hormone
  - Posterior pituitary
  - Decreases urine volume

22

- ADH works by making the collecting tubules more permeable to water.
- If no ADH is present, the tubules are basically impermeable to water, making reabsorption of water from them almost impossible. What happens as a result? (copious urinary output; disease is called Diabetes Insipidus)

Slide 23

Control of Urine Volume (cont'd.)

- Via salt reabsorption
  - **Aldosterone:** Salt and water-retaining hormone
  - **ANH:** Salt and water-releasing hormone
  - Aldosterone and ANH exert their effect mainly via salt reabsorption, which affects water output

23

- Aldosterone controls kidney tubules reabsorption of salt, stimulates faster rate of salt reabsorption, and increases tubular water reabsorption.
- Atrial natriuretic hormone (ANH) is secreted from the atrial wall of the heart.
- What is the effect of ANH? (stimulates kidney tubules to excrete salt and water)

ELSEVIER

Slide 24

Ureters

- Structure
  - Narrow tubes
  - 6 mm wide, 25-30 cm long
  - Upper end terminates in the renal pelvis inside kidney
  - Lined with mucous membrane
  - Muscular wall
- Function
  - Drain urine from renal pelvis to urinary bladder

24

- Note that peristaltic movement in the muscular wall aids transport of urine down the tubes.
- Membrane lining has many nerve cells.
- Path of urine is from the collecting tubules, into the renal pelvis, down the ureters, and into the bladder.

Slide 25

Ureters (cont'd.)

25

- Note the location and path of the ureters.
- Note the location of the urinary bladder and urethra (upcoming topics) just behind the pubic symphysis.
- What structure does the bladder sit in front of in women? (uterus)
- What structure does the bladder sit on top of in men? (prostate)

Slide 26

Urinary Bladder

- Structure
  - Elastic, muscular organ capable of great expansion
  - Mucous membrane lining
  - Rugae
  - Trigone
- Functions
  - Storage of urine before voiding
  - Voiding

26

- What structural features aid the bladder in performing its functions? (elastic and involuntary muscle fibers, rugae, and the trigone)
- How much urine can the bladder hold before the increase in pressure stimulates the emptying reflex? (about 350 ml)

Slide 27

Urinary Bladder (cont'd.)

27

- Note the location of ureter openings.
- Note the location of the trigone. What features differentiate this area structurally from the rest of the bladder? (The trigone is smooth.)
- Note the location of the prostate gland. What disadvantages might there be to this location? (may enlarge and compress the urethra making urination difficulty)

ELSEVIER

Structure & Function of the Body, 13th ed.

Thibodeau/Patton

Slide 28

Urethra

- Structure
  - Narrow tube from urinary bladder to exterior
  - Mucous membrane lining
  - Urinary meatus (opening to the exterior)

- Eight inches long in males, 1½ inches long in females: accounts for more frequent urinary tract infections in females vs. males
- Note that the mucous membrane lining is one continual sheet from the renal cortex to the meatus; this accounts for the fact that infection can spread from the meatus into the kidney.

Slide 29

Urethra (cont'd.)

- Functions
  - Passage of urine from bladder to exterior of the body
  - Passage of male reproductive fluid (semen) from the body

Slide 30

Micturition

- Passage of urine from body
- Regulatory sphincters
  - Internal urethral sphincter (involuntary)
  - External urethral sphincter (voluntary)

- Micturition is also called *urination* or *voiding.*
- At what age are most children toilet trained? (between 2 and 3 years old) What factors play a role? (hereditary factors, psychological)
- At what volume of urine does micturition typically occur in adults? (350 mL)

Slide 31

Micturition (cont'd.)

- Emptying reflex
  - Initiated by stretch reflex in bladder wall
  - Bladder wall contracts
  - Internal sphincter relaxes
  - External sphincter relaxes and urination occurs

- What initiates the emptying reflex? (stretch reflexes in the wall of the bladder)
- If the external sphincter is contracted, will micturition occur if the bladder is full? (not if the sphincter is functioning properly)

ELSEVIER

Structure & Function of the Body, 13th ed.
Thibodeau/Patton

Slide 32

Micturition (cont'd.)

- **Urinary retention:** Urine produced but not voided
- **Urinary suppression:** No urine produced but bladder is normal
- **Incontinence:** Urine voided involuntarily
  - May be caused by spinal injury or stroke
  - Retention of urine may cause cystitis
  - Age

32

- Discuss treatments for urinary retention.
- Why does urinary retention predispose the bladder to infection? (Bacteria may enter the bladder through the urethra. When the urine remains in the bladder for a prolonged period of time, as in retention, the bacteria reproduce and multiply.)
- What are other causes of incontinence? (advanced age or extreme youth, pregnancy, etc.)
- Discuss the terms *anuria* and *oliguria*.

Slide 33

Micturition (cont'd.)

- **Cystitis:** Bladder infection
  - Amounts voided are small
  - Extreme urgency, frequency, and pain are common
  - Pain on urination
- Overactive bladder (interstitial cystitis)
  - No infectious organism detectable
  - Amounts voided are small
  - Extreme urgency and frequency

33

- What are several causes of cystitis in women? (poor hygiene, sexual activity, STDs, incomplete bladder emptying)
- What is the most frequent cause of recurrent cystitis in men? (enlarged prostate)
- What is the difference between urgency and frequency? (Urinary frequency means needing to urinate more often than usual. Urgency is a sudden, compelling urge to urinate, along with discomfort in your bladder.)
- What are common treatments for cystitis? (increased fluids, antibiotics, urinary antiseptics)
- What are common treatments for an overactive bladder? (anticholinergic drugs, kegel exercises, biofeedback)

ELSEVIER

Structure & Function of the Body, 13th ed.

Thibodeau/Patton

18 Lesson Plan
Fluid and Electrolyte Balance

TEACHING FOCUS

In this chapter, students will have the opportunity to learn about body fluids, body fluid compartments, and the avenues by which water enters and leaves the body. Students will have the opportunity to examine the mechanisms that maintain fluid balance, the importance of electrolytes in body fluids, and the aldosterone mechanism of extracellular fluid volume control. They also will explore the interaction between capillary blood pressure and blood proteins, as well as common fluid imbalances.

MATERIALS AND RESOURCES

- ☐ Computer (all Lessons)
- ☐ Poster boards (Lesson 18.1)

LESSON CHECKLIST

Preparations for this lesson include:

- lecture
- guest speakers: medical assistant or nurse
- student performance evaluation of entry-level skills required for student comprehension and application of anatomy and physiology principles including:
  - ○ body fluid compartments
  - ○ importance of electrolytes in body fluids
  - ○ interaction between capillary blood pressure and blood proteins
  - ○ mechanisms of fluid balance

KEY TERMS

decrease in the concentration of plasma
proteins (p. 468)
dehydration (p. 468)
dissociate (p. 464)
diuretic (p. 468)
edema (p. 465)
electrolyte (pp. 459, 464)
extracellular fluid (ECF) (p. 461)

fluid (p. 459)
fluid compartments (p. 461)
increase in capillary blood pressure
(pp. 467, 468)
intracellular fluid (ICF) (p. 461)
nonelectrolytes (p. 464)
retention of electrolytes (p. 468)

ADDITIONAL RESOURCES

AnimationDirect (Book Companion CD)
Instructor's Electronic Resource (IER) (CD)
PowerPoint slides (CD, Evolve)
Test Bank (Evolve)

Legend

ESLR
EVOLVE Student
Learning Resource

EILR TB
EVOLVE Instructor
Learning Resource
Test Bank

AnimationDirect
on Book Companion
CD

PPT
PowerPoint
Slides

SG
Study
Guide

IRM
Instructor's
Resource Manual

Class Activities are indicated in *bold italic*.

LESSON 18.1

PRETEST
Study Guide Multiple Choice questions 1-10 (pp. 226-227)

BACKGROUND ASSESSMENT
Question: Of the hundreds of compounds present in the human body, which is the most abundant? On average, what percentage of the male and female body is composed of this compound? Why is there a difference between the genders in the percentage of this compound?

Answer: Water is the most abundant compound. On average, healthy nonobese young men average about 60% of their body weight in water; for women, the average is 50%. The reason women have less water per pound than men is because they have slightly more fat than males. The more fat present in the body, the less the total water content.

Question: Maintaining a proper body fluid and electrolyte balance is critical for healthy survival. To do this, on what mechanisms does the body rely?

Answer: The body relies on the adjustment of fluid intake and output, the concentration of electrolytes in extracellular fluid, capillary blood pressure, and the concentration of proteins in the blood.

CRITICAL THINKING QUESTION
The body must maintain fairly constant fluid levels to remain healthy. What mechanisms does the body use to accomplish this?

Guidelines: The body relies on regulation of fluid intake through ingested liquids, water in food, and tissue catabolism. The body controls the output of liquids by means of the lungs, skin, kidneys, and large intestine. The proper balance is needed for cellular and chemical functions.

OBJECTIVES	CONTENT	TEACHING RESOURCES
List, describe, and compare the body fluid compartments and their subdivisions.	■ Introduction (p. 459) ■ Body fluids (p. 460) ■ Body fluid compartments (p. 461)	⊠▤ Slides 5-10 📖 Body Fluid questions 1-10 (p. 220) *e* Multiple Choice questions 1-5, 28, 29; True/False questions 1-8, 54-57; Short Answer questions 1, 2 ▧ Multiple Choice questions 9, 10 (pp. 245-246) **Book Resources** Figure 18-1 Relative volumes of three body fluids (p. 460) Table 18-1 Volumes of Body Fluid Compartments (p. 461) Figure 18-2 Proportion of body weight represented by water (p. 461) Quick Check questions 1, 2 (p. 461) Review questions 1, 2 (p. 471) Chapter Test questions 1-5 (p. 472)

ELSEVIER

Structure & Function of the Body, 13th ed.

Thibodeau/Patton

OBJECTIVES	CONTENT	TEACHING RESOURCES
		*Class Activity **Divide the class into small groups. Ask them to discuss the two major fluid compartments: extracellular and intracellular. Ask them to create a poster that lists examples of each type of compartment. Or, using the boxes in the IM (pp. 247-248), have students draw charts and diagrams of intracellular and extracellular fluids.***
		*Class Activity **Divide the class into small groups. Ask each group to research why infants have such a high proportion of body weight as water. Have them create a 30-second Public Service Announcement to warn parents about dehydration issues with their babies and young children, and have them present it to the class.***
Discuss avenues by which water enters and leaves the body and the mechanisms that maintain fluid balance.	■ Mechanisms that maintain fluid balance (p. 462) □ Regulation of fluid intake (p. 463)	Slides 11-13 Mechanisms That Maintain Fluid Balance questions 11-36 (pp. 220-222) Multiple Choice questions 6-11; True/False questions 9-16, 58-61; Short Answer questions 3, 4, 14 Multiple Choice questions 1, 4, 6, 22-24 (pp. 245-247) **Book Resources** Figure 18-3 Sources of fluid intake and output (p. 462) Table 18-2 Typical Normal Values for Each Portal of Water Entry and Exit (p. 463) Quick Check questions 1, 2 (p. 463) Review questions 3, 4 (p. 471) Critical Thinking question 14 (p. 471) Chapter Test questions 6-9 (p. 472) *Class Activity **Divide the class into small groups. Ask each group to list all the sources of fluid intake and output. Have them assign the average amount of water gained or lost through each activity. Ask each group to do a presentation for the class on their findings.***

Thibodeau/Patton

OBJECTIVES	CONTENT	TEACHING RESOURCES
		Class Activity Invite a medical assistant or nurse to field questions from students concerning the importance of, and best means for, maintaining fluid balance and regulating fluid intake. For example, does caffeine affect fluid balance? How? *Class Activity Have the class list the ingredients in the fluid replacement drinks. Are they all the same?*
Discuss the nature and importance of electrolytes in body fluids, and explain the aldosterone mechanism of extracellular fluid volume control.	☐ Importance of electrolytes in body fluids (p. 464)	🖳 Slides 14-18 𝒆 Multiple Choice questions 12-20; True/False questions 17-36, 62; Short Answer questions 5-7 📖 Multiple Choice questions 5, 8, 25, 26 (pp. 245-247) 💿 Aldosterone Regulation Mechanism **Book Resources** Figure 18-4 Homeostasis of the total volume of body water (p. 464) Table 18-3 Common Electrolytes Found in Blood Plasma (p. 465) Figure 18-5 Pitting edema (p. 465) Figure 18-6 Aldosterone mechanism (p. 466) Quick Check questions 1-3 (p. 462) Figure 18-7 Sodium-containing internal secretions (p. 467) Review questions 5-9 (p. 471) Chapter Test questions 10-14 (p. 472) *Class Activity Divide the class into two teams. Write the following words on the board:* **calcium** *(positive),* **chloride** *(negative),* **phosphate** *(negative),* **potassium** *(positive),* *and* **magnesium** *(positive). Ask each team to identify each one as positively or negatively charged ions.* *Class Activity Divide the class into groups. Have them discuss the aldosterone mechanism. Hand out an unlabeled copy of Figure 18-6 (p. 462; available on EILR or IER) and have each team fill in the labels.*

ELSEVIER

OBJECTIVES	CONTENT	TEACHING RESOURCES
Explain the interaction between capillary blood pressure and blood proteins.	☐ Capillary blood pressure and blood proteins (p. 467)	Slide 19 *e* Multiple Choice questions 21-24; True/False questions 37-47, 62; Short Answer questions 8, 9 Multiple Choice questions 3, 7, 20, 21 (pp. 245-247) Fluid Shift **Book Resources** Clinical Application: Diuretics (p. 468) Clinical Application: Edema (p. 468) Review questions 10, 11 (p. 471) Critical Thinking question 15 (p. 471) Chapter Test questions 15, 16 (p. 472) ***Class Activity** Divide the class into groups. Have each group discuss how capillary pressure can increase or decrease and what happens in each scenario. Ask each group to create a role-play to teach patients about this issue. Make sure that everyone in the group has a chance to play the patient and the medical professional.*
Give examples of common fluid imbalances.	■ Fluid imbalances (p. 468)	Slides 20, 21 Fluid Imbalances questions 37-42 (p. 223) *e* Multiple Choice questions 25-27; True/False questions 48-53; Matching questions 4, 8; Short Answer questions 10-13 Multiple Choice question 2 (p. 245) **Book Resources** Review questions 12, 13 (p. 471) ▸ Discuss dehydration and overhydration. Which is more harmful? Which is more common? ***Class Activity** Divide the class into several groups and assign each group one of the following topics:* **edema, dehydration,** *and* **diuretics.** *Have each group research its keyword in relation to fluid imbalances. Have each group present its findings to the class.*

OBJECTIVES	CONTENT	TEACHING RESOURCES
		Class Activity Have the class research a common diuretic, such as Lasix (furosemide). Discuss its indications and side effects.
Performance Evaluation		![e] Chapter 18 Computerized Test Bank questions
		![IRM] Chapter 18 questions
		![e] Student Post-Test questions
		Book Resources
		Review questions (p. 471)
		Critical Thinking questions (p. 471)
		Chapter Test (p. 472)

18.1 Homework/Assignments:

18.1 Teacher's Notes:

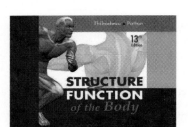

Slide 1

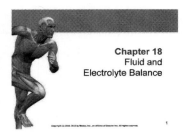

Chapter 18
Fluid and
Electrolyte Balance

Slide 2

Learning Objectives

- List, describe, and compare the body fluid compartments and their subdivisions
- Discuss avenues by which water enters and leaves the body and the mechanisms that maintain fluid balance

2

Slide 3

Learning Objectives (cont'd.)

- Discuss the nature and importance of electrolytes in body fluids and explain the aldosterone mechanism of extracellular fluid volume control
- Explain the interaction between capillary blood pressure and blood proteins
- Give examples of common fluid imbalances

3

Thibodeau/Patton

Slide 4

Chapter 18
Lesson 18.1

Slide 5

Body Fluids

- Water is the most abundant body compound
  - References to "average" body water volume based on healthy, nonobese, 70 kg (154 lb.) male
  - Water is 60% of body weight in males; 50% in females
  - Volume averages 40 L in 70 kg male

Slide 6

Body Fluids (cont'd.)

- Variation in total body water is related to
  - Total body weight of individual
  - Fat content of body—the more fat, the less water (adipose tissue is low in water content)
  - Sex—female body about 10% less than male body

- Why do obese people have less body water per kilogram? (Adipose tissue contains the least amount of water of any body tissue.)

Slide 7

Body Fluids (cont'd.)

- Age
  - In newborn infants, water may account for 80% of total body weight
  - In elderly, water per pound of weight decreases (muscle tissue, 65% water, is replaced by fat, which is 20% water)

- Because infants' bodies have such a high percentage of water, fluid imbalance caused by diarrhea is very serious.

- The percentage of body water decreases during the first 10 years of life, and by adolescence, adult values are reached and gender differences appear.

ELSEVIER

Thibodeau/Patton

Slide 8

- Why do women have less body water? (The female body contains slightly more fat than the male body.)

Slide 9

- The types of extracellular fluid are:

  - Plasma

  - Interstitial fluid (IF)

  - Miscellaneous: Lymph, joint fluids, cerebrospinal fluids, eye humors

- Discuss the volumes of plasma, interstitial fluid, and intracellular fluid in infants, adult males, and adult females.

Slide 10

- Intracellular fluid refers to the largest volume of water by far.

Slide 11

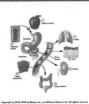

- Some sources are measurable, some are not. Those that are not are called *insensible*.

Thibodeau/Patton

Slide 12

> ### Mechanisms That Maintain Fluid Balance
>
> - Fluid output, mainly urine volume, adjusts to fluid intake
>   - Antidiuretic hormone (ADH) from posterior pituitary gland acts to increase kidney tubule reabsorption of sodium and water from tubular urine into blood
>
> 12

- ADH tends to increase the extracellular fluid and total body fluid by decreasing urine volume.

Slide 13

> ### Mechanisms That Maintain Fluid Balance (cont'd.)
>
> - Concentration of electrolytes (primarily sodium) in extracellular fluid influences volume of extracellular fluid
>   - Increase in sodium in the blood tends to increase volume of blood by
>   - Increasing movement of water out of ICF
>   - Increasing ADH secretion, which decreases urine volume, and this, in turn, increases ECF volume
>
> 13

- Sometimes people retain fluid due to excess sodium intake.

Slide 14

> ### Electrolytes in Body Fluid
>
> - Importance of electrolytes in body fluids
>   - **Nonelectrolytes:** Organic substances that do not break up or dissociate when placed in water solution (example: glucose)
>   - **Electrolytes:** Compounds that break up or dissociate in water solution into separate particles called *ions* (example: ordinary table salt or sodium chloride)
>
> 14

- The dissociated particles of an electrolyte are ions; they carry an electrical charge.

Slide 15

> ### Electrolytes in Body Fluid (cont'd.)
>
> - **Ions:** The dissociated particles of an electrolyte that carry an electrical charge
>   - **Positively charged ions:** Potassium (K^+) and sodium (Na^+)
>   - **Negatively charged ions:** Chloride (Cl^-) and bicarbonate (HCO_3^-)
>   - Electrolyte composition of blood plasma
>
> 15

- A variety of electrolytes have important nutrient or regulatory roles in the body.
- Many ions are major or important trace elements; for example iron and iodine.

Slide 16

Electrolytes in Body Fluid (cont'd.)

- Sodium: Most abundant and important positively charged ion of plasma
  - Normal plasma level—142 mEq/L
  - Average daily intake (diet)—100 mEq
  - Chief method of regulation—kidney
  - Aldosterone increases Na reabsorption in kidney tubules
  - Containing internal secretions

- Where sodium goes, water soon follows.
- If, for example, the concentration of sodium in blood increases, the volume of blood soon increases.
- Conversely, if blood sodium concentration decreases, blood volume soon decreases.
- mEq is short for *milliequivalent*.

Slide 17

Electrolytes in Body Fluid (cont'd.)

Aldosterone Mechanism

- What is the aldosterone mechanism? How does it work? (Aldosterone, secreted by the adrenal cortex, increases sodium reabsorption by the kidney tubules. Water reabsorption also increases, causing an increase in ECF volume.)

Slide 18

Electrolytes in Body Fluid (cont'd.)

Sodium-Containing Internal Secretions

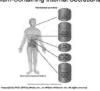

- Why should caregivers pay special attention to the use of diuretics with patients? (The use of diuretics in patients can cause a decrease in fluid volume and dehydration. Diuretics can also cause a patient to lose important electrolytes.)

Slide 19

Capillary Blood Pressure

- Capillary blood pressure pushes water out of blood into interstitial fluid (IF)
- Blood protein concentration pulls water into blood from interstitial fluid
  - These two forces regulate plasma and interstitial fluid volume under usual conditions

- Plasma proteins act as a water-pulling or water-holding force.
- They hold water in the blood and pull it into the blood from IF.
- Of the three main body fluids, IF volume varies the most.
- Plasma volume usually fluctuates only slightly; if a pronounced change occurs, adequate circulation cannot be maintained.

Slide 20

Fluid Imbalances

- **Dehydration:** Total volume of body fluids less than normal
  - Interstitial fluid volume shrinks first; if treatment is not given, intracellular fluid volume and plasma volume decrease
  - Dehydration occurs when fluid output exceeds intake for an extended period

20

- Dehydration is a potentially dangerous condition.
- What is an easy way to test for dehydration? (skin pinch test, but can also assess patient's mucous membranes)

Slide 21

Fluid Imbalances (cont'd.)

- **Overhydration:** Total volume of body fluids greater than normal
  - Occurs when fluid intake exceeds output
    - Various factors may cause this
      - Giving excessive amounts of intravenous fluids
      - Giving intravenous fluids too rapidly

21

- The danger of overhydration is that it puts a heavy burden on the heart.

Structure & Function of the Body, 13th ed.
Thibodeau/Patton

19 Lesson Plan
Acid–Base Balance

TEACHING FOCUS

In this chapter, the student will have the opportunity to learn the concepts of pH, including acid–base balance, buffer, and buffer pair, as well as contrasting strong and weak bases. The student also will have the opportunity to examine and contrast the respiratory and urinary mechanisms of pH control and compensatory mechanisms that may help correct blood pH imbalances. Metabolic and respiratory types of imbalances will be compared and contrasted.

MATERIALS AND RESOURCES

☐ Computer (Lesson 19.1)

LESSON CHECKLIST

Preparations for this lesson include:

- lecture/discussion
- demonstration
- guest speakers: medical assistant or nurse
- student performance evaluation of all entry-level skills required for student comprehension and application of acid–base balance principles including:
  - o learning the concepts of pH and acid–base balance
  - o defining buffer and buffer pair
  - o contrasting respiratory and urinary mechanisms of pH control
  - o contrasting metabolic and respiratory types of pH balances

Thibodeau/Patton

KEY TERMS

acid–base balance (p. 475)
acid solution (p. 476)
acidosis (p. 481)
aerobic respiration (p. 477)
alkaline solution (p. 476)
alkalosis (p. 481)
base (p. 477)
bicarbonate (p. 478)
buffer (p. 477)
buffer pairs (p. 477)
carbonic anhydrase (p. 477)
cellular respiration (p. 477)

diabetic ketoacidosis (p. 480)
emesis (p. 483)
hydrogen ions (H^+) (p. 475)
hydroxide ions (OH^-) (p. 475)
ketone bodies (p. 480)
metabolic acidosis (p. 482)
metabolic alkalosis (p. 482)
pH (p. 475)
respiratory acidosis (p. 482)
respiratory alkalosis (p. 482)
uncompensated metabolic acidosis (p. 484)

ADDITIONAL RESOURCES

AnimationDirect (Book Companion CD)
Instructor's Electronic Resource (IER) (CD)
PowerPoint slides (CD, Evolve)
Test Bank (Evolve)

ESLR EVOLVE Student Learning Resource	**EILR TB** EVOLVE Instructor Learning Resource Test Bank	AnimationDirect on Book Companion CD	**PPT** PowerPoint Slides	**SG** Study Guide	**IRM** Instructor's Resource Manual

Legend

Class Activities are indicated in ***bold italic.***

Structure & Function of the Body, 13th ed.
Thibodeau/Patton

LESSON 19.1

PRETEST
Study Guide Multiple Choice questions 1-10 (pp. 235-236)

BACKGROUND ASSESSMENT
Question: Do all body fluids have roughly the same pH level?
Answer: For homeostasis to occur, there must be equilibrium between intracellular and extracellular fluid volume. However, chemical pH of body fluids is equally important in homeostasis. The pH value is the degree of acidity and alkalinity of a body fluid. The neutral point, pH 7, is when a fluid is neither acid nor alkaline. (Increasing acidity is expressed as less than 7; increasing alkalinity is expressed as greater than 7). Examples of body fluids that are acidic are gastric juice (1.6) and urine (6.0), while blood (7.45) is considered alkaline. Maintaining the acid–base balance of body fluids is a matter of vital importance. If the balance varies even slightly, necessary chemical and cellular reactions cannot occur.

Question: What are buffers and how do they help regulate the pH of body fluids?
Answer: The body uses three mechanisms to regulate the pH of its fluids: the buffer mechanism, the respiratory mechanism, and the urinary mechanisms. Together, they keep blood slightly alkaline with a pH that stays remarkably constant. Buffers are chemical substances that prevent a sharp change in the pH of a fluid when an acid or base is added to it. This is paramount; survival depends on protecting the body from drastic changes in pH. An example of buffers, which consist of two kinds or "pairs" of substances, is ordinary baking soda ($NaHCO_3$) and carbonic acid (H_2CO_3).

CRITICAL THINKING QUESTION
Josie is in her second trimester of pregnancy and has been vomiting constantly for several days. On the advice of her physician, Josie is admitted to the hospital, where she receives intravenous administrations of normal saline. Why?
Guidelines: Severe vomiting, as in Josie's case, can be caused by pregnancy, and it can be life-threatening. It may result in metabolic alkalosis, which is due to a massive loss of chloride from the stomach. The loss of chloride causes a compensatory increase of bicarbonate in the extracellular fluid, which is why Josie is getting an intravenous administration of normal saline, a chloride-containing solution. The chloride ions of the solution replace bicarbonate ions and help relieve the bicarbonate excess responsible for the imbalance.

OBJECTIVES	CONTENT	TEACHING RESOURCES
Discuss the concept of pH, and define the term acid–base balance.	■ pH of body fluids (p. 475) ■ Mechanisms that control pH of body fluids (p. 477)	Slides 5, 6 pH of Body questions 1-10 (p. 230) Mechanisms that Control pH of Body Fluids questions 11, 18 (pp. 230-231) Check Your Knowledge questions 1, 2, 6 (pp. 235-236) Multiple Choice questions 1-6, 31, 32; True or False questions 1-11, 57-60, 62; Short Answer question 1 **Book Resources** Figure 19-1 The pH range (p. 476)

OBJECTIVES	CONTENT	TEACHING RESOURCES
		Class Activity Invite a medical assistant or nurse to field questions from students on pH of body fluids and the three mechanisms that control pH of body fluids: the **buffer** *mechanism, the* **respiratory mechanism,** *and the* **urinary mechanism.** *Class Activity To demonstrate the pH range of common substances, assign each student a substance such as gastric fluid, coffee, or Milk of Magnesia (see Figure 19-1). Have the students line up according to the pH balance of their substance, from acidic to basic.*
Define the terms *buffer* **and** *buffer pair* **and contrast strong and weak acids and bases.**	☐ Buffers (p. 477)	Slides 7-10 Mechanisms that Control pH of Body Fluids and pH Imbalances questions 13-16, 20, 21 (pp. 230-231) Applying What You Know question 47 (p. 233) Check Your Knowledge questions 3, 4 (p. 236) Multiple Choice questions 7-17, 33, 34; True or False questions 12-25, 61, 63; Short Answer questions 2-4 **Book Resources** Figure 19-2 Buffering action of sodium bicarbonate (p. 478) Figure 19-3 Buffering action of carbonic acid (p. 479) Quick Check questions 1, 2 (p. 479) Critical Thinking question 14 (p. 488) *Class Activity Divide the class into small teams. To reinforce the concept of buffers, have each team sketch out how buffering takes place, using the examples of sodium bicarbonate and hydrochloric acid and sodium chloride and carbonic acid (see Figures 19-2 and 19-3). Ask each team to present their findings to the class.*

Thibodeau/Patton

OBJECTIVES	CONTENT	TEACHING RESOURCES
Contrast the respiratory and urinary mechanisms of pH control.	☐ Respiratory mechanism of pH control (p. 479) ☐ Urinary mechanism of pH control (p. 481)	Slides 11-14 Mechanisms that Control pH of Body Fluids and pH Imbalances questions 17-30 (pp. 231-232) Applying What You Know question 48 (p. 241) Multiple Choice questions 18-23, 35; True or False questions 26-44, 64, 65; Short Answer questions 5, 6, 11 Urinary Mechanism of pH Control **Book Resources** Figure 19-4 Lactic acid buffered by sodium bicarbonate (p. 480) Clinical Application: Diabetic Ketoacidosis (p. 480) Figure 19-5 Acidification of urine and conservation of base by distal renal tubule secretion of H^+ ions (p. 482) Figure 19-6 Acidification of urine by tubule secretion of ammonia (NH_3) (p. 483) Quick Check questions 1, 2 (p. 481) *Class Activity **Divide the class into small teams. Have them discuss what happens to the body's blood pH level when the breath is held for a minute. Ask students to discuss what causes these changes. Ask each group to role-play teaching patients about this concept.*** *Class Activity **Divide the class into small teams. Have them discuss why urine is usually acidic. Give each team a copy of Figure 19-6, taking care to delete the labels. Ask each team to fill in the labels as part of this discussion.***
Discuss compensatory mechanisms that may help return blood pH to near-normal levels in cases of pH imbalances.	■ pH imbalances (p. 481)	Slides 15, 16 Multiple Choice questions 24-26; True or False questions 45-48, 66, 67; Matching questions 1-10 *Class Activity **Divide the class into two groups. Assign one group the topic "pH regulation by the kidneys" and one group the topic "pH regulation by the respiratory system." Ask each team to create scenarios of how their body system can restore pH balance. Then have each group share this information with the rest of the class.***

OBJECTIVES	CONTENT	TEACHING RESOURCES
Compare and contrast metabolic and respiratory types of pH imbalances.	☐ Metabolic and respiratory disturbances (p. 482) ☐ Vomiting (p. 483)	Slides 16-18 pH Imbalances, Metabolic and Respiratory Disturbances, and Vomiting questions 31-40 (p. 232) Applying What You Know question 47 (p. 233) Check Your Knowledge questions 5, 7-10 (p. 236) Multiple Choice questions 27-30; True or False questions 49-56, 68-70; Short Answer questions 7-10 **Book Resources** Clinical Application: Lactic Acidosis and Metformin (p. 484) Figure 19-7 The vomit reflex (p. 485) Quick Check questions 1-4 (p. 485) Critical Thinking question 13 (p. 488) *Class Activity **Divide the class into four teams. Assign each team one of the following topics: metabolic acidosis, metabolic alkalosis, respiratory acidosis, or respiratory alkalosis. Have students make up index cards or posters outlining the definition, causes, and treatments. Have each team discuss this type of disturbance and give examples of it. Ask each group to present their results to the class.*** *Class Activity **Divide the class into small groups, and have them discuss the impact that vomiting can have on blood pH levels. Ask each group to develop a brochure to teach patients about this issue.*** *Class Activity **Divide the class into small teams. Ask them to discuss what the normal ratio of sodium bicarbonate to carbonic acid in the blood is. Have each team describe the differences between uncompensated metabolic acidosis and compensated metabolic acidosis. Ask each team to create a poster to explain these concepts.***
Performance Evaluation		Chapter 19 Computerized Test Bank questions Chapter 19 activities and questions Student Post-Test questions

OBJECTIVES	CONTENT	TEACHING RESOURCES
		Book Resources
		Review questions (p. 488)
		Chapter Test (pp. 488-489)

19.1 Homework/Assignments:

19.1 Teacher's Notes:

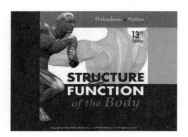

Slide 1

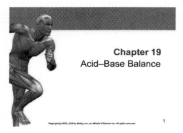

Chapter 19
Acid–Base Balance

1

Slide 2

Learning Objectives

- Discuss the concept of pH and define the term *acid–base balance*
- Define the terms *buffer* and *buffer pair* and contrast strong and weak acids and bases
- Contrast the respiratory and urinary mechanisms of pH control

2

Slide 3

Learning Objectives (cont'd.)

- Discuss compensatory mechanisms that may help return blood pH to near-normal levels in cases of pH imbalances
- Compare and contrast metabolic and respiratory types of pH imbalances

3

Slide 4

Chapter 19
Lesson 19.1

Slide 5

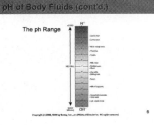

pH of Body Fluids

- Definition of **pH**: A number that indicates the hydrogen ion (H⁺) concentration of a fluid
  - pH 7 indicates neutrality
  - pH higher than 7 indicates alkalinity
  - pH less than 7 indicates acidity
- Normal arterial blood pH is about 7.45
- Normal venous blood pH is about 7.35

- What do water and all water solutions contain? (Hydrogen [H^+] and hydroxide [OH^-] ions)
- What does pH 7 mean? (the solution contains an equal number of hydrogen and hydroxide ions)

Slide 6

pH of Body Fluids (cont'd.)

The ph Range

- Note the neutral pH of 7.

Slide 7

Mechanisms That Control pH

- **Buffers**
  - Substances that prevent a sharp change in the pH of a fluid when an acid or base is added to it
  - **Fixed acids:** Buffered mainly by sodium bicarbonate ($NaHCO_3$)
  - Buffers consist of two substances and are often called *buffered pairs*

- Main blood buffer pairs are baking soda (sodium bicarbonate) and carbonic acid.
- Strong acids and bases, if added to blood, would disassociate almost completely.
- This would release large quantities of H or OH ions and create drastic changes in blood pH.

Slide 8

Mechanisms That Control pH (cont'd.)

- Changes in blood are produced by buffering of fixed acids in the tissue capillaries
  - Amount of carbonic acid (H_2CO_3) in blood increases slightly
  - Amount of $NaHCO_3$ in blood decreases
  - H^+ concentration of blood increases slightly
  - Blood pH decreases slightly below arterial level

8

- Ratio of amount of $NaHCO_3$ to H_2CO_3 does not normally change; normal ratio is 20:1.
- Fixed acids do not break down to form a gas.
- Lactic acid is one of the most abundant fixed acids.

Slide 9

Mechanisms That Control pH (cont'd.)

Buffering Action of Sodium Bicarbonate

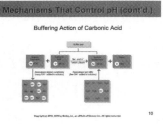

9

- Both sodium bicarbonate and carbonic acid can act as buffers.

Slide 10

Mechanisms That Control pH (cont'd.)

Buffering Action of Carbonic Acid

10

- Both sodium bicarbonate and carbonic acid can act as buffers.

Slide 11

Respiratory Mechanism of pH Control

- Respiratory mechanism of pH control—respirations remove some CO_2 from blood
  - As blood flows through lung capillaries, the amount of H_2CO_3 in blood is decreased
  - Thereby its H^+ concentration is decreased
  - This increases blood pH from its venous to its arterial level

11

- How does holding your breath affect blood pH?
- Decreasing respirations will produce acidosis.
- Increasing respirations will produce alkalosis.

ELSEVIER

Structure & Function of the Body, 13th ed.

Thibodeau/Patton

Slide 12

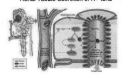

- Urinary mechanism of pH control is the body's most effective regulator of blood pH
    - Kidneys acidify urine by the distal tubules secreting hydrogen ions and ammonia (NH₃) into the urine from blood in exchange for reabsorption of NaHCO₃ into the blood

12

- Kidneys usually excrete acids, but they can excrete bases if necessary. Lungs cannot excrete base.
- More acids than bases usually enter the blood.

Slide 13

Urinary Mechanism of pH Control (cont'd.)
Acidification of Urine and Conservation of Base by Distal Renal Tubule Secretion of H+ Ions

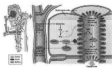

13

- Kidneys are more efficient than lungs in regulating pH, but they take longer.

Slide 14

Urinary Mechanism of pH Control (cont'd.)
Acidification of Urine by Tubule Secretion of Ammonia (NH₃)

14

Slide 15

pH Imbalances

- Acidosis and alkalosis are the two kinds of pH or acid–base imbalances
- Disturbances in acid–base balance depend on relative quantities of NaHCO₃ and H₂CO₃ in the blood
- The body can regulate both of the components of the NaHCO₃-H₂CO₃ buffer system

15

- Blood levels of $NaHCO_3$ are regulated by kidneys.
- H_2CO_3 levels are regulated by respiratory system (lungs).
- The blood pH falls as H+ ion concentration increases or due to a loss of bases.
- Rarely does blood pH fall as low as 7.
- Blood pH almost never falls below 7; death would happen first.

Structure & Function of the Body, 13th ed.
Thibodeau/Patton

Slide 16

pH Imbalances (cont'd.)

- Two basic types of pH disturbances—metabolic and respiratory—can alter the normal 20:1 ratio of $NaHCO_3$ to H_2CO_3 in blood
  - Metabolic disturbances affect the $NaHCO_3$ levels in blood
  - Respiratory disturbances affect the H_2CO_3 levels in blood

16

Slide 17

pH Imbalances (cont'd.)

- Types of pH or acid–base imbalances
  - Metabolic disturbances
    - **Metabolic acidosis:** Bicarbonate ($NaHCO_3$) deficit
    - **Metabolic alkalosis:** Bicarbonate ($NaHCO_3$) excess; complication of severe vomiting
  - Respiratory disturbances
    - Respiratory acidosis (H_2CO_3 excess)
    - Respiratory alkalosis (H_2CO_3 deficit)

17

- Patients with metabolic acidosis often suffer from renal disease, uncontrolled diabetes, prolonged diarrhea, or have ingested toxic chemicals such as antifreeze.
- From what can metabolic alkalosis result? (bulimia)
- What causes respiratory acidosis? (retention of too much carbon dioxide as seen in COPD)
- What causes respiratory alkalosis? (hyperventilation)

Slide 18

pH Imbalances (cont'd.)

- Vomiting can cause metabolic alkalosis
- Uncompensated metabolic acidosis: The normal ratio of $NaHCO_3$ to H_2CO_3 is changed
- Compensated metabolic acidosis: The ratio remains at 20:1, but the total amount of $NaHCO_3$ and H_2CO_3 changes

18

- Treatment of vomiting includes intravenous administration of chloride-containing solutions such as normal saline.
- The chloride ions of the solution replace the bicarbonate ions and help relieve the bicarbonate excess responsible for the imbalance.

Thibodeau/Patton

TEACHING FOCUS

In this chapter, students will have the opportunity to investigate the essential and accessory organs of the male and female reproductive systems and the general functions of each, including the gross and microscopic structures of the gonads in both sexes and the developmental steps in spermatogenesis and oogenesis. Students will have the opportunity to examine the primary functions of sex hormones and to identify the cell type and structure responsible for their secretion. They will also have the opportunity to identify and describe the structures of external male and female genitalia and to discuss the endometrial or menstrual cycle and its phases in a typical 28-day cycle.

MATERIALS AND RESOURCES

- ☐ 3x5 cards to make flash cards (all Lessons)
- ☐ Computer (all Lessons)
- ☐ Unlabeled copies of Figure 20-1 (p. 489) (Lesson 20.1)
- ☐ Unlabeled copies of Figure 20-7 (p. 497) (Lesson 20.2)

- ☐ Unlabeled display of Figure 20-6 (p. 495) (Lesson 20.1)
- ☐ Unlabeled display of Figure 20-11 (p. 502) (Lesson 20.2)

LESSON CHECKLIST

Preparations for this lesson include:

- lecture
- guest speakers: physician, medical assistant, nurse
- student performance evaluation of all entry-level skills required for student comprehension and application of anatomical and physiological principles including:
  - ○ male reproductive system
  - ○ female reproductive system

KEY TERMS

accessory organ (p. 492)
acrosome (p. 495)
amenorrhea (p. 510)
areola (p. 505)
Bartholin's glands (p. 505)
benign prostatic hypertrophy (p. 499)
body (of the uterus) (p. 504)
breasts (p. 505)
bulbourethral glands (p. 499)
cervix (p. 504)
circumcision (p. 499)
clitoris (p. 506)
corpora cavernosa (p. 499)
corpus luteum (p. 501)
corpus spongiosum (p. 499)
cryptorchidism (p. 498)
ductus deferens (p. 497)
ectopic pregnancy (p. 505)
ejaculatory duct (p. 498)
endometrium (p. 504)
epididymis (p. 497)

episiotomy (p. 506)
essential organ (p. 492)
estrogen (p. 502)
external genitalia (p. 506)
fallopian tubes (p. 503)
fimbriae (p. 503)
foreskin (p. 499)
fundus (p. 504)
gametes (p. 491)
genitalia (p. 499)
glans (p. 499)
gonads (p. 492)
Graafian follicle (p. 501)
granulosa cells (p. 501)
greater vestibular glands (p. 505)
hymen (p. 506)
interstitial cells (p. 494)
labia majora (p. 506)
labia minora (p. 506)
lactiferous ducts (p. 505)
mature follicles (p. 501)

Copyright © 2008, 2005 by Mosby, Inc., an affiliate of Elsevier Inc.   Thibodeau/Patton

ADDITIONAL RESOURCES

AnimationDirect (Book Companion CD)

Instructor's Electronic Resource (IER) (CD)

PowerPoint slides (CD, Evolve)

Test Bank (Evolve)

Legend

ESLR
EVOLVE Student
Learning Resource

EILR TB
EVOLVE Instructor
Learning Resource
Test Bank

AnimationDirect
on Book Companion
CD

PPT
PowerPoint
Slides

SG
Study
Guide

IRM
Instructor's
Resource Manual

Class Activities are indicated in ***bold italic.***

Structure & Function of the Body, 13th ed.

Thibodeau/Patton

LESSON 20.1

PRETEST

Study Guide Multiple Choice questions 1-10 (pp. 248-249)

BACKGROUND ASSESSMENT

Question: New human life results from the equal contribution of two parent cells, one from a male and one from a female. What cell does each contribute?
Answer: The male contributes sperm and the female contributes ova.

Question: The complex systems in both the male and female reproductive systems have, as their ultimate goal, the merging of sperm and ova. What is the successful completion of this function called?
Answer: The successful completion of the sperm merging with the ova is called *fertilization*.

CRITICAL THINKING QUESTION

The human reproductive process depends on different multiple organs from both male and female reproductive systems performing key functions of the process. Based on your knowledge of reproductive organs, how do a vasectomy (blocking the vas deferens in the male) and tubal ligation (blocking the fallopian tubes in the female) work to interrupt the reproductive process?
Guidelines: In a vasectomy, the vas deferens from each testicle in the male is blocked. This stops sperm from mixing with other seminal fluids produced in the seminal vesicles and prostrate gland as it passes through the urethra during ejaculation. Therefore, fertilization cannot take place without sperm in the semen. Although oogenesis continues ova development, tubal ligation ties, blocks, or cuts the fallopian tubes so that eggs cannot travel down the tubes to the uterus. Because of this, the sperm can never fertilize the egg and the egg cannot implant in the uterus.

OBJECTIVES	CONTENT	TEACHING RESOURCES

List the essential and accessory organs of the male and female reproductive systems, and give the general function of each.	■ Common structural and functional characteristics between the sexes (p. 492)
	
	 ■ Male reproductive system (p. 492)
	
	 □ Structural plan (p. 492)
	
	   – Essential organs (p. 492)
	
	   – Accessory organs (p. 492)
		Slides 5-9
		
		 Male Reproductive System and Structural Plan questions 1-10 (p. 240)
		
		 Multiple Choice questions 1, 41, 42; True or False questions 1, 2, 58-61
		
		 Book Resources
		
		 Table 20-1 Male Reproductive Organs (p. 493)
		
		 Figure 20-1 Organization of the male reproductive organs (p. 493)
		
		 Chapter Test question 1 (p. 517)
		
		 Clear View of the Human Body
		
		 Class Activity Have students create flash cards listing the male reproductive organs and each organ's functions. Divide the class into teams and have them quiz each other.

Thibodeau/Patton

OBJECTIVES	CONTENT	TEACHING RESOURCES
		Class Activity Create a mock game show, inviting three students to be contestants. Describe the function of an organ; the contestant who correctly says the right organ gets a point. The first student to reach ten points wins.
Describe the gross and microscopic structure of the gonads in both sexes, and explain the developmental steps in spermatogenesis and oogenesis.	☐ Testes (p. 493) – Structure and location (p. 493)	Slides 10, 11 Testes questions 11-15 (pp. 240-241) Multiple Choice questions 2, 3; True or False questions 3-5, 62, 63; Matching questions 1-10, 21; Short Answer question 1 **Book Resources** Figure 20-2 Tubules of the testis and epididymis (p. 494) Figure 20-3 Testis tissue (p. 494) Review question 1 (p. 516) Chapter Test questions 2-4 (p. 517) *Class Activity Divide the class into small groups. Distribute an unlabeled handout of Figure 20-1 (p. 493; available on EILR or IER). Have each group label the figure and discuss the functions of the organs.*
Discuss the primary functions of the sex hormones, and identify the cell type or structure responsible for their secretion.	– Testis functions (p. 495)	Slides 12-14 Testes questions 15-27 (pp. 241-242) Multiple Choice questions 4-9; True or False questions 6-13, 64-67; Short Answer questions 2-4 **Book Resources** Figure 20-4 Spermatogenesis (p. 496) Quick Check questions 1-3 (p. 497) Figure 20-5 Human sperm (p. 497) Review questions 2, 3 (p. 516) Chapter Test questions 5-8 (p. 517) *Class Activity To help students better understand spermatogenesis, divide the class into small groups. Have them diagram the process of sperm production.* *Class Activity Divide the class into small groups. Have them discuss the functions that testosterone serves.*

Structure & Function of the Body, 13th ed.

Thibodeau/Patton

OBJECTIVES	CONTENT	TEACHING RESOURCES
Describe the gross and microscopic structure of the gonads in both sexes, and explain the developmental steps in spermatogenesis and oogenesis.	☐ Reproductive ducts (p. 497) – Epididymis (p. 497) – Ductus (vas) deferens (p. 497) – Ejaculatory duct and urethra (p. 498) ☐ Accessory or supportive sex glands (p. 498) – Seminal vesicles (p. 498) – Prostate gland (p. 498) – Bulbourethral glands (p. 499)	⊠▦ Slides 15-18 Reproductive Ducts, Accessory or Supportive Sex Glands, and External Genitalia questions 28-37 (p. 242) *e* Multiple Choice questions 10-15, 43-46; True or False questions 14-21, 68, 69; Short Answer questions 5, 6 Male Reproductive Ducts **Book Resources** Review questions 4, 5 (p. 516) Critical Thinking question 18 (p. 516) Chapter Test questions 9-12 (p. 517)
Identify and describe the structures that constitute the external genitals in both sexes.	☐ External genitals (p. 499)	⊠▦ Slides 19-21 *e* Multiple Choice question 16; True or False questions 22, 23; Matching questions 1-10 **Book Resources** Figure 20-6 Penis (p. 500) Critical Thinking question 18 (p. 516) Chapter Test question 13 (p. 517) Clear View of the Human Body ***Class Activity Show the class an unlabeled copy of Figure 20-6 (p. 500; available on EILR or IER). Ask students to volunteer to fill in the labels. If possible, ask students to describe the function of each part of the penis.***

20.1 Homework/Assignments:

20.1 Teacher's Notes:

Thibodeau/Patton

LESSON 20.2

CRITICAL THINKING QUESTION

The reproductive mechanisms in both sexes are complex. However, the female reproductive system is even more complex than the male's. Why is this so?

Guidelines: The female reproductive system not only must produce the egg to complement the male sperm, it must provide all necessary elements for the fertilized egg to develop through all prenatal phases. For example, the uterus serves multiple purposes, functioning in menstruation, pregnancy, and labor. Furthermore, the vagina serves the dual purposes of a passage for sperm to enter during their journey to meet the ovum and as the organ by which a baby emerges at birth.

OBJECTIVES	CONTENT	TEACHING RESOURCES
List the essential and accessory organs of the male and female reproductive systems and give the general function of each.	■ Female reproductive system (p. 499) □ Structural plan (p. 499) – Essential organs (p. 501) – Accessory organs (p. 501)	Slides 23-25 Female Reproductive System and Structural Plan questions 38-42 (p. 243) Multiple Choice question 17; True or False questions 24, 25 **Book Resources** Table 20-2 Female Reproductive Organs (p. 501) Figure 20-7 Organization of the female reproductive organs (p. 502) Chapter Test question 14 (p. 516) Clear View of the Human Body *Class Activity Have students create flash cards listing the female reproductive organs and each organ's functions. Divide students into teams and have them quiz each other.* *Class Activity Create a mock game show, inviting three students to be contestants. Describe the function of an organ; the contestant who correctly says the right organ gets a point. The first student to reach ten points wins.*
Describe the gross and microscopic structure of the gonads in both sexes and explain the developmental steps in spermatogenesis and oogenesis.	□ Ovaries (p. 501) – Structure and location (p. 501)	Slides 26, 27 Female Reproductive System and Structural Plan questions 43-50 (p. 243) True or False questions 26-29; Matching questions 11-20, 70, 71; Short Answer question 7 **Book Resources** Review question 6 (p. 516) Chapter Test question 15 (p. 517)

Structure & Function of the Body, 13th ed.
Thibodeau/Patton

OBJECTIVES	CONTENT	TEACHING RESOURCES
		*Class Activity **Divide the class into small groups. Give them an unlabeled copy of Figure 20-7 (p. 502; available on EILR or IER). Have each group label the figure and discuss the functions of the organs.***
Discuss the primary functions of the sex hormones, and identify the cell type or structure responsible for their secretion.	– Ovary functions (p. 501)	Slides 29, 30 Ovaries questions 51-61 (p. 243) Multiple Choice questions 18-24, 47; True or False questions 30-35, 55, and 72; Short Answer question 8 **Book Resources** Figure 20-8 Diagram of ovary and oogenesis (p. 503) Quick Check questions 1-4 (p. 503) Review questions 7-9 (p. 516) Chapter Test questions 16, 17 (p. 517) *Class Activity **To help students better understand oogenesis, divide the class into small groups. Have students detail the process of female sex cells. For help, they can reference Figure 20-8 (p. 503).*** *Class Activity **Divide the class into small groups. Have them discuss the functions that estrogen and progesterone perform.***
Describe the gross and microscopic structure of the gonads in both sexes, and explain the developmental steps in spermatogenesis and oogenesis.	☐ Reproductive ducts (p. 503) – Uterine tubes (p. 503) – Uterus (p. 504) – Vagina (p. 505) ☐ Accessory or supportive sex glands (p. 505) – Bartholin's glands (p. 505) – Breasts (p. 505)	Slides 31-35 Female Reproductive Ducts questions 62-71 (p. 244) Multiple Choice questions 25-29, 48; True or False questions 36-45; Short Answer questions 9-11 Female Reproductive Ducts **Book Resources** Figure 20-9 Uterus (p. 504) Figure 20-10 Lateral view of the breast (p. 506) Review questions 10-13 (p. 516) Chapter Test questions 18-24 (p. 517)

Thibodeau/Patton

OBJECTIVES	CONTENT	TEACHING RESOURCES
Identify and describe the structures that constitute the external genitalia in both sexes.	☐ External genitalia (p. 506)	Slides 36, 37 Accessory or Supportive Sex Glands questions and External Genitalia of the Female 72-81 (p. 244) Multiple Choice question 30; True or False question 46; Matching questions 11-30; Short Answer questions 1-6 **Book Resources** Quick Check questions 1 (p. 511) Figure 20-11 External genitalia of the female (p. 507) Clear View of the Human Body ***Class Activity Show the class an unlabeled copy of Figure 20-11 (p. 507; available on EILR or IER). Ask students to volunteer to fill in the labels. If possible, ask students to describe the function of each part of the external genitalia.***

Identify and discuss the phases of the endometrial or menstrual cycle, and correlate each phase with its occurrence in a typical 28-day cycle.	☐ Menstrual cycle (p. 506)
	  – Phases and events (p. 506)
	  – Control of menstrual cycle changes (p. 507)
	■ Summary of male and female reproductive systems (p. 511)
		Slides 38-42
		
		Menstrual Cycle questions 82-92 (p. 245)
		
		Multiple Choice questions 31-40; True or False questions 47-54, 56, 57, and 73; Matching questions 22-30; Short Answer questions 12-16
		
		Book Resources
		
		Figure 20-12 The 28-day menstrual cycle (p. 508)
		
		Table 20-3 Analogous Features of the Reproductive Systems (p. 511)
		
		Review questions 14-16 (p. 516)
		
		Critical Thinking questions 17, 19 (p. 51)
		
		Class Activity Divide the class into small groups. Ask them to create flash cards with the details of the four phases of the 28-day menstrual cycle. Have them quiz each other.

Performance Evaluation		Chapter 20 Computerized Test Bank questions Chapter 20 activities and questions Student Post-Test questions

OBJECTIVES	CONTENT	TEACHING RESOURCES
		Book Resources
		Review questions (p. 516)
		Critical Thinking questions 17-19 (p. 516)
		Chapter Test (p. 517)

20.2 Homework/Assignments:

20.2 Teacher's Notes:

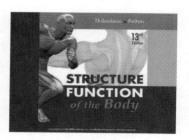

Slide 1

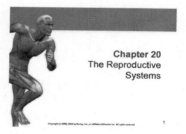

Chapter 20
The Reproductive
Systems

Slide 2

Learning Objectives

- List the essential and accessory organs of the male and female reproductive systems and describe the general function of each
- Describe the gross and microscopic structure of the gonads in both sexes and explain the developmental steps in spermatogenesis and oogenesis

Slide 3

Learning Objectives (cont'd.)

- Discuss the primary functions of the sex hormones and identify the cell type or structure responsible for their secretion
- Identify and describe the structures that constitute the external genitals in both sexes
- Identify and discuss the phases of the endometrial or menstrual cycle and correlate each phase with its occurrence in a typical 28-day cycle

Slide 4

Chapter 20
Lesson 20.1

Slide 5

Common Structural and Functional Characteristics Between the Sexes

- Common general structure and function can be identified between the systems in both sexes
- Systems adapted for development of sperm or ova followed by successful fertilization, development, and birth of offspring

- What advantages for humans come from a sexual rather than an asexual reproductive system? (Variation in genetic make-up.)

Slide 6

Common Structural and Functional Characteristics Between the Sexes (cont'd.)

- Sex hormones in both sexes are important in development of secondary sexual characteristics and normal reproductive system activity

- Organs of both men and women adapted to specific functions in sequence.
- Male organs: produce, store, and introduce mature sperm into female reproductive tract.
- Female organs: produce ova, receive sperm, permit fertilization, and develop ovum to allow it to mature before birth.

Slide 7

Male Reproductive System

- Structural plan
  - Reproductive organs are classified as essential or accessory
  - Essential organs of reproduction are the gonads (testes in males), which produce sex cells called sperm

- Essential organs of reproduction in both men and women are called *gonads*.
- Why are the testes classified as essential? (The production of sex cells are necessary for the reproduction of human life.)

Slide 8

Male Reproductive System (cont'd.)

- Accessory organs
  - **Ducts:** Passageways that carry sperm from testes to exterior
  - **Sex glands:** Produce protective and nutrient secretions for sperm
  - External genitals

8

- The ducts consist of two each of the following: epididymis, vas deferens, ejaculatory duct, and urethra.
- Supportive sex glands are the seminal vesicles, bulbourethral or Cowper's gland, and the prostrate gland.

Slide 9

Organization of the Male Reproductive Organs

9

- Which of the organs shown here are essential organs? (sex cells of testes) Accessory organs? (The duct system and the sex glands are accessory.)
- What are the elements of the duct system? (epididymis, vas deferens, ejaculatory duct, and urethra)
- What are the elements of the supportive sex glands? (Supportive sex glands are the seminal vesicles, bulbourethral or Cowper's gland, and the prostrate gland.)

Slide 10

Testes

- **Testes:** the gonads of men
  - Structure and location
    - Testes in scrotum—lower temperature
    - Covered by tunica albuginea, which divides testis into lobules containing seminiferous tubules
    - Interstitial cells produce testosterone

10

- Testes are in pairs.
- Scrotum is 1 degree Celsius (3 degrees Fahrenheit) cooler than normal body temperature.
- What is the importance of the lower temperature of the scrotum? (Cooler temperatures are necessary for sperm cells to generate.)

Slide 11

Testes (cont'd.)

Tubules of the Testis and Epididymis

11

- In the photograph, the testicle is the darker sphere in the center.

Thibodeau/Patton

Slide 12

> **Testes (cont'd.)**
>
> • Testis functions
>   • **Spermatogenesis:** process of sperm production
>   ▫ Sperm precursor cells called *spermatogonia*
>   ▫ Meiosis produces primary spermatocyte, which forms four spermatids with 23 chromosomes
>   ▫ **Spermatozoa:** Highly specialized cells
>
> 12

- Primary spermatocyte—one of the daughter cells produced when spermatogonium divide.

- Spermatids: daughter cells.

- Each primary spermatocyte produces four sperm cells.

- Spermatazoa: heads contain genetic material, acrosomes contain enzymes to assist sperm to penetrate ovum, and mitochondria provide energy for movement.

Slide 13

> **Testes (cont'd.)**
>
> Spermatogenesis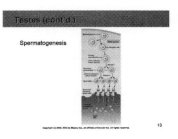
>
> 13

- What are the steps in the process of spermatogenesis? (Mitotic division, Meiosis I, and Meiosis II)

Slide 14

> **Testes (cont'd.)**
>
> • Production of testosterone
>   • Carried on by the interstitial cells of the testes
>   • Testosterone "masculinizes" and promotes and maintains development of the male accessory organs
>   • Stimulates protein anabolism and development of muscle strength
>
> 14

- Production of testosterone is not carried on in the seminiferous tubules.

- What is protein anabolism? (the "building up" of a structure such as muscle using amino acids)

Slide 15

> **Reproductive Ducts**
>
> • Sperm pass through reproductive ducts after exiting testes until they exit from the body
>   • Epididymis
>   ▫ Single, coiled tube about 6 m in length
>   ▫ Lies along the top and behind the testis in the scrotum
>   ▫ Sperm mature and develop the capacity for mobility as they pass through the epididymis
>
> 15

- Sperm are formed within the walls of the seminiferous tubules of the testes.

- What is the pathway of sperm from their formation in the seminiferous tubules until they exit the body? (epididymis, vas deferens, also known as the ductus deferens, ejaculatory duct, urethra)

ELSEVIER

Structure & Function of the Body, 13th ed.

Thibodeau/Patton

Slide 16

- Ductus (vas) deferens
  - Receives sperm from the epididymis and transports them from scrotal sac through the abdominal cavity
  - Passes through inguinal canal
  - Joins duct of seminal vesicle to form the ejaculatory duct
- Ejaculatory duct and urethra
  - Passes through the substance of the prostate gland and permits sperm to empty into the urethra

18

- Spermatic cord—connective tissue sheath that also encloses blood vessels and nerves.
- What function does the urethra have other than its part in reproduction? (excretion of urine)

Slide 17

- Sex glands produce semen
  - Mixture of sperm and secretions of accessory sex glands
  - Averages 3 to 5 ml per ejaculation, with 100 million sperm per ml
  - Seminal vesicles
    - Pouchlike glands that produce about 60% of seminal volume
    - Secretion is yellowish, thick, rich in fructose to provide energy needed by sperm for mobility

17

- The accessory glands contribute more than 95% of the secretions to the gelatinous fluid part of the semen.
- The seminiferous tubules contribute somewhat less than 5% to semen.
- What is the benefit of semen being alkaline? (protection form acidic environment of vagina)
- Why might so many sperm be necessary? (many do not survive)

Slide 18

- Prostate gland
  - Urethra passes through the gland
  - Thin, milk-colored secretion represents 30% of seminal fluid volume
- Bulbourethral (Cowper's) glands
  - Resemble peas in size and shape
  - Secrete mucous-like fluid constituting less than 5% of seminal fluid volume

18

- The prostate is shaped like a doughnut and located below the bladder.
- What other purpose does the secretion of the prostate serve? (provides an alkaline "protection" for sperm)
- Bulbourethral secretion often releases just before most of the semen is ejaculated; sometimes called *preejaculate.*

Slide 19

- The penis and scrotum constitute the external reproductive organs or genitalia of men
  - Scrotum
    - Skin-covered pouch suspended from the groin
    - Internally divided into two sacs by the septum

19

- What constitutes the genitalia of women? (Vulva, mons pubis, clitoris, orifice of urethra, labia, hymen, orifice of Bartholin gland duct, and orifice of vagina.)
- What is contained in the scrotum? (testes)

Structure & Function of the Body, 13th ed.

Thibodeau/Patton

Slide 20

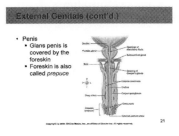

External Genitals (cont'd.)

- Penis
  - Three columns of erectile tissue
  - Two dorsal columns called *corpora cavernosa*
  - One ventral column surrounding the urethra called *corpus spongiosum*

- What is the purpose of erectile tissue? (Facilitates sexual activity. Erectile tissue fills with blood allowing the penis to become stiff so that it may enter the vagina to deposit sperm.)

Slide 21

External Genitals (cont'd.)

- Penis
  - Glans penis is covered by the foreskin
  - Foreskin is also called *prepuce*

- The surgical removal of the foreskin is called *circumcision.*
- Discuss the pros and cons of circumcision.
- Recap the order and functions of the seminal vesicles, prostate gland, and bulbourethral glands.

Slide 22

Chapter 20
Lesson 20.2

Slide 23

Female Reproductive System

- Structural plan
  - Essential organs, or gonads, in women are the ovaries
  - Ovaries produce sex cells called *ova*

- Reiterate the meaning of the term *essential.*

Slide 24

Female Reproductive System (cont'd.)

- Accessory organs
  - Ducts or modified ducts—including oviducts, uterus, and vagina
  - Sex glands—including those in the breasts
  - External genitals

- Contrast the term *accessory* to the term *essential*.

Slide 25

Female Reproductive System (cont'd.)

Organization of the Female Reproductive Organs

- Note the normal position of the uterus; it is nearly horizontal.
- Discuss the fingerlike protrusions on the fallopian tubes. What purpose do they serve? (to facilitate the movement of the egg [ova] into the fallopian tube)

Slide 26

Ovaries

- Structure and location
  - Paired glands weighing about 3 g each
  - Resemble large almonds
  - Attached to ligaments in pelvic cavity on each side of uterus

- How does the location of the female gonads differ from the location of the male gonads? (Female structures are internal, whereas the male gonads are external to the body.)

Slide 27

Ovaries (cont'd.)

- Microscopic structure
  - Ovarian follicles—contain oocyte, an immature sex cell (about 1 million at birth)
  - Primary follicles—are covered with granulosa cells (about 400,000 at puberty)
  - Secondary follicles have a hollow chamber called the *antrum*
  - Corpus luteum forms after ovulation from ruptured follicle

- Follicles that do not mature degenerate and are reabsorbed into the ovarian tissue.
- About 350 to 500 mature follicles ovulate during the reproductive lifetime of most women; sometimes called *Graafian follicles*.
- Corpus luteum means "yellow body" in Latin to describe its appearance.
- Refer to Figure 20-8. (following slide)

Slide 28

Ovaries (cont'd.)

Diagram of Ovary and Oogenesis

28

- Would all of the states of Graafian follicle and ovum development be visible at one time? (No, the states are progressive.)

Slide 29

Ovaries (cont'd.)

- Ovary Functions
  - **Oogenesis:** the production of female gametes or sex cells
    - Meiotic cell division produces daughter cells with equal chromosome numbers (23) but unequal cytoplasm
      - Ovum is large
      - Polar bodies are small and degenerate

29

- The ovum, with its large supply of cytoplasm, is one of the body's largest cells.

- The ovum is uniquely designed to provide nutrients for rapid development of the embryo until implantation into the uterus.

- At fertilization, the sex cells from both parents fuse and the normal chromosome number, 46, is achieved.

- Discuss some of the actions of estrogen.

Slide 30

Ovaries (cont'd.)

- Estrogen and progesterone
  - Granulosa cells surrounding the oocyte in the mature female, and growing follicles produce estrogen
  - Corpus luteum produces progesterone

30

- What is the role of the corpus luteum if fertilization occurs? (to continue to secrete progesterone)

- What is the function of estrogen? (feminization; assist in the development of the uterine lining)

- What is the function of progesterone? (stimulates the proliferation and vascularization of the endometrium)

- In menopausal women, how would the loss of estrogen affect their bodies? (loss of estrogen curtails the ability to produce ova) Have students offer other characteristics of the menopausal period.

Slide 31

Reproductive Ducts

- Uterine tubes
  - Also called *fallopian tubes* or *oviducts*
  - Extend about 10 cm from uterus into abdominal cavity
  - Expanded distal end surrounded by fimbriae
  - Mucosal lining of tube is directly continuous with lining of abdominal cavity

31

- What are fimbriae? (fringelike projections at the outer ends of the oviducts)

- After ovulation, the discharged ovum enters the abdominal cavity and then enters the uterine tube assisted by the wavelike movement of the fimbriae.

- After leaving the tube, the ovum begins its journey to the uterus.

ELSEVIER

Slide 32

> Reproductive Ducts (cont'd.)
>
> - Uterus
>   - Composed of body, fundus, and cervix
>   - Lies in pelvic cavity just behind urinary bladder
>   - Myometrium is the muscle layer
>   - Endometrium lost in menstruation
>
> 32

- The uterus is nearly all muscle with a small cavity inside.
- What three processes does the uterus function in? (menstruation, pregnancy, and delivery)
- What is the menstrual cycle? (The cycle is usually 28 days in which an ovum is matured and the endometrial lining proliferates. Should an ovum not be fertilized, the endometrial tissue sloughs off and is expelled through the vagina.)
- What is endometriosis? (Endometriosis is a condition in which the endometrial tissue lies outside of the uterus.)
- What is menopause and when does it typically take place? (It makes the end of the repetitive menstrual cycles, occurring usually between 45-52 years old.)
- Refer to Figure 20-9 (p. 504)

Slide 33

> Reproductive Ducts (cont'd.)
>
> - Vagina
>   - Distensible tube about 10 cm long
>   - Located between urinary bladder and rectum in the pelvis
>
> 33

- What dual purposes does the vagina serve? (Deposition of sperm and the exit route for the delivery of a baby.)

Slide 34

> Accessory or Supportive Sex Glands
>
> - Bartholin's (greater vestibular) glands
>   - Secretes mucous lubricating fluid
>   - Ducts open between labia minora
> - Breasts
>   - Located over pectoral muscles of thorax
>   - Size determined by fat quantity
>   - Lactiferous ducts drain at nipple, which is surrounded by pigmented areola
>
> 34

- Why does the size of the breast have little to do with its ability to secrete adequate amounts of milk after the birth of a baby? (Size is determined by the amount of fat and not the amount of milk glands.)

Slide 35

> Accessory or Supportive Sex Glands (cont'd.)
>
> Lateral View of the Breast
>
>
>
> 35

- Nursing mothers may experience blocked lactiferous ducts.
- This can cause swelling around the areola, redness, and a slightly higher skin temperature.

ELSEVIER

Slide 36

- Female external genitals include
  - Mons pubis
  - Clitoris
  - Orifice of urethra
  - Bartholin's glands
  - Vagina
  - Labia minora and majora
  - Hymen

36

- The perineum is the area between the vaginal opening and the anus.
- In an episiotomy, this area is sometimes surgically cut during delivery.

Slide 37

External Genitals of the Female

37

- What is the importance of a PAP smear? (Pap smears can detect early cervical cancer.)

Slide 38

- Menstrual cycle involves many changes in the uterus, ovaries, vagina, and breasts
- Lasts about 28 days, varies from month to month among individuals and in the same individual
- Each cycle consists of three phases
  - Menses
  - Proliferative phase
  - Secretory phase

38

- In general, only one ovum matures each month.
- Ovulation occurs 14 days before the next menses begins; in a 28-day cycle, ovulation occurs on day 14.
- Why is the time of ovulation important? (Ovulation time is a fertile time. Couples can use this knowledge to either plan or avoid a pregnancy.)

Slide 39

The Human Menstrual Cycle

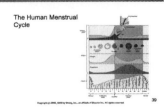

39

- The first menses or menstrual flow is called *menarche*.
- Point out the critical balance between pituitary, ovarian, and uterine hormones to maintain the cycle.
- What factors can affect this cycle? (stress, diet, hormone levels)

Slide 40

Menstrual Cycle (cont'd.)

- Menses
  - About the first 4 or 5 days of the cycle
  - Characterized by sloughing of bits of endometrium (uterine lining) with bleeding
- Proliferative phase
  - Between menses and secretory phases
  - Varies in length; characterized by repair of endometrium
- Secretory phase
  - Days between ovulation and next menses
  - Secretory about 14 days before next menses

40

- What day is considered the first day of the cycle? (first day of menstrual flow)
- What occurs during the proliferative phase? (repair of the endometrium)
- How many ova usually mature in one month? (one)
- The combined actions of the anterior pituitary hormones FSH and LH cause ovulation.
- Sudden sharp decrease in estrogen and progesterone brings on menstruation if pregnancy does not occur.

Slide 41

Summary of Male and Female Reproductive Systems

- In men and women the organs of the reproductive system are adapted for the specific sequence of functions that permit
  - Development of sperm or ova
  - Successful fertilization
  - Normal development and birth of offspring

41

- Refer to Table 20-3 (p. 511).
- List the commonalities and distinctions between the male and female reproductive systems.

Slide 42

Summary of Male and Female Reproductive Systems (cont'd.)

- Male organs
  - Designed to produce, store, and introduce mature sperm into the female reproductive tract
- Female organs
  - Designed to produce ova, receive the sperm, permit fertilization, facilitate fetal development and birth, and perform lactation

42

- Production of sex hormones is required for development of secondary sex characteristics and for normal reproductive functions in both sexes.

21 Lesson Plan
Growth and Development

TEACHING FOCUS

In this chapter, students will have the opportunity to learn about the concept of development as a biological process of continuous modification and change, including the prenatal stage from fertilization to birth. Students will be shown the three primary germ layers and several derivatives in the adult body that develop from each layer. Additionally, students will examine the three stages of labor in normal vaginal birth, the four postnatal periods of life, and the developmental changes that characterize each. The effects of aging on the major organ systems of the body will also be discussed.

MATERIALS AND RESOURCES

- ☐ Computer (Lesson 21.1)
- ☐ Flash cards (Lesson 21.1)
- ☐ Photocopies of Figure 21-8 (Lesson 21.1)

LESSON CHECKLIST

Preparations for this lesson include:
- lecture/discussion
- guest speaker: medical assistant for an OB/GYN
- student performance evaluation of all entry-level skills required for student comprehension of growth and development principles including:
  - ○ the stages of development during the prenatal period
  - ○ the process of labor
  - ○ the divisions of the postnatal period
  - ○ the effects of aging on the body

ELSEVIER

KEY TERMS

adolescence (p. 534)
adulthood (p. 535)
amniotic cavity (p. 524)
antenatal medicine (p. 532)
arteriosclerosis (p. 538)
atherosclerosis (p. 538)
blastocyst (p. 523)
birth defects (p. 530)
cataract (p. 539)
childhood (p. 534)
chorion (p. 525)
ectoderm (p. 527)
embryology (pp. 522, 538)
endoderm (p. 527)
fetal alcohol syndrome (p. 536)
fertilization (p. 522)
gerontology (p. 535)
gestation (p. 527)
glaucoma (p. 539)
histogenesis (p. 527)
hypertension (p. 538)
implantation (p. 523)
infancy (p. 533)

laparoscope (p. 526)
mesoderm (p. 527)
morula (p. 523)
neonatal period (p. 533)
neonate (p. 533)
neonatology (p. 533)
older adulthood (p. 535)
organogenesis (p. 527)
osteoarthritis (p. 536)
parturition (p. 530)
placenta (p. 525)
postnatal period (pp. 521, 530)
prenatal period (p. 521)
prenatal stage of development (p. 522)
presbyopia (p. 539)
primary germ layers (p. 527)
quickening (p. 532)
secondary sex characteristics (p. 534)
senescence (p. 535)
stem cells (p. 535)
teratogen (p. 530)
yolk sac (p. 524)
zygote (p. 523)

ADDITIONAL RESOURCES

AnimationDirect (Book Companion CD)
Instructor's Electronic Resource (IER) (CD)
PowerPoint slides (CD, Evolve)
Test Bank (Evolve)

Legend

ESLR
EVOLVE Student
Learning Resource

EILR TB
EVOLVE Instructor
Learning Resource
Test Bank

AnimationDirect
on Book Companion
CD

PPT
PowerPoint
Slides

SG
Study
Guide

IRM
Instructor's
Resource Manual

Class Activities are indicated in **bold italic**.

Structure & Function of the Body, 13th ed.

Thibodeau/Patton

LESSON 21.1

PRETEST

Study Guide Multiple Choice questions 1-10 (pp. 265-266)

BACKGROUND ASSESSMENT

Question: What are the functions of the placenta during pregnancy?
Answer: The placenta, which is composed of tissues from both the mother and child, functions as a pathway for nutrients to reach the fetus. It is also used as an excretory, respiratory, and endocrine organ, and it provides a thin barrier against some harmful substances.

Question: From fertilization through birth and to early adulthood, the body builds organs to sustain life. As humans enter late adulthood, these organs change and lose some of their capabilities. What organs and functions are most affected?
Answer: The brain, basal metabolic rate, liver weight and blood flow, cardiac output, respiratory capacity, kidney mass, and the conduction velocity of nerve fiber can all lose capacity.

CRITICAL THINKING QUESTION

Dana, a 24-year-old patient who is five weeks pregnant with her first child, is visiting the office for a routine checkup. She says that birth defects are common in her family, and she is concerned about the possibility that her baby will have defects as well. What should you tell her?
Guidelines: Tell Dana that birth defects can be caused by genetic or environmental factors. While it is still too early in her pregnancy to detect genetic birth defects, the physician will eventually perform a series of tests to determine if the fetus has any defects such as abnormal genes or an abnormal number of chromosomes. In the meantime, remind Dana to avoid environmental factors such as drugs, cigarettes, alcohol, and x-rays.

OBJECTIVES	CONTENT	TEACHING RESOURCES
Discuss the concept of development as a biological process characterized by continuous modification and change.	■ Introduction (p. 521)	*E* True or False question 52 ***Class Activity** Divide students into small groups and have them discuss the life cycle from conception to death. Have each group make a list of the stages—such as the prenatal period, childhood, and adulthood—and the biological changes that occur during each stage.*
Discuss the major developmental changes characteristic of the prenatal stage of life from fertilization to birth.	■ Prenatal period (p. 522) □ Fertilization to implantation (p. 522) □ Periods of development (p. 527)	Slides 5-10 Prenatal Period questions 1-20 (p. 258) *E* EILR TB Multiple Choice questions 1-6; True or False questions 1-17, 26, 53-57; Short Answer questions 1-3 Multiple Choice questions 21, 29-32, 34; Identification question 37 Fertilization and Implantation **Book Resources** Figure 21-1 Fertilization (p. 522)

OBJECTIVES	CONTENT	TEACHING RESOURCES
		Figure 21-2 Fertilization and implantation (p. 523)
		Figure 21-3 Early stages of human development (p. 524)
		Figure 21-4 Implantation and early development (p. 525)
		Research, Issues and Trends: In Vitro Fertilization (p. 526)
		Figure 21-5 The placenta: interface between maternal and fetal circulation (p. 526)
		Research, Issues and Trends: How Long Does Pregnancy Last? (p. 527)
		Figure 21-6 Human embryos and fetuses (p. 528)
		Figure 21-7 Critical periods of neonatal development (p. 529)
		Critical Thinking questions 15-17 (p. 543)
		Class Activity Divide students into small groups. Have each group discuss the fertilization and implantation process and sketch the journey from ovulation to implantation.
		Class Activity Divide students into small groups. Have each group discuss the placenta and make a two-column table, listing the placenta's functions in one column and its limitations in the other.
Identify the three primary germ layers and several derivatives in the adult body that develop from each layer.	☐ Formation of the primary germ layers (p. 521) ☐ Histogenesis and organogenesis (p. 521) ☐ Birth defects (p. 523)	Slides 11, 12 Multiple Choice questions 7-10, 24; True or False questions 18-25, 58-60; Matching questions 1-10; Short Answer questions 4, 5 **Book Resources** Table 21-1 Primary Germ Layer Derivatives (p. 529) Quick Check questions 1-4 (p. 530) *Class Activity Have students create flash cards of the primary germ layer derivatives of the endoderm, ectoderm, and mesoderm. Divide students into teams and have them quiz each other.*

Thibodeau/Patton

OBJECTIVES	CONTENT	TEACHING RESOURCES
Discuss the three stages of labor that characterize a normal vaginal birth.	■ Birth or parturition (p. 530) ☐ Stages of labor (p. 530)	🖾▣ Slide 13 ✇ Multiple Choice question 11; True or False questions 27-32, 61; Short Answer question 6 ◉ Three Stages of Birth **Book Resources** Figure 21-8 Parturition (p. 531) Health and Well-Being: Quickening (p. 532) Research, Issues and Trends: Antenatal Diagnosis and Treatment (p. 536) *Class Activity **Divide students into small groups. Give each group a copy of Figure 21-8 (available on EILR or IER), taking care to delete the legend. Ask each group to define the three stages of labor. Then, ask each group to match the stage of labor with the proper part of the figure.*** *Class Activity **Invite a medical assistant, nurse, or an OB/GYN physician to speak to the class.***
List and discuss the major developmental changes characteristic of the four postnatal periods of life.	■ Postnatal period (p. 530) ☐ Infancy (p. 533) ☐ Childhood (p. 534) ☐ Adolescence and adulthood (p. 534) ☐ Older adulthood (p. 535)	🖾▣ Slides 14-18 Postnatal Period questions 21-44 (pp. 259-261) ✇ Multiple Choice questions 12-14; True or False questions 33-41, 62, 63; Matching questions 11-20; Short Answer questions 7, 8 Multiple Choice questions 23, 24, 27, 28, 33, 35, 36 **Book Resources** Figure 21-9 Changes in the proportions of body parts from birth to maturity (p. 533) Figure 21-10 The neonate infant (p. 533) Figure 21-11 Normal lumbar curvature of a toddler's spine (p. 534) Research, Issues and Trends: Freezing Umbilical Cord Blood (p. 535) Quick Check questions 1-4 (p. 536) ▸ Discuss Research, Issues and Trends: Fetal Alcohol Syndrome (p. 536). What information will students share with pregnant patients? Are there conflicting views about alcohol use by pregnant women?

ELSEVIER

Structure & Function of the Body, 13th ed.

Thibodeau/Patton

OBJECTIVES	CONTENT	TEACHING RESOURCES
		Class Activity Divide the class into four groups. Assign each group to read and report to the class on one of the following stages of postnatal life (this can be done during the class period): Infancy (p. 533), Childhood (p. 534), Adolescence and adulthood (p. 534), Older adulthood (p. 535).
Discuss the effects of aging on the major body organ systems.	■ Effects of aging (p. 536) □ Skeletal system (p. 536) □ Integumentary system (skin) (p. 536) □ Urinary system (p. 536) □ Respiratory system (p. 538) □ Cardiovascular system (p. 538) □ Special senses (p. 538)	Slides 19-24 Effects of Aging questions 45-54 (p. 261) Multiple Choice questions 15-20; True or False questions 42-51, 64; Short Answer questions 9-11 Multiple Choice questions 22, 25, 26 (p. 296) **Book Resources** Figure 21-12 Some biological changes associated with maturity and aging (p. 536) Quick Check questions 1-4 (p. 539) ▶ Discuss Research, Issues and Trends: Extending the Human Lifespan (p. 539). Ask students to discuss costs, advantages, and disadvantages. *Class Activity Divide the students into small groups. Assign each group to review the effects of aging on a particular body system, such as the integumentary system, urinary system, respiratory system, or cardiovascular system. Ask each group to share their information with the class.*
Performance Evaluation		Chapter 21 Computerized Test Bank questions Chapter 21 activities and questions Student Post-Test questions **Book Resources** Review questions (p. 543) Critical Thinking questions 15-17 (p. 543) Chapter Test (p. 544)

Thibodeau/Patton

21.1 Homework/Assignments:

21.1 Teacher's Notes:

Slide 1

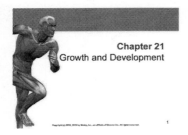

Chapter 21
Growth and Development

Slide 2

Learning Objectives

- Discuss the concept of development as a biological process characterized by continuous modification and change
- Discuss the major developmental changes characteristic of the prenatal stage of life from fertilization to birth
- Discuss the three stages of labor that characterize a normal vaginal birth

Slide 3

Learning Objectives (cont'd.)

- Identify the three primary germ layers and several derivatives in the adult body that develop from each layer
- List and discuss the major developmental changes characteristic of the four postnatal periods of life
- Discuss the effects of aging on the major body organ systems

Slide 4

Chapter 21
Lesson 21.1

Slide 5

Prenatal Period

- Prenatal period begins at conception and continues until birth
- Science of fetal growth and development is called *embryology*

- Approximately how long does pregnancy last? (40 weeks)
- Discuss the importance of prenatal care.

Slide 6

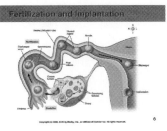

Fertilization and Implantation

- How long does the process of fertilization and implantation take? (10 days)
- Go through the process step by step, and discuss each step with students.

Slide 7

Fertilization and Implantation (cont'd.)

- After three days of cell division, the zygote has developed into a solid cell mass called a *morula*
- Continued cell division of the morula produces a hollow ball of cells called a *blastocyst*
- The blastocyst implants in the uterine wall about 10 days after fertilization
- The blastocyst forms the amniotic cavity and chorion of the placenta

- As the blastocyst develops, it forms a structure with two cavities: the *yolk sac* and the *amniotic cavity*.

  - The yolk sac produces blood cells.

  - The amniotic cavity becomes the amniotic sac.

- The chorion develops into the placenta.

- Chorionic villi connect the blood vessels of the chorion to the placenta.

Slide 8

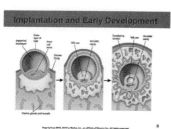

- How does the embryo receive nutrients before the placenta is functional? (uterine fluids provide nutrients)

Slide 9

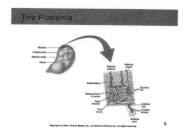

- What are the functions of the placenta? (To provide nutrients to the developing fetus, it acts as an "anchor" for the fetus and attaches to the umbilical cord.)
- Maternal and fetal blood do not mix.
- The very thin layer of placental tissues that separates maternal and fetal blood serves as a barrier that can protect the baby from many substances. Discuss the types of substances that can cross this barrier (alcohol, rubella, etc.).

Slide 10

- Discuss the periods of prenatal development and what happens during each stage.
- See Figure 21-6, p. 528.

Slide 11

- What are the three primary germ layers? (endoderm, ectoderm, and mesoderm)
- Discuss the derivatives listed in the table.
- What are *histogenesis* and *organogenesis?* (The process by which the primary germ layers develop into many different types of tissues is called histogenesis. The way in which the tissues arrange themselves into organs is called organogenesis.)

Slide 12

> Birth Defects
>
> • **Birth defect:** Any structural or functional abnormality present at birth
>   ▪ May be caused by genetic factors
>   ▫ Abnormal genes
>   ▫ Abnormal number of chromosomes
>   ▪ May be caused by environmental factors
>   ▫ Environmental factors are called teratogens
>   ▫ Especially harmful during the first trimester
>
> 12

- Teratogens can cause miscarriage if significant damage occurs during the preembryonic stage.
- What are some examples of teratogens? (radiation, chemicals, infections, medications)
- Use Figure 21-7 (p. 529) to show when teratogenic agents are most dangerous.

Slide 13

> Birth, or Parturition

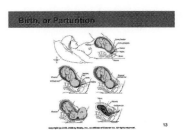

> 13

- Define the stages of labor. (see p. 530)
- Describe the birth process according to the figure.

Slide 14

> Postnatal Period
>
> • Postnatal period begins at birth and lasts until death
> • Divisions of postnatal period into isolated time frames can be misleading
> • Life, growth, and development are continuous
> • Obvious changes in the physical appearance occur between birth and maturity
>
> 14

- The early postnatal period is a time of rapid growth and development.
- Many of the changes that occur in the later years of life do not result in increased function.

Slide 15

> Infancy
>
> • First four weeks is called *neonatal period*
> • Cardiovascular and respiratory changes occur at birth
>   ▪ Fetus is totally dependent on mother
>   ▪ Newborn must immediately become totally self-supporting
>
> 15

- What is neonatology? (the medical and nursing specialty concerned with the diagnosis and treatment of disorders of the newborn.)
- Many changes occur in the cardiovascular and respiratory system when the baby takes their first breath. (closure of the ductus arteriosis and foramen ovale)
- Babies are expected to triple their birth weight by what time period? (one year)

ELSEVIER

Slide 16

Childhood

- Extends from end of infancy to puberty
- Overall rate of growth remains rapid but decelerates
- Continuing development of motor and coordination skills
- Loss of deciduous or baby teeth and eruption of permanent teeth

16

- By age 6, the child appears more like a preadolescent than an infant or toddler.
- Child becomes less chubby, potbelly becomes flatter, and face loses its babyish look.
- Permanent teeth (except for wisdom teeth) have erupted by age 14.
- At what age do girls and boys usually hit puberty? (can vary greatly but around 13 years old)

Slide 17

Adolescence

- Average age range of adolescence varies from 13 to 19 years
- Period of rapid growth results in sexual maturity (adolescence)
- Appearance of secondary sex characteristics regulated by secretion of sex hormones
- Growth spurt typical of adolescence; begins in girls at age 10 and in boys at age 12

17

- Breast development usually begins at about age 10.
- Most girls begin to menstruate (menarche) at age 12 or 13, which is about three years earlier than a century ago.
- Boys begin signs of testicle enlargement between 10 and 13.

Slide 18

Adulthood

- Bones' growth plates are fully closed in adult
- Other structures such as the sinuses acquire adult placement
- Adulthood characterized by maintenance of existing body tissues
- Older adulthood
  - Every organ system of the body undergoes degenerative changes

18

- Many body traits do not become apparent until adulthood, such as normal balding patterns.
- What is gerontology? (the study of aging)
- What is senescence? (a synonym for the older adulthood period)
- What are some biological changes associated with maturity and aging? (dry and thin skin, presbyopia, decreased calcification of bones)

Slide 19

Effects of Aging

- Skeletal system
  - Aging causes changes in the texture, calcification, and shape of bones
  - Bone spurs develop around joints
  - Bones become porous and fracture easily

19

- What is lipping? (Older bones develop indistinct and shaggy-appearing margins with spurs. This can restrict mobility.)
- Changes in calcification may reduce bone size.
- What is a common degenerative joint disease seen in the elderly? (arthritis)

Slide 20

Effects of Aging (cont'd.)

- Integumentary system (skin)
    - With age, skin sags and becomes
        - Thin
        - Dry
        - Wrinkled

20

- What other changes occur in the integumentary system during the aging process? (decreased pigmentation and hair loss)

Slide 21

Effects of Aging (cont'd.)

- Urinary system
    - Nephron units decrease in number by 50% between ages 30 and 75
    - Blood flow to kidney and ability to form urine decrease

21

- Incontinence is not a normal sign of aging, but rather a pathology that can be treated.

Slide 22

Effects of Aging (cont'd.)

- Respiratory system
    - Calcification of costal cartilages makes it difficult for rib cage to expand and contract normally
    - Wasting of respiratory muscles decreases respiratory efficiency
    - Respiratory membrane thickens; movement of oxygen from alveoli to blood is slowed

22

- What is barrel chest? (Ribs become "fixed" to the sternum; rib cage remains in a more expanded position; respiratory efficiency decreases.)
- What causes it? (Cartilages that connect ribs to sternum become calcified.)
- Conversion of muscle cells to connective tissue decreases the strength of the muscles associated with inspiration and expiration.

Slide 23

Effects of Aging (cont'd.)

- Cardiovascular system
    - Degenerative heart and blood vessel disease is among the most common and serious effects of aging
    - Hardening of arteries (arteriosclerosis) may result in rupture of blood vessels
    - Hypertension or high blood pressure is common in older adulthood

23

- What is atherosclerosis? (presence of fat plaques in the blood vessels)
- Atherosclerosis often leads to blockage of the coronary arteries and a heart attack.
- What is a brain attack? (a condition previously referred to as a stroke in which the blood supply to the brain is disrupted)

ELSEVIER

Thibodeau/Patton

Slide 24

- Special senses
  - Eye lenses become hard and cannot accommodate for near vision
  - Decreased transmission of sound waves caused by loss of elasticity of eardrum and fixing of the bony ear ossicles is common
    - Some degree of hearing impairment is universally present in the aged

24

- All sense organs show a gradual decline in performance with age.

- Inability of eyes to accommodate for near vision is called *presbyopia*.

- Discuss the need for reading glasses and bifocals.

- What are cataracts? (cloudiness of the eye lens)

- What is glaucoma? (increased intraocular pressure)

- What causes a decline in the ability to hear? (loss of cells in the organ of Corti and immobility of the ossicles)

- Only about 40% of the taste buds present at age 30 remain at age 75.